INSTRUCTOR'S SOLUTIONS MANUAL

MARTHA J. SIEGEL

FINITE MATHEMATICS
AND ITS APPLICATIONS
Fifth Edition

Larry J. Goldstein
David I. Schneider
Martha J. Siegel

D1313885

PRENTICE HALL, Englewood Cliffs, NJ 07632

© 1995 by **PRENTICE-HALL, INC.**
A Simon & Schuster Company
Englewood Cliffs, NJ 07632

10 9 8 7 6 5 4 3 2 1

ISBN 0-13-321027-8

Printed in the United States of America

CONTENTS

INTRODUCTION

This *Instructors' Solution Manual* for the Fifth Edition of *Finite Mathematics and Its Applications* has been prepared to aid faculty by providing the solutions to all the problems in the text. We call attention to the teaching and learning tools that are available in connection with this edition.

Explorations in Finite Mathematics is software written by David Schneider, one of the authors of the text, and it has been customized for the present edition. It is available either wrapped with the textbook or separately and directly from Prentice Hall. We strongly urge faculty to use the software and to introduce it to students. We believe that you will find it helpful in grading students' solutions and in preparing examples and examination questions, although solutions given in this manual are independent of its capabilities. We feel confident that if students have access to it, they will find that it is an excellent learning tool. It was designed to help the student understand the material and to monitor progress through the many steps in problem solving. The calculator we used for the several problems that require it was the TI-82.

Learning aids in the text itself include the many Examples and Practice Problems in each section. Students should **read** the book. They should have pencil and paper at hand to try the Examples and Practice Problems before they attempt the Exercises. The Supplementary Exercises at the end of each chapter provide students an opportunity to review and synthesize the material appearing throughout the chapter. A test item file and a test generator are available also.

We certainly have tried to keep the solutions error free. Please let us know if you have any comments or corrections. We welcome them.

Larry J. Goldstein
David I. Schneider
    University of Maryland
    College Park
Martha J. Siegel
    Towson State University

LINEAR EQUATIONS AND STRAIGHT LINES

1.1 Coordinate Systems and Graphs

1.- 6.

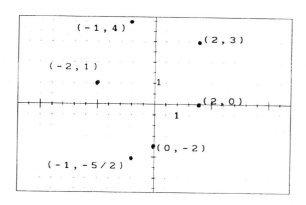

7.- 8.

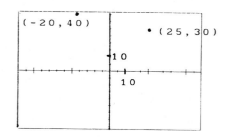

9. m = 5, b = 8

10. m = -2, b = -6

11. m = 0, b = 3 since y = 0·x + 3

12. m = $\frac{2}{3}$, b = 0 since y = $\frac{2}{3}$·x + 0

13. To change into standard form, solve for y:
$$14x + 7y = 21$$
$$7y = -14x + 21$$
$$y = -\frac{14}{7} x + 3$$
$$y = -2x + 3$$

14. To change into standard form, solve for y:
$$x - y = 3$$
$$- y = -x + 3$$
$$y = x - 3$$

15. Here y does not occur, so we solve for x: x = $\frac{5}{3}$.

16. To change into standard form, solve for y:

$$-\frac{1}{2}x + \frac{2}{3}y = 10$$

$$\frac{2}{3}y = \frac{1}{2}x + 10$$

$$2y = \frac{3}{2}x + 30$$

$$y = \frac{3}{4}x + 15$$

17. The x-intercept is found by setting y= 0, and solving for x:

$$-4x + 8 = 0$$
$$-4x = -8$$
$$x = 2$$

Hence, the x-intercept is (2,0).
The y-intercept is found by setting x = 0:

$$y = -4\cdot0 + 8$$
$$y = 8 \qquad \text{So the y-intercept is (0,8).}$$

18. The line y = 5 is a horizontal line 5 units above the x-axis. Hence, it has no x-intercept and its y-intercept is (0,5)

19. The line x = 7 is a vertical line 7 units to the right of the y-axis. Hence, it has no y-intercept and its x-intercept is (7,0).

20. To find the x-intercept, set y = 0; then -8x = 0. So, $x = -\frac{0}{8} = 0$.

To find the y-intercept, set x = 0; then y = -8·0 = 0.
The two intercepts are the same point: (0,0), (0,0).

21. Graph $y = \frac{1}{3}x - 1$

When y = 0, x = 3   Point is (3,0)
When x = 0, y = -1   Point is (0,-1)

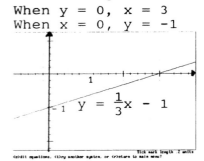

Tick mark length 2 units
<e>dit equations, <t>ry another system, or <r>eturn to main menu?

22. Graph y = 2x.
    When y = 0, x = 0   Point is (0,0).
    When x = 2, y = 4   Point is (2,4).

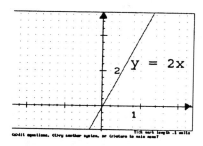

23. The graph y = $\frac{5}{2}$. is a horizontal line $\frac{5}{2}$ units above the x-axis.

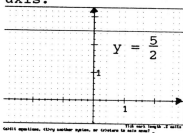

24. Graph x = 0. This is the y-axis.

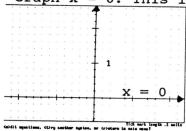

25. Graph 3x + 4y = 24. Since 3 and 4 divide 24 evenly, the intercept method is an easy approach. When x = 0, we have:

    3·0 + 4y = 24
          4y = 24
           y = 6   The point is (0,6).

    and when y = 0, we have:

    3x + 4·0 = 24
          3x = 24
           x = 8   The point is (8,0).

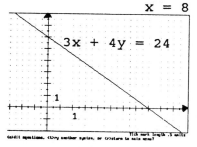

26.   Graph x + y = 3. When x = 0, we have:
           0 + y = 3
               y = 3   The point is (0,3).
      and when y = 0, we have:
           x + 0 = 3
               x = 3   The point is (3,0).

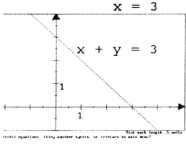

27.   The standard form of $2x + 3y = 6$ is $y = -\frac{2}{3}x + 2$.

   (a) $4x + 6y = 12$
                $6y = -4x + 12$
                 $y = -\frac{2}{3}x + 2$ yes.

   (b) $y = -\frac{2}{3}x + 2$ yes, automatic.

   (c) $x = 3 - \frac{3}{2}y$

            $\frac{3}{2}y = -x + 3$

            $y = -\frac{2}{3}x + 2$ yes

   (d) $6 - 2x - y = 0$
                     $y = -2x + 6$ no, not the same standard form.

   (e) $y = 2 - \frac{2}{3}x$

         $y = -\frac{2}{3}x + 2$ yes

   (f) $x + y = 1$
              $y = -x + 1$ no

   The equations with the same standard form are (a), (b), (c),
   and (e).

28.   The standard form of $\frac{1}{2}x - 5y = 1$ is $y = \frac{1}{10}x - \frac{1}{5}$.

   (a) $2x - \frac{1}{5}y = 1$

            $-\frac{1}{5}y = -2x + 1$

                 $y = 10x - 5$ no, not the same standard form.

   (b) $-5y = -x + 2$
            $y = \frac{1}{5}x + \frac{2}{5}$ no

   (c) $10y = 5x - 2$
            $y = \frac{1}{2}x - \frac{1}{5}$ no

4

(d) $\qquad y = -\frac{1}{10}(x-2)$

$\qquad\qquad y = \frac{1}{10}x - \frac{1}{5}$ yes

(e) $\quad 10y = x - 2$

$\qquad\qquad y = \frac{1}{10}x - \frac{1}{5}$ yes

(f) $\quad 1 + .5x = 2 + 5y$

$\qquad -1 + .5x = 5y$

$\qquad -\frac{1}{5} + .1x = y$

$\qquad\qquad y = \frac{1}{10}x - \frac{1}{5}$ yes

The equations with the same standard form are (d), (e), (f).

29. (a) $x + y = 3$ has the points $(3,0)$ and $(0,3)$ as x- and y-intercepts, respectively. So L_3 matches with this equation.

(b) $2x - y = -2$ has the points $(-1,0)$ and $(0,2)$ as x- and y-intercepts, respectively. So L_1 matches with this equation.

(c) $x = 3y + 3$ has the points $(0,-1)$ and $(3,0)$ as x- and y-intercepts, respectively. So L_2 matches with this equation.

30. From the points $(1,2)$ and $(5,4)$ we get values for x and y that can be placed in the equations (a), (b) and (c). We discard (a) because $5 + 4 \neq 3$ and (b) because $2 \neq 1 - 1$. Equation (c) holds for both points: $2 \cdot 2 = 1 + 3$ and $2 \cdot 4 = 5 + 3$.

31. (a) When the water boils, the temperature y is 212.

$\qquad$ So $212 = 30x + 72$

$\qquad\qquad 140 = 30x$

$\qquad\qquad x = 4\frac{2}{3}$ minutes or 4 min. 40 sec.

(b) The y-intercept gives the temperature when $x = 0$.

$\qquad$ i.e., the initial temperature, which is $72°F$.

(c) The x-intercept shows the number of minutes until the water is $0°F$. since it begins at $72°F$ and is heating, this is not a meaningful physical interpretation.

32. (a) The y intercept is $(0,130)$ also $(8,105)$ is a point on the graph.
So the graph is:

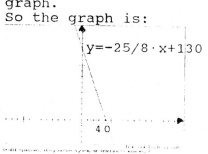

$y = -25/8 \cdot x + 130$

4 0

(b) The y intercept is when x = 0 or when the time is zero
    years after 1969. Therefore in 1969 the amount of
    rainforest will be 130 thousand square miles.
(c) When will y = 80 thousand square miles? Substitute 80
    for y and solve for x.

$$80 = -\frac{25}{8} \cdot x + 130 \qquad \text{So } x = 16$$

The rainforest will be 80 thousand square miles in 1985,
16 years after 1969.
(d) The year 2001 is 32 (2001 - 1969) years after 1969, so x
    = 32. When x = 32 y = 30. Therefore there will be
    30,000 m² of rain forest in the year 2001.

33.(a) The y intercept is (0,2.5) also (4,.3) is a point on the
       graph. So the graph is:

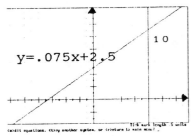

y=.075x+2.5

(b) The y intercept (0,2.5) represents the 0 years after
    1960 when the world wide consumption of cigarettes was
    2.5 trillion.
(c) This means that y = 4. When y = 4 then x = 20. So the
    world wide consumption of cigarettes was 4 trillion in
    1980 (1960 + 20).
(d) The year 2020 is 60 years after 1960 so x = 60. When
    x = 60 then y = 7. Therefore in the year 2020 the world
    wide consumption of cigarettes will be 7 trillion.

34. The y-intercept (0,5) gives us the value of b. We can use
     this information and the x-intercept to find m:
     $0 = m \cdot 4 + 5$
     $m = -\frac{5}{4}$ So the equation of the line is $y = -\frac{5}{4}x + 5$.

35. Up, because the slope doesn't change, but the y-intercept
     moves upward.

36. Yes. The x-axis (y = 0) is the only line with more than one
     x-intercept.

37. From the standard form: y = mx + b, m = 0 because the x-axis
     is a horizontal line and b = 0 since the y-intercept is
     (0,0). So the equation of the x-axis is y = 0.

38. Since m = 0 for every horizontal line, the equation of a
     line that is parallel to the x-axis is: y = b.

39. No. For instance, x = 5 has no y-intercept.

6

40. No. For instance, $y = 5$ has no x-intercept.

41. The x- and y-intercepts are the same when the line passes through $(0,0)$, the only common point of both.

42. To find the x-intercept, set $y = 0$; then $x = a$.
    To find the y-intercept, set $x = 0$; then $y = b$.
    The x- and y-intercepts are $(a,0)$ and $(0,b)$, respectively.

1.2 Linear Inequalities

1. False

2. True

3. True

4. False

5. $2x \geq 8$
   $x \geq 4$

6. $3x \leq 9$
   $x \leq 3$

7. $-5x + 13 \leq -2$
   $-5x \leq -15$
   $x \geq 3$
   (reverse inequality when dividing by a negative number)

8. $-x + 1 \leq 3$
   $-x \leq 2$
   $x \geq -2$
   (reverse inequality when dividing by a negative number)
   The answer is (d).

9. $2x + y \leq 5$
   $y \leq -2x + 5$

10. $-3x + y \geq 1$
    $y \geq 3x + 1$

11. $5x - \frac{1}{3}y \leq 6$
    $-\frac{1}{3}y \leq -5x + 6$
    $-y \leq -15x + 18$
    $y \geq 15x - 18$
    (reverse inequality when dividing by a negative number)

12. $\frac{1}{2}x - y \leq -1$

$\qquad -y \leq -\frac{1}{2}x - 1$

$\qquad y \geq \frac{1}{2}x + 1$

(reverse inequality when dividing by a negative number)

13. Since y does not appear, we solve for x:

$\qquad x \geq -\frac{3}{4}$ This is the standard form.

14. Since y does not appear, we solve for x:

$\qquad -2x \leq 4$

$\qquad \quad x \geq -2$

(reverse inequality when dividing by a negative number)

15. Yes. By substituting x = 2 and y = 1 in the inequality, we obtain

$\qquad 3 \cdot 2 + 5 \cdot 1 \leq 12$ or $11 \leq 12$, which is true.

16. Yes. By substituting x = 3 and y = 15 in the inequality, we obtain

$\qquad -2 \cdot 3 + 15 \geq 9$ or $9 \geq 9$, which is true.

17. No. By substituting x = 3 and y = 0 in the inequality, we obtain

$\qquad 0 \geq -2 \cdot 3 + 7$ or $0 \geq 1$, which is false.

18. No. By substituting x = 4 and y = 6 in the inequality, we obtain

$\qquad 6 \leq \frac{1}{2} \cdot 4 + 3$ or $6 \leq 5$, which is false.

19. Yes. By substituting x = 3 and y = 5, we obtain

$\qquad 5 \leq 3(3) - 4$ or $5 \leq 5$, which is true.

20. Yes. By substituting x = -3 and y = -2 in the inequality, we obtain

$\qquad -2 \geq -3$, which is true.

21. Yes. By substituting x = 7 in the inequality, we obtain $7 \geq 5$, which is true.

22. Yes. By substituting x = 0 in the inequality, we obtain $0 \leq 7$, which is true.

23.

y = 1/3x + 1

24.

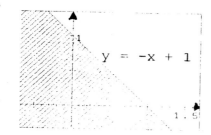

$y = -x + 1$

25. Points to the right of or on the line x = 4 have x-coordinates ≥ 4.

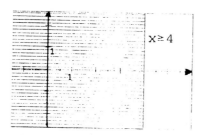

$x \geq 4$

26. Points above or on the line y = 2 have y-coordinates ≤ 2.

$y \leq 2$

27.

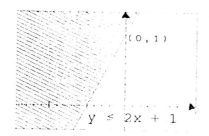

(0,1)

$y \leq 2x + 1$

28.

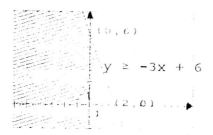

(0,6)

$y \geq -3x + 6$

(2,0)

29.

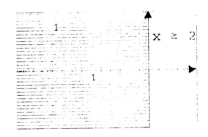

$x \geq 2$

30.

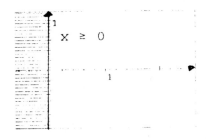

$x \geq 0$

31. $x + 4y \geq 12$
$y \geq -\frac{1}{4}x + 3$ Points *above* or on the line satisfy the inequality.

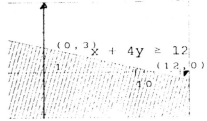

$(0, 3)$ $x + 4y \geq 12$
$(12, 0)$

32. $4x - 4y \geq 8$
$y \leq x - 2$ Points *below* or on the line satisfy the inequality.

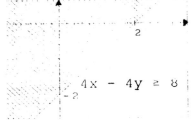

$4x - 4y \geq 8$

33. $4x - 5y + 25 \geq 0$
   $y \geq 4/5 \cdot x + 5$ Points below or on the line satisfy the
                                  inequality

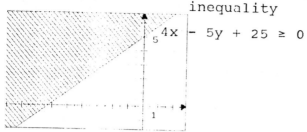

$4x - 5y + 25 \geq 0$

34. $.2y - x \geq .4$ or in standard form $y \geq 5x + 2$

$.2y - x \geq .4$

35. $1/2 \cdot x - 1/3 \cdot y \leq 1$ or in standard form $y \geq 3/2 \cdot x - 3$

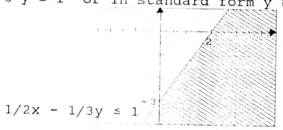

$1/2x - 1/3y \leq 1$

36. $3y - 3x \leq 2y + x + 1$ or in standard form $y \leq 4x + 1$

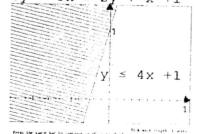

$y \leq 4x + 1$

11

37.

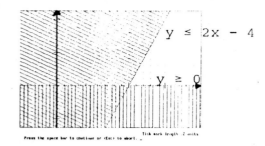

$y \leq 2x - 4$

$y \geq 0$

38.

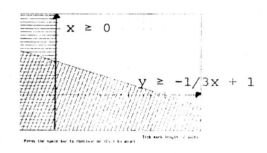

$x \geq 0$

$y \geq -1/3x + 1$

39.

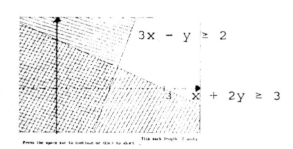

$3x - y \geq 2$

$3x + 2y \geq 3$

40.

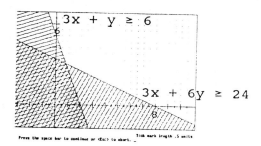

41.

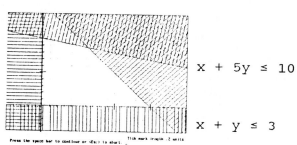

42.

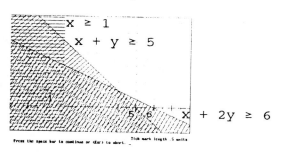

43. (8,7) must satisfy all inequalities to be in the feasible
    set.   6·8 + 3·7 = 69, which is ≤ 96.
              8 + 7 = 15, which is ≤ 18.
              2·8 + 6·7 = 58, which is ≤ 72.
              8 ≥ 0 and 7 ≥ 0,
    So (8,7) is IN the feasible set.

44. (14,3) must satisfy all inequalities to be in the feasible
    set.   6·14 + 3·3 = 93, which is ≤ 96.
              14 + 3 = 17, which is ≤ 18.
              2·14 + 6·3 = 46, which is ≤ 72.
              14 ≥ 0 and 3 ≥ 0,
    So (14,3) is IN the feasible set.

45. (9,10) must satisfy all inequalities to be in the feasible
    set.   6·9 + 3·10 = 84, which is ≤ 96.
              9 + 10 = 19, which is not ≤ 18.
    So (9,10) is NOT IN the feasible set.

13

46. (16,0) must satisfy all inequalities to be in the feasible set. $6 \cdot 16 + 3 \cdot 0 = 96$, which is ≤ 96.
    $16 + 0 = 16$, which is ≤ 18.
    $2 \cdot 16 + 6 \cdot 0 = 32$, which is ≤ 72.
    $16 \geq 0$ and $0 \geq 0$,
    So (16,0) is IN the feasible set.

47. Substituting 3 for x and 9 for y in $y = 2x + 5$ gives 9 on the left and 11 on the right. $9 \leq 11$, so (3,9) is below the line.

48. First the equation must be in standard form:
    $$3x - y = 4$$
    $$-y = -3x + 4$$
    $$y = 3x - 4$$
    Now substituting 2 for x and 3 for y in $y = 3x - 4$ gives 3 on the left and 2 on the right. $3 \geq 2$, so (2,3) is above the line.

49. First the equation must be in standard form:
    $$7 - 4x + 5y = 0$$
    $$5y = 4x - 7$$
    $$y = \frac{4}{5}x - \frac{7}{5}$$

    Now substituting zeros for x and y in $y = \frac{4}{5}x - \frac{7}{5}$ gives 0 on the left and $-\frac{7}{5}$ on the right. $0 \geq -\frac{7}{5}$, so (0,0) is above the line.

50. Substituting 6 for x and 1 for y in $y = \frac{x}{2} - \frac{5}{2}$ (the equation in standard form) gives 1 on the left and $\frac{1}{2}$ on the right. $1 \geq \frac{1}{2}$, so (6,1) is above the line.

51. The standard form of the given pair of lines is $y = 2x - 1$ and $y = 2x$. Since $y = 2x$ is above $y = 2x - 1$ ($b = 0$ for the first line and $b = -1$ for the second one), the region is above $y = 2x - 1$ and below $y = 2x$. The system of inequalities is: $\begin{cases} y \geq 2x - 1 \\ y \leq 2x \end{cases}$

52. Find the slope of the line passing through (-4,0) and (0,5):
    $m = \dfrac{5 - 0}{0 - (-4)} = \dfrac{5}{4}$; the equation of the line is $y = \dfrac{5}{4}x + 5$
    and the region below or on this line is indicated by:
    $y \leq \dfrac{5}{4}x + 5$ written as $4y \leq 5x + 20$ or $-5x + 4y \leq 20$.
    Find the slope of the line passing through (5,0) and (0,2):
    $m = \dfrac{2 - 0}{0 - 5} = -\dfrac{2}{5}$; the equation of the line is $y = -\dfrac{2}{5}x + 2$
    and the region below or on this line is indicated by:

$y \le -\frac{2}{5}x + 2$ written as $y \le -\frac{2}{5}x + 2$, $5y \le -2x + 10$ or $2x + 5y \le 10$.

Find the slope of the line passing through $(5,0)$ and $(0,-3)$: $m = \frac{-3-0}{0-5} = \frac{3}{5}$; the equation of the line is $y = \frac{3}{5}x - 3$ and the region above or on this line is indicated by: $y \ge \frac{3}{5}x - 3$ written as $5y \ge 3x - 15$ or $-3x + 5y \ge -15$.

Find the slope of the line passing through $(-2,0)$ and $(0,-5)$: $m = \frac{-5-0}{0-(-2)} = -\frac{5}{2}$; the equation of the line is $y = -\frac{5}{2}x - 5$ and the region above or on this line is indicated by: $y \ge -\frac{5}{2}x - 5$ written as $2y \ge -5x - 10$ or $5x + 2y \ge -10$.

So the system of linear inequalities is:
$-5x + 4y \le 20$, $2x + 5y \le 10$, $-3x + 5y \ge -15$, $5x + 2y \ge -10$

53. Find the slope of the line passing through $(3,0)$ and $(0,2)$: $m = \frac{2-0}{0-3} = -\frac{2}{3}$; the equation of the line is $y = -\frac{2}{3}x + 2$ and the region below or on this line is indicated by: $y \le -\frac{2}{3}x + 2$ written as $3y \le -2x + 6$ or $2x + 3y \le 6$.

The two vertical lines have $x = -2$ and $x = 4$ as equations, respectively. The region between these lines is expressed by $x \ge -2$ and $x \le 4$. The horizontal line has $y = -3$ as its equation and the region above or on this line is indicated by $y \ge -3$. So the system of linear inequalities is:
$x \ge -2$, $x \le 4$, $2x + 3y \le 6$, $y \ge -3$

54. (a) $(2,5)$ (b) $3.2, 6.8)$ (c) $(2.67, 6)$ (d) $11.067, 18.6)$

55. (a) $(2, -1.533)$ (b) $(10, 3.8)$ (c) $(10.3, 4)$
     (d) $(11.5, 4.8)$

56. (a) $(3.6, 3.7)$ (b) below   57. (a) $(6, 2.5)$ (b) above

1.3 The Intersection Point of a Pair of Lines

1. Set y values equal and solve for x:
$$4x - 5 = -2x + 7$$
$$6x = 12$$
$$x = 2$$
$$y = 4(2) - 5 = 3$$
Intersection point is (2, 3).

2. Set y values equal and solve for x:
$$3x - 15 = -2x + 10$$
$$5x = 25$$
$$x = 5$$
$$y = 3 \cdot 5 - 15 = 0$$
Intersection point is (5,0).

3. Get the standard forms, set y values equal and solve for x:
$$\frac{x}{4} + \frac{1}{2} = -\frac{x}{2} + 2$$
$$\frac{3}{4}x = \frac{3}{2}$$
$$x = 2$$
$$y = \frac{2}{4} + \frac{1}{2} = 1$$
Intersection point is (2,1).

4. Substituting the value of y = 3 in the first equation:
$$2x - 3 \cdot 3 = 3$$
$$2x = 12$$
$$x = 6$$
Intersection point is (6,3).

5. Substituting the value of x = 12 in the first equation:
$$y = \frac{1}{3} \cdot 12 - 1 = 3$$
Intersection point is (12,3).

6. Substituting the value of x = 6 in the first equation:
$$2(6) - 3y = 3$$
$$-3y = -9$$
$$y = 3$$
Intersection point is (6,3).

7. x = 6 and y = 4 must satisfy both equations:
$$6 - 3 \cdot 4 = -6 \qquad \text{True}$$
$$3 \cdot 6 - 2 \cdot 4 = 18 - 8 = 10 \qquad \text{True}$$
therefore yes (6,4) satisfies the system of equations.

8. x = 12 and y = 4 must satisfy both equations:
$$4 = \frac{1}{3} \cdot 12 - 1, \quad 4 = 3 \text{ is false.}$$
(12,4) does not satisfy the system of linear equations.

9. Get the standard forms, set y values equal and solve for x:
$$7 - 2x = x - 3$$
$$-3x = -10$$
$$x = \frac{10}{3}$$
$$y = 7 - 2 \cdot \frac{10}{3} = \frac{1}{3}$$
The solution is $\left(\frac{10}{3}, \frac{1}{3} \right)$.

10. Get the standard forms, set y values equal and solve for x:

$$-\frac{x}{2} + 2 = -x + 6$$

$$\frac{x}{2} = 4$$

$$x = 8$$

$$y = -8 + 6 = -2 \qquad \text{The solution is } (8,-2).$$

11. Get the standard forms, set y values equal and solve for x:

$$\frac{5}{2}x - \frac{1}{2} = -2x - 4$$

$$\frac{9}{2}x = -\frac{7}{2}$$

$$x = -\frac{7}{9}$$

$$y = -2 \cdot \left(-\frac{7}{9}\right) - 4 = -\frac{22}{9} \qquad \text{The solution is } \left(-\frac{7}{9}, -\frac{22}{9}\right).$$

12. Get the standard forms, set y values equal and solve for x:

$$-\frac{x}{2} + 3 = 3x - 12$$

$$-\frac{7}{2}x = -15$$

$$x = \frac{30}{7}$$

$$y = 3 \cdot \left(\frac{30}{7}\right) - 12 = \frac{6}{7} \qquad \text{The solution is } \left(\frac{30}{7}, \frac{6}{7}\right).$$

13. Point A has x-coordinate = 3. It is on the line x = 3. When x = 3,

$$2(3) + 3y = 18$$
$$6 + 3y = 18$$
$$3y = 12$$
$$y = 4$$

So the coordinates of vertex A are (3,4).

Point B has y-coordinate = 2. It is on the line y = 2. When y = 2,

$$2x + 3 \cdot 2 = 18$$
$$2x = 12$$
$$x = 6$$

So the coordinates of vertex B are (6,2).

14. Point A is on the y-axis, so x = 0 in the equation

$$y = \frac{x}{3} + 7: \qquad y = \frac{0}{3} + 7 = 7$$

So the coordinates of vertex A are (0,7).

Point B is the intersection of $y = -\frac{x}{3} + 7$ and $y = -x + 9$.

Setting y values equal and solving for x:

$$-\frac{x}{3} + 7 = -x + 9$$

$$\frac{2}{3}x = 2$$

$$x = 3$$

$$y = -\frac{1}{3} \cdot 3 + 7 = 6 \qquad \text{The coordinates of vertex B are}$$

(3,6).
Point C is the intersection of $y = -x + 9$ and $y = -3x + 19$.
Setting y values equal and solving for x:
$-x + 9 = -3x + 19$
$\quad 2x = 10$
$\quad\ x = 5$
$\quad\ y = -3 \cdot 5 + 19 = 4$ The coordinates of vertex C are (5,4).
Point D is on the x-axis, so $y = 0$ in the equation
$\quad y = -3x + 19:$ $\qquad\qquad 0 = -3x + 19$
$$3x = 19$$
$$x = \frac{19}{3}$$
So the coordinates of vertex D are $\left(\frac{19}{3}, 0\right)$.

15. The coordinates of vertices A and D are easy to determine:
A = (0,0) is the origin and D = (5,0) is the intersection of
the x-axis
and the line $x = 5$.
Point B is the intersection of lines $y = 2x$ and
$y = \frac{1}{2}x + 3$.
Setting y values equal and solving for x:
$2x = \frac{1}{2}x + 3$

$\frac{3}{2}x = 3$

$\ x = 2$
$\ y = 2 \cdot 2 = 4$ $\qquad$ So the coordinates of vertex B are (2,4).
Point C has x-coordinate $x = 5$. Replacing this value in
$\quad y = \frac{1}{2}x + 3;$ $\qquad y = \frac{1}{2} \cdot 5 + 3 = \frac{11}{2}$.
So the coordinates of vertex C are $\left(5, \frac{11}{2}\right)$.

16. Point A is on the y-axis, so $x = 0$ in the equation
$2x + y = 14;$ $\qquad 2 \cdot 0 + y = 14$
$\qquad\qquad\qquad\qquad\qquad y = 14$
So the coordinates of vertex A are (0,14).
Point D is on the x-axis, so $y = 0$ in the equation
$x + 2y = 12:$ $\qquad x + 2 \cdot 0 = 12$
$\qquad\qquad\qquad\qquad\quad x = 12$
So the coordinates of vertex D are (12,0).
Point B is the intersection of $2x + y = 14$ and $3x + 2y = 24$.
Getting the standard forms, setting y values equal and
solving for x:
$$-2x + 14 = -\frac{3}{2}x + 12$$
$$-\frac{1}{2}x = -2$$
$$x = 4$$
$y = -2 \cdot 4 + 14 = 6$. So the coordinates of vertex B are (4,6).
Point C is the intersection of $3x + 2y = 24$ and $x + 2y = 12$.
Getting the standard forms, setting y values equal and
solving for x:

$$-\frac{3}{2}x + 12 = -\frac{x}{2} + 6$$
$$-x = -6$$
$$x = 6$$

$y = -\frac{1}{2} \cdot 6 + 6 = 3$. So the coordinates of vertex C are $(6,3)$.

17.

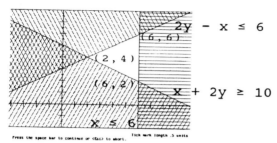

To find the coordinates of the vertices, we write the set of inequalities as equalities in standard form and find the intersection between each pair of the lines:

$$y = \frac{x}{2} + 3, \quad y = -\frac{x}{2} + 5 \quad \text{and} \quad x = 6.$$

The intersection of the first two lines is

$$\frac{x}{2} + 3 = -\frac{x}{2} + 5$$

$x = 2$ and $y = 4$, the point $(2,4)$.
The other two vertices are on the line $x = 6$ with:

$y = \frac{6}{2} + 3 = 6$, therefore the point is $(6,6)$.

$y = -\frac{6}{2} + 5 = 2$, therefore the point is $(6,2)$.

18.

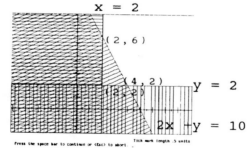

$(2,2)$ is the intersection of $x = 2$ and $y = 2$.
Replacing $x = 2$ in the equation $y = -2x + 10$ from $2x + y = 10$ gives:

$y = -2 \cdot 2 + 10 = 6$, the point of intersection is $(2,6)$.

Replacing $y = 2$ in the equation $x = -\frac{y}{2} + 5$ from $2x + y = 10$ gives:

$x = -\frac{2}{2} + 10 = 9$, the point of intersection is $(4,2)$.

$(2,6)$ and $(4,2)$ are the vertices of the feasible set and $(2,2)$ is not since it lies outside of the set.

19

19.

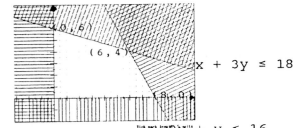

First, solve each inequality for y:

$$x + 3y \leq 18$$
$$3y \leq -x + 18$$
$$y \leq -\frac{1}{3}x + 6 \qquad \text{When } x = 0, \ y = 6$$
$$\text{When } y = 0, \ x = 18$$

$$2x + y \leq 16$$
$$y \leq -2x + 16 \qquad \text{When } x = 0, \ y = 16.$$
$$\text{When } y = 0, \ x = 8.$$

The intersection of the last two lines is:

$$-\frac{1}{3}x + 6 = -2x + 16,$$
$$\frac{5}{3}x = 10$$
$$x = 6 \qquad \text{Using either inequality, when } x = 6,$$
$$y = 4 \text{ so the point is } (6,4)$$

The vertices of the feasible set are (0,0), (0,6), (6,4) and (8,0). The other points of intersection (0,16) and (18,0) lay outside of the feasible set so they are not vertices. All have to be tested for feasibility however.

20.

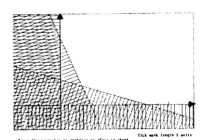

First, solve each inequality for y:

$$5x + 2y \geq 14$$
$$2y \leq -5x + 14$$
$$y \leq -\frac{5}{2}x + 7 \qquad \text{When } x = 0, \ y = 7$$
$$\text{When } y = 0, \ x = \frac{14}{5} = 2.8$$

$$x + 3y \leq 8$$
$$y \leq -\frac{1}{3}x + \frac{8}{3} \qquad \text{When } x = 0, \ y = \frac{8}{3}.$$
$$\text{When } y = 0, \ x = 8.$$

The intersection of the last two lines is:

$$-\frac{5}{2}x + 7 = -\frac{1}{3}x + \frac{8}{3}$$

$$-\frac{13}{6}x = -\frac{13}{3}$$

$$x = 2$$ Using either inequality, when x = 2,
y = 2 so the point is (2,2)

The vertices of the feasible set are (0,7), (2,2) and (8,0).
The other points of intersection (0,0) (0,8/3) and (2.8,0)
lie outside of the feasible set so they are not vertices.
All have to be tested for feasibility, however.

21.

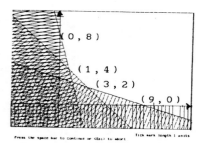

First, solve each inequality for y:

$$4x + y \geq 8$$
$$y \geq -4x + 8$$ When x = 0, y = 8
     When y = 0, x = 2

$$x + y \geq 5$$
$$y \geq -x + 5$$ When x = 0, y = 5
     When y = 0, x = 5

$$x + 3y \geq 9$$
$$3y \geq -x + 9$$

$$y \geq -\frac{1}{3}x + 3$$ When x = 0, y = 3

     When y = 0, x = 9

The intersection of the first and second lines is:

$$-4x + 8 = -x + 5$$
$$-3x = -3$$
$$x = 1$$ Using either inequality, when x = 1,
y = 4 so the point is (1,4)

The intersection of the second and third lines is:

$$-x + 5 = -\frac{1}{3}x + 3$$

$$-\frac{2}{3}x = -2$$

$$x = 3$$ Using either inequality, when x = 3,
y = 2 so the point is (3,2)

The vertices of the feasible set are (0,8), (1,4), (3,2) and
(9,0). The other points of intersection (0,5), (0,3), (5,0)
and (2,0) lie outside of the feasible set so they are not
vertices. All have to be tested for feasibility, however.

21

22.

(0,7)
(4,6)
(7,3)
(8,0)

$x + 4y \leq 28$

$x + y \leq 10$

$3x + y \leq 24$

First, solve each inequality for y:

$$x + 4y \leq 28$$
$$4y \leq -x + 28$$
$$y \leq -\frac{1}{4}x + 7 \qquad \text{When } x = 0, y = 7.$$
$$\text{When } y = 0, x = 28.$$

$$x + y \leq 10$$
$$y \leq -x + 10 \qquad \text{When } x = 0, y = 10.$$
$$\text{When } y = 0, x = 10.$$

$$3x + y \leq 24$$
$$y \leq -3x + 24$$
$$y \leq -3x + 24 \qquad \text{When } x = 0, y = 24.$$
$$\text{When } y = 0, x = 8.$$

The intersection of the first and second lines is:

$$-\frac{1}{4}x + 7 = -x + 10$$

$$\frac{3}{4}x = 3$$

$$x = 4 \qquad \text{Using either inequality, when } x = 4,$$
$$y = 6 \text{ so the point is } (4,6).$$

The intersection of the second and third lines is:

$$-x + 10 = -3x + 24$$
$$2x = 14$$
$$x = 7 \qquad \text{Using either inequality, when } x = 7,$$
$$y = 3 \text{ so the point is } (7,3).$$

Therefore the vertices are (0,7) since 7 < 10 < 24, (4,6), (7,3) and (8,0) since 8 < 10 < 28.
The vertices of the feasible set are (0,0), (0,7), (4,6), (7,3) and (8,0). The other points of intersection (0,10), (0,8), (10,0) and (28,0) lie outside of the feasible set so they are not vertices. All have to be tested for feasibility, however.

23. (a) For q = 10,000p - 500 when p = $2

$$q = 10,000(2) - 500$$
$$q = 20,000 - 500 = 19,500 \text{ units will be sold.}$$

(b) If q = 0, then
$$0 = 10,000p - 500$$
$$500 = 10,000p$$
$$p = \$0.05 \text{ or } 5 \text{ cents per unit.}$$

24. (a) p = $1 per unit, so q = -1,000·1 + 32,500 = 31,500.
(b) q = 0, so 0 = -1000p + 32500. Solving for p, p = $32.50.

22

25. (a) Solving the system of linear equations
$$q = 10,000p - 500 \text{ and } q = -1000p + 32,500 \text{ so}$$
$$10000p - 500 = -1000p + 32500$$
$$11000p = 33000$$
$$p = \$3$$
(b) Replacing $p = \$3$ in any of the two equations:
$$q = 10,000 \cdot 3 - 500 = 29,500 \text{ units.}$$

26. From the equation of L_1 we get the x- and y-intercepts: $(-2,0)$ and $(0,6)$; hence, the x- and y-intercepts of L_2 are: $(-1,0)$ and $(0,8)$. We can find the equation of L_2 using its x-intercept and the slope/y-intercept formula:
$$0 = m_2 \cdot -1 + 8$$
$$m_2 = 8 \quad \text{so the equation of } L_2 \text{ is } y = 8x + 8.$$
Equating L_1 and L_2: $3x + 6 = 8x + 8$
$$-5x = 2$$
$$x = -\frac{2}{5}$$
Substituting $x = -\frac{2}{5}$ we get $y = 3 \cdot -\frac{2}{5} + 6 = \frac{24}{5}$.

So the point of intersection of L_1 and L_2 is $\left(-\frac{2}{5}, \frac{24}{5}\right)$.

27. Let x be the number of hours working on the assembly line and y the number of hours supervising the work of others. We know the total number of working hours is 40, therefore:
$$x + y = 40$$
and the plant supervisor's earnings of the week are $504 so:
$$12x + 15y = 504.$$
Get the standard forms, set y values equal and solve for x:
$$40 - x = \frac{168}{5} - \frac{4}{5}x$$
$$200 - 5x = 168 - 4x$$
$$x = 32 \quad \text{and } 32 + y = 40, \text{ so } y = 8.$$
The supervisor spends 32 hours working and 8 supervising.

28. (1.5, 3) 29. (4, 2) 30. (1, 1) 31. (2, .75) 32. (1, -2)

33. (b) (2, 1) (c) yes 34. (b) (3, 2) (c) no

23

1.4 The Slope of a Straight Line

1. $y = \frac{2}{3}x + 7$ is in slope-intercept form, so the slope $m = \frac{2}{3}$.

2. When we write the equation in standard form $y = 0 \cdot x - 4$, we see that $m = 0$.

3. When we write the equation in standard form $y = 5x + 23$, we see that $m = 5$.

4. When we write the equation in standard form $y = -\frac{7}{5}x + 2$, we see that $m = -\frac{7}{5}$.

5. Graph line between (3,4) and (7,9) Slope $= \frac{9 - 4}{7 - 3} = \frac{5}{4}$

6. Graph line between (-2,1) and (3, -3) Slope $= \frac{-3 - 1}{3 - (-2)} = -\frac{4}{5}$

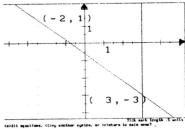

7. Graph line between (0,0) and (5,4) Slope $= \frac{4-0}{5-0} = \frac{4}{5}$

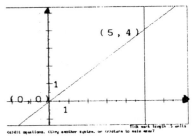

24

8. Graph line between (4, 17) and (-2, 17)   Slope = $\dfrac{17 - 17}{-2 - 4} = 0$

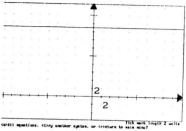

9. Not defined.

10. Because the line is vertical and its slope is not defined.

11. Graph y = -2x + 1

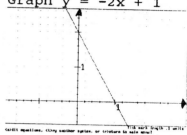

12. Graph y = 4x -2

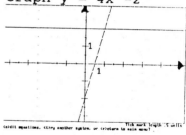

13. Graph y = 3x

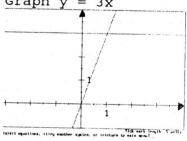

14. Graph y = -2

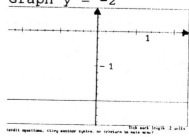

Use the point-slope formula for 15-22.

15. $m = -\frac{2}{1} = -2$, $\quad y - 3 = -2 \cdot (x - 2)$,

$$y = -2x + 7$$

16. $m = \frac{1/2}{1} = \frac{1}{2}$, $\quad y - 1 = \frac{1}{2} \cdot (x - 3)$,

$$y = \frac{1}{2}x - \frac{1}{2}$$

17. $m = \frac{0 - 2}{2 - 1} = -2$, $\quad y - 2 = -2 \cdot (x - 1)$,

$$y = -2x + 4$$

18. $m = \frac{2 - 1/2}{1 - (-1)} = \frac{3/2}{2} = \frac{3}{4}$, $\quad y - 2 = \frac{3}{4} \cdot (x - 1)$,

$$y = \frac{3}{4}x + \frac{5}{4}$$

19. Since L is perpendicular to $y = -4x + 10$, its slope is $\frac{1}{4}$.

$$y - 2 = \frac{1}{4}(x - 2)$$

$$y - 2 = \frac{1}{4}x - \frac{1}{2}$$

$$y = \frac{1}{4}x + \frac{3}{2} \qquad \text{or} \qquad 4y = x + 6.$$

20. Since L is parallel to $y = \frac{1}{3}x$, its slope is $\frac{1}{3}$.

$$y - 3 = \frac{1}{3} \cdot (x - 5), \quad y = \frac{1}{3}x + \frac{4}{3}.$$

21. Since L is parallel to $y = -x + 2$, its slope is -1.
L passes through the origin: $y - 0 = -1 \cdot (x - 0)$, $\quad y = -x$

22. Since L is perpendicular to $y = -\frac{1}{2}x$, its slope is 2.

$$y - (-1) = 2 \cdot (x - 2), \quad y = 2x - 5.$$

23. Since the line is parallel to the x-axis, its slope is 0:
$y - 3 = 0 \cdot (x - 2)$, $\quad y = 3$,

24. $y - 0 = \frac{3}{2} \cdot (x - 0)$, $\quad y = \frac{3}{2}x$

25. $y - 6 = \frac{3}{5}(x - 5)$

$$y = \frac{3}{5}x - 3 + 6$$

$$y = \frac{3}{5}x + 3 \qquad\qquad \text{The y-intercept is } (0,3).$$

26. $m = \frac{4 - 4}{0 - 1} = 0$

27. Each unit sold yields a commission of \$5. In addition, she receives \$60 per week base pay.

28. $y = 4x + 2000$

29. (a) $1200; at $1200, no one will buy the item
    (b) 400 items; even if the item is given away, only 400 people will want it
    (c) - 3; to sell an additional item, the price must be reduced by $3
    (d) p = -3·350 + 1200 = -1050 + 1200, p = $150
    (e) 300 = -3q + 1200, q = 300 items
    (f)

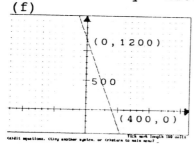

30. (a) (F,c) Two points are known (68,124) and (80,172).
    $m = \dfrac{172 - 124}{80 - 68} = \dfrac{48}{12} = 4$, c - 172 = 4 (F - 80)

    $c = 4 \cdot F - 148$ or $F = \dfrac{1}{4}c + 37$

    (b) The linear equation $F = \dfrac{1}{4}c + 37$ takes (c) chirps per minute, divides it by 4 which gives the number of chirps per 15 seconds, and adds 37 to get temperature. Since we already have the number of chirps per 15 seconds then to get the temperature we need only add 37.

31. (a) Let y = cost and x = number of radios. One then knows the points (20,6800) and (50,9500),
    therefore the slope is $m = \dfrac{9500-6800}{50-20} = 90$ and
    y -6800 = 90(x - 20)
         y = 90x + 5000
    (b) The fixed cost is the y-intercept = $5000.
    (c) The marginal cost of production is the slope = $90.
    (d)

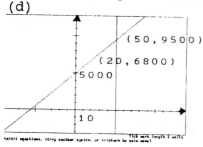

32. (a) y = 40·100 + 2400 = $6400
    (b) 3600 = 40x + 2400, x = 30 coats
    (c) y = 40·0 + 2400 = 2400, y-intercept is (0,2400); fixed costs are $2400.
    (d) The slope is 40; it represents the variable cost: each additional coat costs an additional $40 to make.

33. (a) $y = 100 \cdot 300 = \$30,000$,
    (b) $6000 = 100x$, $x = 60$ coats,
    (c) $(0,0)$; if no coats are sold, there is no revenue,
    (d) $\$100$, each additional coat yields an additional $\$100$ in revenue. Therefore, $\$100$ is the selling price of the coat.

34. (a) $y = \text{revenue} - \text{cost} = 100x - (40x + 2400) = 60x - 2400$
    (b) $(0,-2400)$; If no coats are sold, $\$2400$ will be lost. That is, the fixed costs are $\$2400$.
    (c) $(40,0)$; The break even point is $x = 40$. Less than 40 coats made and sold yields a loss, more than 40 coats yields a profit.
    (d) 60; Each additional coat the company makes and sells yields an additional $\$60$ profit.
    (e) $y = 60 \cdot 80 - 2400 = 4800 - 2400 = \$2400$
    (f) $6000 = 60x - 2400$, $x = \frac{8400}{60} = 140$ coats

    (g)

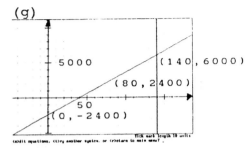

35. $y = 30,000 - 400t$
    When $t = 0$, $y = 30,000$.
    When $t = 50$, $y = 10,000$.
    When $t = 75$, $y = 0$.

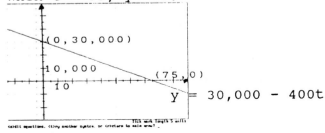

36. $y = 30000 - 400 \cdot 31 = 17,600$ gallons

37. $y = 30000 - 400 \cdot 45 = 12,000$ gallons

38. $y = 30000 - 400 \cdot 0 = 30000$. The y-intercept is $(0,30,000)$; on Jan. 1 the tank contained 30,000 gallons of oil.

39. $0 = 30000 - 400t$, $t = \frac{30000}{400} = 75$. The t-intercept is $(75,0)$; the tank will be empty after 75 days.

28

40.

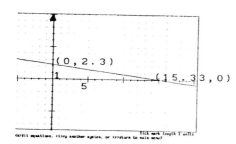

41. July 16 is 15 days after July 1, so t = 15. Then
$$y = 2.3 - (.15)(15)$$
$$y = 2.3 - 2.25 = \$0.05 \text{ million or } \$50,000.$$

42. $y = 2.3 - .15 \cdot 0 = 2.3$. So the y-intercept is $(0, 2.3)$; it means that \$2.3 million is the amount of cash reserves on July 1.

43. $0 = 2.3 - .15t$, $.15t = 2.3$, $t = \dfrac{2.3}{.15} = 15.33$ or $15\frac{1}{3}$. The t-intercept is $(15\frac{1}{3}, 0)$. It means that the cash reserves will be depleted after $15\frac{1}{3}$ days; that is, during July 16.

44. $y = 2.3 - .15 \cdot 3 = \$1.85 \text{ million}$

45. $.8 = 2.3 - .15t$, $.15t = 1.5$, $t = 10$. The cash reserves will be \$.8 million the morning of July 11, that is, after 10 days.

46. Let y = # of accidents and x = # of overtime hours. Two points are $(1000, 8)$ and $(400, 5)$; the slope is: $m = \dfrac{8-5}{1000-400} = \dfrac{3}{600} = \dfrac{1}{200}$.

$$y - 8 = \frac{1}{200}(x - 1000)$$
$$y = \frac{1}{200}x - 5 + 8$$
$$y = \frac{1}{200}x + 3$$

47. $y = \dfrac{1}{200} \cdot 0 + 3 = 3$, so, $x = 0$ hours, we expect 3 accidents.

48. $y = \dfrac{1}{200} \cdot 2000 + 3 = 10 + 3 = 13$ accidents

49. $10 = \dfrac{1}{200}x + 3$, $7 = \dfrac{1}{200}x$, $x = 1400$ hours

50. $y = .10x + 160$

51. $y = .10 \cdot 1000 + 160 = \$260.00$

52. $500 = .10x + 160$, $.10x = 340$, $x = \$3400$

53. $y = 3x - 1$

54. $y = -\frac{1}{2}x$

55. $m = 1$, $y - 2 = 1 \cdot (x - 1)$ or $y = x + 1$

56. $m = -\frac{1}{3}$, $y - (-2) = -\frac{1}{3} \cdot (x - 6)$ or $y = -\frac{1}{3}x$

57. $m = -7$, $y - 0 = -7 \cdot (x - 5)$ or $y = -7x + 35$

58. $m = \frac{1}{2}$, $y - (-3) = \frac{1}{2} \cdot (x - 2)$ or $y = \frac{1}{2}x - 4$

59. Slope = 0 implies a horizontal line, so noting point (7,4), $y = 4$.

60. (0,5) is the y-intercept (0,b), the equation is $y = -\frac{2}{5}x + 5$.

61. The slope is: $m = \frac{2 - 1}{4 - 2} = \frac{1}{2}$

    $y - 1 = \frac{1}{2} (x - 2)$ or $y = \frac{1}{2}x$

62. The slope is: $m = \frac{3 - (-3)}{-1 - 5} = -1$

    $y - (-3) = -1 \cdot (x - 5)$ or $y = -x + 2$

63. The slope is $m = -\frac{2}{1} = -2$ and the equation is $y = -2x$

64. Both points have -1 as y-coordinate, so the line is horizontal: $y = -1$.

65. The equation is $y - 3 = 2 \cdot (x - 1)$ or $y = 2x + 1$
    First point: $y = 2 \cdot 2 + 1 = 5$ (2,5)
    Second point: $y = 2 \cdot 0 + 1 = 1$ (0,1)
    Third point: $y = 2 \cdot -1 + 1 = -1$ (-1,-1)

66. The equation is $y - 2 = -3(x - 2)$ or $y = -3x + 8$
    First point: $y = -3 \cdot 3 + 8 = -1$ (3,-1)
    Second point: $y = -3 \cdot 4 + 8 = -4$ (4,-4)
    Third point: $y = -3 \cdot 1 + 8 = 5$ (1,5)

67. The equation is $y - (-1) = -\frac{1}{4} \cdot (x - (-1))$ or $y = -\frac{1}{4}x - \frac{5}{4}$

    First point: $y = -\frac{1}{4} \cdot 0 - \frac{5}{4} = -\frac{5}{4}$ $(0,-\frac{5}{4})$

    Second point: $y = -\frac{1}{4} \cdot 1 - \frac{5}{4} = -\frac{3}{2}$ $(1,-\frac{3}{2})$

    Third point: $y = -\frac{1}{4} \cdot -2 - \frac{5}{4} = -\frac{3}{4}$ $(-2,-\frac{3}{4})$

68. The equation is $y - 2 = \frac{1}{3} \cdot (x - (-5))$ or $y = \frac{1}{3}x + \frac{11}{3}$

First point: $y = \frac{1}{3} \cdot -4 + \frac{11}{3} = \frac{7}{3}$ $\qquad$ $(-4, \frac{7}{3})$

Second point: $y = \frac{1}{3} \cdot -3 + \frac{11}{3} = \frac{8}{3}$ $\qquad$ $(-3, \frac{8}{3})$

Third point: $y = \frac{1}{3} \cdot -2 + \frac{11}{3} = 3$ $\qquad$ $(-2, 3)$

69. l_1

70. l_2

71. Using (C, F) points $(0, 32)$ and $(100, 212)$, $m = \frac{180}{100} = \frac{9}{5}$ and

$F - 32 = \frac{9}{5}(C - 0)$

$F = \frac{9}{5}C + 32$

72. Using the points $(4, 1500)$ and $(8, 2100)$,

the slope is $m = \frac{2100 - 1500}{8 - 4} = \frac{600}{4} = 150$.

$y - 1500 = 150 \cdot (x - 4)$, $y = 150x + 900$
To look for relics from 3000 B.C., he should dig:

$\qquad 3000 = 150x + 900$

$\qquad 2100 = 150x$

$\qquad x = 14$ feet.

73. When $y = 6$ million then $x = 0$, since 1920 is zero years after 1920. When $y = 2$ million then $x = 60$ since 1980 is 60 years after 1920. The slope then of the equation passing by $(0, 6)$ and $(60, 2)$ is

$m = \frac{2 - 6}{60 - 0} = -\frac{1}{15}$.

The y intercept of the equation is $(0, 6)$ so the equation is:

$$y = -\frac{1}{15}x + 6.$$

1965 is 45 years after 1920 so $x = 45$. We use the equation

to calculate y. $\qquad y = -\frac{1}{15} \cdot 45 + 6$

$\qquad\qquad y = -3 + 6 = 3$

Therefore, there were 3 million farms in the U.S. in 1965.

74. When $y = 100$ acres then $x = 0$ since 1920 is zero years after 1920. When $y = 700$ acres then $x = 60$ since 1980 is 60 years after 1920. The slope then of the equation passing by $(0, 100)$ and $(60, 700)$ is

$m = \frac{700 - 100}{60 - 0} = \frac{600}{60} = 10$.

The y intercept of is $(0, 100)$ so the equation is:

$\qquad\qquad y = 10x + 100$.

The size of the farm will be 600 acres when y = 600. We use
the equation to calculate x.   600 = 10x + 100
                                  500 = 10x
                                    x = 50
The size of the farm will be 600 acres 50 years after 1920,
or in 1970.

75. Counterclockwise

76. The equation of the line is y = 2x + 1. The inequality is
     y ≤ 2x + 1.

77. The equation of the line is y = .4x + 3. The inequality is
     y ≥ .4x + 3.

78. Find the slope of the line passing through (-2,5) and (2,8):
     $m = \dfrac{8 - 5}{2 - (-2)} = \dfrac{3}{4}$; the equation of the line is

     $y - 8 = \dfrac{3}{4} \cdot (x - 2)$ or $y = \dfrac{3}{4}x + \dfrac{13}{2}$ or -3x + 4y = 26.
     The region below or on the line is written: -3x + 4y ≤ 26.
     Find the slope of the line passing through (2,8) and (5,1):
     $m = \dfrac{1 - 8}{5 - 2} = -\dfrac{7}{3}$; the equation of the line is

     $y - 1 = -\dfrac{7}{3} \cdot (x - 5)$ or $y = -\dfrac{7}{3}x + \dfrac{38}{3}$ or 7x + 3y = 38.
     The region below or on the line is written: 7x +3y ≤ 38.
     Find the slope of the line passing through (5,1) and (-2,5):
     $m = \dfrac{5 - 1}{-2 - 5} = -\dfrac{4}{7}$; the equation of the line is

     $y - 1 = -\dfrac{4}{7} \cdot (x - 5)$ or $y = -\dfrac{4}{7}x + \dfrac{27}{7}$ or 4x + 7y = 27.
     The region above or on the line is written: 4x + 7y ≥ 27.

     So the system of linear inequalities is: $\begin{cases} -3x + 4y \le 26 \\ 7x + 3y \le 38 \\ 4x + 7y \ge 27 \end{cases}$

79. The region is limited by the x- and y-axis: x ≥ 0 and y ≥ 0.
     Find the slope of the line passing through (0,4) and (2,3):
     $m = \dfrac{3 - 4}{2 - 0} = -\dfrac{1}{2}$; the equation of the line is

     $y = -\dfrac{1}{2}x + 4$ or x + 2y = 8.
     The region below or on this line is written: x + 2y ≤ 8.
     Find the slope of the line passing through (2,3) and (4,1):
     $m = \dfrac{1 - 3}{4 - 2} = -\dfrac{2}{2} = -1$; the equation of the line is
     y - 1 = -1·(x - 4) or y = -x + 5 or x + y = 5.
     The region below or on this line is written: x + y ≤ 5.
     Find the slope of the line passing through (4,1) and (3,0):
     $m = \dfrac{0 - 1}{3 - 4} = 1$; the equation of the line is
     y - 0 = 1·(x - 3) or y = x - 3 or -x + y = -3.
     The region above or on this line is written: -x + y ≥ -3.

So the system of linear inequalities is: $\begin{cases} x + 2y \le 8 \\ x + y \le 5 \\ -x + y \ge -3 \\ x \ge 0, \ y \ge 0 \end{cases}$

80. The slope of the line passing through $(1,3)$ and $(2,4)$ is:
$$m_1 = \frac{4 - 3}{2 - 1} = 1$$
The slope of the line passing through $(1,3)$ and $(3,-1)$ is:
$$m_2 = \frac{-1 - 3}{3 - 1} = -2$$
m_1 and m_2 are different, so the points are not on the same line.

81. Choosing two pairs of points, we should get the same slope:
$$\frac{k - 7}{3 - 2} = \frac{7 - 5}{2 - 1} \text{ or } k - 7 = 2 \text{ or } k = 9.$$

82. If the lines are parallel, then they have the same slope:
$$\frac{-3.1 - 1}{2 - a} = \frac{2.4 - 0}{3.8 - (-1)}$$
$$4.8 \cdot (-4.1) = 2.4 \cdot (2 - a)$$
$$-8.2 = 2 - a \qquad \text{or } a = 10.2$$

83. The line through $(-1,0)$ and $(3.8,2.4)$ has slope $= \frac{2.4}{4.8} = \frac{1}{2}$
Thus a line perpendicular to the one above has a slope $= -2$
To find a in $(a,1)$ and $(2,-3.1)$,
$$\frac{1-(-3.1)}{a - 2} = -2$$
$$4.1 = -2a + 4$$
$$0.1 = -2a$$
$$a = -\frac{1}{20} \text{ or } -.05$$

84. Assume the lines cross. Then there is an x such that the lines are equal. we then have $mx + b = m'x + b'$ and solve for x, $x = \frac{-b + b'}{m - m'}$ has a solution unless the denominator is zero, i.e. $m - m' = 0$ or $m = m'$. Therefore, if the slopes are equal we have a contradiction and the lines do not cross i.e. they are parallel.

85. With the assumptions of the hint, we have three right triangles in the figure:
l_1 hypotenuse length a, legs m_1 and 1
l_2 hypotenuse length b, legs $-m_2$ and 1
$l_1 + l_2$ hypotenuse length $m_1 - m_2$, legs a and b.

By the Pythagorean property

I. $a^2 = m_1^2 + 1^2$ II. $b^2 = m_2^2 + 1^2$

III. $(m_1 - m_2)^2 = a^2 + b^2$

Substituting I. and II. into III.

$$(m_1 - m_2)^2 = m_1^2 + 1^2 + m_2^2 + 1^2$$
$$m_1^2 - 2m_1m_2 + m_2^2 = m_1^2 + m_2^2 + 2$$
$$- 2m_1m_2 = 2$$
$$m_1m_2 = -1$$
$$m_1 = \frac{-1}{m_2}$$

To show the converse, we assume that $d_1 = m_1 = a$ and $d_2 = m_2 = -b$. Then show that the Pythagorean property holds in the triangle POQ. The Pythagoran property holds in each of the small triangles since PQ was drawn perpenicular to the x-axis. Thus, $a^2 = 1 + d_1^2$ and $b^2 = 1 + d_2^2$. And, $a^2 + b^2 = (1 + d_1^2) + (1 + d_2^2) = (d_1 + d_2)^2$ because $d_1d_2 = 1$.

86. -.75 88. (-21, 17)

34

SUPPLEMENTARY EXERCISES

1. The equation of the y-axis is x = 0.

2.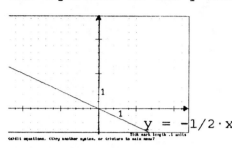

$$y = -1/2 \cdot x$$

3. Put in standard form:

   Solve for y : x - 5y = 6   Solve for x (since no y):

   $$-5y = -x + 6$$ $$3x = 6$$

   $$y = \frac{1}{5}x - \frac{6}{5}$$ $$x = 2$$

   Set x = 2 $$y = \frac{1}{5}(2) - \frac{6}{5} = -\frac{4}{5}$$

   So the point of intersection is (2,-4/5)

4. Writing 3x - 4y = 8 in the standard form:

   $$-4y = -3x + 8 \text{ or } y = \frac{3}{4}x - 2$$

   The slope is $\frac{3}{4}$

5. The slope is $m = \frac{0 - 5}{10 - 0} = -\frac{1}{2}$ and b = 5, since y-intercept is

   (0, 5). The equation of the line is $y = -\frac{1}{2} x + 5$

6.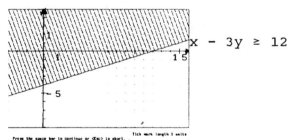

   $$x - 3y \geq 12$$

7. Yes.   When x = 1 and y = 2, 3(1) + 4(2) ≥ 11 or 11 ≥ 11.

8. Put in standard form:

   2x - y = 1   x + 2y = 13

   $$y = 2x - 1$$ $$2y = -x + 13$$

   $$y = -\frac{1}{2}x + \frac{13}{2}.$$

   $$2x - 1 = -\frac{x}{2} + \frac{13}{2}$$

   $$4x - 2 = -x + 13$$

   $$5x = 15$$

   $$x = 3$$

   $$y = 2\cdot3 - 1 = 5 \text{ So the point of intersection is } (3,5).$$

9. The standard form of the equation of $2x - 10y = 7$ is:
    $$y = \frac{1}{5}x - \frac{7}{10}.$$
    So the slope of the straight line is $\frac{1}{5}$. The equation of the line passing through $(15,16)$ and with slope $1/5$ is:
    $$y - 16 = \frac{1}{5}(x - 15)$$
    $$y = \frac{1}{5}x + 13$$

10. Replacing $x = 1$ in the equation of the line:
    $$y = 3 \cdot 1 + 7 = 10$$

11. The x-intercept has 0 as its y-coordinate and since the x-coordinate is always 5, the x-intercept is $(5,0)$.

12.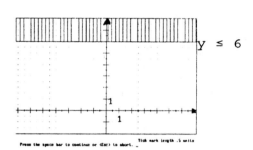

13. $\quad 3x - 2y = 1$
    $\quad\ 2x + y = 24 \qquad\qquad$ Solve for y in both equations and set them equal to each other.
    $$y = \frac{3}{2}x - \frac{1}{2} = -2x + 24$$
    $$x = 7 \qquad \text{Substitute } x = 7 \text{ in either equation.}$$
    $$3(7) - 2y = 1$$
    $$21 - 2y = 1$$
    $$20 = 2y$$
    $$y = 10 \text{ so the solution is } (7, 10).$$

14.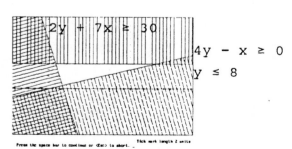

15. The equation of the line is $y - 9 = \frac{1}{2}(x - 4)$ or $y = \frac{1}{2}x + 7$. When $x = 0$, $y = 7$; the y-intercept is $(0,7)$.

36

16. Moving costs are \$35 per hour with an additional fixed cost (called running time) of \$20.

17. The slope of the line that passes through (1,2) and (2,0) is: $m_1 = \frac{0 - 2}{2 - 1} = -2$.

    The slope of the line that passes through (2,0) and (3,1) is: $m_2 = \frac{1 - 0}{3 - 2} = 1$.

    m_1 and m_2 are different, so the points are not on the same line.

18. Find the slope: $m = \frac{-2 - 0}{0 - 3} = \frac{2}{3}$. From y-intercept $b = -2$.

    So the equation of the line is $y = \frac{2}{3}x - 2$

19. Solving each for y:
    $$y = -\frac{4}{6}x + \frac{a}{6} = -\frac{2}{3}x + \frac{a}{6}$$
    $$y = -\frac{2}{3}x + \frac{b}{3}$$
    Since the slopes are equal, the lines are parallel and have no solution unless $\frac{a}{6} = \frac{b}{3}$ or $a = 2b$. Then the lines coincide in all points.

20. The equation of the line is $y = \frac{2}{3}x + \frac{3}{2}$. We are interested in the half-plane below the line, so the inequality is
    $$y \leq \frac{2}{3}x + \frac{3}{2}.$$

21. The slope is: $m = \frac{8.6 - (-1)}{6 - 2} = 2.4$ and the equation of the line is: $y - (-1) = 2.4 \cdot (x - 2)$ or $y = 2.4x - 5.8$.
    We are interested in the half-plane above the line, so the inequality is $y \geq 2.4x - 5.8$.

22. First switch the order of the terms in the second equation.
    1.2x + 2.4y = .6   Multiply the first equation by -2.
    -1.6x + 4.8y = 2.4

           -2.4x - 4.8y = -1.2
           -1.6x + 4.8y = 2.4   Adding
           ─────────────────────
            -4x   = 1.2   or   x = -.3
    Calculate y by substituting x = -.3 into either equation.
         2.4y = .6 - 1.2(-.3)
         2.4y = .96   or   y = .4

37

23. We first find the intersection of the lines by setting the values of y equal and solving for x:

$$-x + 1 = 2x + 3$$
$$-3x = 2$$
$$x = -\frac{2}{3} \quad \text{and} \quad y = -\left(-\frac{2}{3}\right) + 1 = \frac{5}{3}$$

Now we find the line through $\left(-\frac{2}{3}, \frac{5}{3}\right)$ and $(1,1)$:

$$m = \frac{1 - 5/3}{1 - (-2/3)} = -\frac{2}{5} \quad \text{and} \quad y - 1 = -\frac{2}{5} \cdot (x - 1) \quad \text{or} \quad y = -\frac{2}{5}x + \frac{7}{5}$$

24.
$$2x + 3(x-2) \geq 0$$
$$2x + 3x - 6 \geq 0$$
$$5x \geq 6$$
$$x \geq \frac{6}{5}$$

25. First solve the equation for y. $x + \frac{1}{2}y = 4$

$$y = -2x + 8$$

The slope is -2, and the y-intercept is (0,8)
To find the x intercept set y = 0 in the original equation.
$x + 0 = 4$ or $x = 4$ The x-intercept is (4,0)

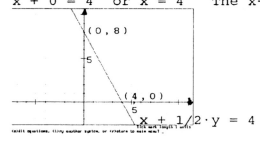

26. Find the intersection of $2x - 3y = 1$ $(y = \frac{2}{3}x - \frac{1}{3})$ and

$5x + 2y = 0$ $(y = -\frac{5}{2}x)$:

$$\frac{3}{2}y + \frac{1}{2} = -\frac{2}{5}y$$
$$3y + 1 = -\frac{4}{5}y$$
$$15y + 5 = -4y$$
$$19y = -5 \quad \text{or} \quad y = -\frac{5}{19} \quad \text{and} \quad x = -\frac{2}{5} \cdot -\frac{5}{19} = \frac{2}{19} \quad \left(\frac{2}{19}, \frac{-5}{19}\right)$$

Replacing these values in the third equation:

$\frac{2}{19} + \left(-\frac{5}{19}\right) = 1$, not true, so the equation does not hold.
We conclude then that there is not a common point.

27. The slope of the line with equation $2x - 3y = 1$ is $m = \frac{2}{3}$.

The slope of the line with equation $3x + 2y = 4$ is $n = -\frac{3}{2}$.

m and n are negative reciprocals of one another, so the two lines are perpendicular.

38

28. (A) with (b) Since the line must have a negative slope and the inequality must be ≤.
(B) with (c) Since the line must have a positive slope and inequalities must be ≥ when one solves for y.
(C) with (a) Since the line must have a negative slope and inequality must be ≥.
(D) with (d) Since the line must have a positive slope and inequality must be ≤.

29. (a) L_3: The line must have negative slope and y-intercept >4
(b) L_1: The line must have positive slope
(c) L_2: The line must have negative slope and y-intercept <4

30. Both axes delimit the feasible set: $x \geq 0$ and $y \geq 0$.

Find the line through $(0,5)$ and $(4,\frac{3}{2})$:

$m = \dfrac{3/2 - 5}{4 - 0} = -\dfrac{7/2}{4} = -\dfrac{7}{8}$, and the y intercept is $(0,5)$ so the equation of the line is: $y = -\dfrac{7}{8}x + 5$.

The inequality is $y \leq -\dfrac{7}{8}x + 5$ or $7x + 8y \leq 40$.

The line perpendicular to the previous one has slope $\dfrac{8}{7}$.

The equation of this line is: $y - \dfrac{3}{2} = \dfrac{8}{7} \cdot (x - 4)$ or

$$y = \dfrac{8}{7}x - \dfrac{43}{14}.$$

The inequality is $14y \geq 16x - 43$ or $16x - 14y \leq 43$.

$\begin{cases} 7x + 8y \leq 40 \\ 16x - 14y \leq 43 \\ x \geq 0, \ y \geq 0 \end{cases}$ is the system of linear inequalities is

To find the coordinates of the unspecified vertex, replace $y = 0$ in the equation $y = \dfrac{8}{7}x - \dfrac{43}{14}$: $0 = \dfrac{8}{7}x - \dfrac{43}{14}$

$$0 = 16x - 43 \quad \text{or} \quad x = \dfrac{43}{16}.$$

The coordinates are $\left(\dfrac{43}{16}, 0\right)$.

31. Supply curve should have positive slope (supply increases as price increases) and have a non-positive y-intercept (supply should run out on or before selling price is zero).
$q = 150p - 100$ satisfies these conditions.
Demand curve should have negative slope (demand decreases as price increases) and have a non-negative y-intercept (Demand should exist when price is zero). $q = -75p + 500$ satisfies these conditions.

$150p - 100 = -75p + 500$

$\qquad 225p = 600$

$\qquad\quad p = \dfrac{8}{3}$

$\qquad\quad q = 150\left(\dfrac{8}{3}\right) - 100 = 300$

The intersection of the demand and supply curves is $(\dfrac{8}{3}, 300)$.

32. To find the coordinates of the vertices, we write the set of inequalities as equalities in standard form and find the intersection of each pair of lines that define the feasible set:

$$x = 0, \quad y = 0, \quad y = -5x + 50, \quad y = -\frac{2}{3}x + 11, \quad y = \frac{x}{2} + 4.$$

So, the vertices are $(0, 0)$, $(0, 4)$, $(6, 7)$, $(9, 5)$, $(0, 10)$

33. Label the points on the line closest to the three points $(2,4)$, $(5,8)$ and $(7,9)$ as P,Q, and R respectively. If the linear equation is
$y = mx + b$ then $P = (2, 2m+b)$,
$Q = (5, 5m+b)$ and $R = (7, 7m+b)$ and the distances are :

$d_1 = 2m + b - 4$

$d_2 = 8 - (5m+b)$

$d_3 = 7m + b - 9$

Setting $d_1 = d_3$, we have $2m + b - 4 = 7m + b - 9$

$$5 = 5m$$
$$1 = m$$

With $m = 1$ and setting $d_1 = d_2$ we have

$$2(1) + b - 4 = 8 - (5(1) + b)$$
$$b - 2 = 8 - (5+b)$$
$$b - 2 = 3 - b$$
$$2b = 5$$
$$b = \frac{5}{2}$$

So, $y = x + \frac{5}{2}$ is the equation of the line.

34. (a) $y - 4000 = 10 \cdot (x - 1000)$ or $y = 10x - 6000.$
    (b) $y = 10 \cdot 0 - 6000 = -6000$, y-intercept is $(0, -6000)$.
        $0 = 10x - 6000$ or $x = 600$; x-intercept is $(600, 0)$.
    (c)

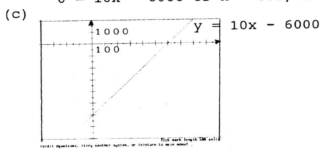

35. (a) A: $y = .10x + 50$;   B: $y = .20x + 40$;
    (b) A: $y = .10 \cdot 80 + 50 = \$58$; B: $y = .20 \cdot 80 + 40 = \$56$.
        Answer: B since the cost is less.
    (c) A: $y = .10 \cdot 160 + 50 = \$66$; B: $y = .20 \cdot 160 + 40 = \$72$.
        Answer: A since the cost is less.
    (d) $.10x + 50 = .20x + 40$; $.10x = 10$; $x = 100$ miles.
        The companies have the same value at 100 miles.

40

36. (a) $m = \dfrac{1000 - 5000}{1994 - 1986} = -\dfrac{4000}{8} = -500$, b = 5000.

     The equation is: y = -500x + 5000

   (b) y = -500·4 + 5000 = $3000

   (c) 2000 = -500x + 5000

        -500x = -3000

        x = 6.   The computers will value $2000 in 1992.

37. Graph x ≤ 3y + 2.   When x = 2, y = 0.   When x = -1, y = -1.
     Since 3y ≥ x - 2, then the solution is all points on or
     above the line.

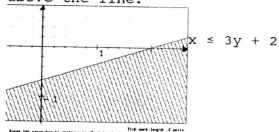

x ≤ 3y + 2

Press the space bar to continue or <Esc> to abort.   Tick mark length .2 units

38. First weekly salary: y = .03x + 200.

     Second weekly salary: y = .05x + 100.

     Let y values be equal: .03x + 200 = .05x + 100

                            100 = .02x   or x = $5000.

41

MATRICES

2.1 Solving Systems of Linear Equations, I

1.   (2) $\frac{1}{2}$x − (2)(3y) = (2)(2)

    x − 6y = 4

    Abbreviation 2[1]

    New system: $\begin{cases} x - 6y = 4 \\ 5x + 4y = 1 \end{cases}$

2. $\begin{cases} x + 4y = 6 \\ y = -2 \end{cases}$

    (−1) [2]

3. $\begin{cases} x + 2y = 3 \\ 14y = 16 \end{cases}$

    [2] + (5)[1]

4. $\begin{cases} x - 6y = 4 \\ 5y = -1 \end{cases}$

    [2] + (−$\frac{1}{2}$)[1]

5. $\begin{cases} x - 2y + z = 0 \\ y - 2z = 4 \\ 9y - z = 5 \end{cases}$

    [3] + (−4)[1]

6. $\begin{cases} x + 6y - 4z = 1 \\ y + 3z = 1 \\ 16z = 5 \end{cases}$

    [3] + 3[2]

7. $\begin{bmatrix} 1 & -\frac{1}{2} & \bigm| & 3 \\ 0 & 1 & \bigm| & 4 \end{bmatrix}$ Multiply 2nd row by $\frac{1}{2}$ gives $\begin{bmatrix} 0 & \frac{1}{2} & \bigm| & 2 \end{bmatrix}$

Adding this to the 1st row gives the new matrix of

$\begin{bmatrix} 1 & 0 & \bigm| & 5 \\ 0 & 1 & \bigm| & 4 \end{bmatrix}$ Note that the 2nd row remains the same.

Abbreviation: [1] + $\frac{1}{2}$ [2]

8. $\begin{bmatrix} 1 & 0 & 7 & | & 9 \\ 0 & 1 & -2 & | & 3 \\ 0 & 0 & 16 & | & -7 \end{bmatrix}$

   Abbreviation: $[3] + -4[2]$

9. $[2] + 2[1]$

10. $\frac{1}{2}[2]$

11. $[1] + (-2)[2]$

12. $[3] + (-4)[1]$

13. Since the given matrix has a zero in the upper left corner and we want a 1 in that position, we must interchange Row 1 with Row 2 or Row 3 as the first step.

14. $(-\frac{1}{3})[2]$

15. $[1] + (-3)[3]$

16. Interchange rows 2 and 3

17. $\begin{bmatrix} 3 & 9 & | & 6 \\ 2 & 8 & | & 6 \end{bmatrix} \xrightarrow{1/3\ [1]} \begin{bmatrix} 1 & 3 & | & 2 \\ 2 & 8 & | & 6 \end{bmatrix} \xrightarrow{-2\ [1]\ +\ [2]}$

    $\begin{bmatrix} 1 & 3 & | & 2 \\ 0 & 2 & | & 2 \end{bmatrix} \xrightarrow{1/2\ [2]} \begin{bmatrix} 1 & 3 & | & 2 \\ 0 & 1 & | & 1 \end{bmatrix} \xrightarrow{-3\ [2]\ +\ [1]}$

    $\begin{bmatrix} 1 & 0 & | & -1 \\ 0 & 1 & | & 1 \end{bmatrix} \qquad x = -1,\ y = 1$

18. $\begin{bmatrix} 1/3 & 2 & | & 1 \\ -2 & -4 & | & 6 \end{bmatrix} \xrightarrow{3\ [1]} \begin{bmatrix} 1 & 6 & | & 3 \\ -2 & -4 & | & 6 \end{bmatrix} \xrightarrow{2\ [1]\ +\ [2]}$

    $\begin{bmatrix} 1 & 6 & | & 3 \\ 0 & 8 & | & 12 \end{bmatrix} \xrightarrow{1/8\ [2]} \begin{bmatrix} 1 & 6 & | & 3 \\ 0 & 1 & | & 3/2 \end{bmatrix} \xrightarrow{-6\ [2]\ +\ [1]}$

    $\begin{bmatrix} 1 & 0 & | & -6 \\ 0 & 1 & | & 3/2 \end{bmatrix} \qquad x = -6,\ y = \frac{3}{2}$

19. $\begin{bmatrix} 1 & -3 & 4 & | & 1 \\ 4 & -10 & 10 & | & 4 \\ -3 & 9 & -5 & | & -6 \end{bmatrix} \xrightarrow{-4\ [1]\ +\ [2]} \begin{bmatrix} 1 & -3 & 4 & | & 1 \\ 0 & 2 & -6 & | & 0 \\ -3 & 9 & -5 & | & -6 \end{bmatrix}$

    $\xrightarrow{3\ [1]\ +\ [3]} \begin{bmatrix} 1 & -3 & 4 & | & 1 \\ 0 & 2 & -6 & | & 0 \\ 0 & 0 & 7 & | & -3 \end{bmatrix} \xrightarrow{1/2\ [2]}$

$$\begin{bmatrix} 1 & -3 & 4 & | & 1 \\ 0 & 1 & -3 & | & 0 \\ 0 & 0 & 7 & | & -3 \end{bmatrix} \xrightarrow{3\ [2]\ +\ [1]} \begin{bmatrix} 1 & 0 & -5 & | & 1 \\ 0 & 1 & -3 & | & 0 \\ 0 & 0 & 7 & | & -3 \end{bmatrix} \xrightarrow{1/7\ [3]}$$

$$\begin{bmatrix} 1 & 0 & -5 & | & 1 \\ 0 & 1 & -3 & | & 0 \\ 0 & 0 & 1 & | & -3/7 \end{bmatrix} \xrightarrow{5\ [3]\ +\ [1]} \begin{bmatrix} 1 & 0 & 0 & | & -8/7 \\ 0 & 1 & -3 & | & 0 \\ 0 & 0 & 1 & | & -3/7 \end{bmatrix}$$
$$\xrightarrow{3\ [3]\ +\ [2]}$$

$$\begin{bmatrix} 1 & 0 & 0 & | & -8/7 \\ 0 & 1 & 0 & | & -9/7 \\ 0 & 0 & 1 & | & -3/7 \end{bmatrix} \qquad x = -\frac{8}{7}\ y = -\frac{9}{7},\ z = -\frac{3}{7}$$

20. $$\begin{bmatrix} 1/2 & 1 & 0 & | & 4 \\ -4 & -7 & 3 & | & -31 \\ 6 & 14 & 7 & | & 50 \end{bmatrix} \xrightarrow{2\ [1]} \begin{bmatrix} 1 & 2 & 0 & | & 8 \\ -4 & -7 & 3 & | & -31 \\ 6 & 14 & 7 & | & 50 \end{bmatrix} \xrightarrow{4\ [1]\ +\ [2]}$$

$$\begin{bmatrix} 1 & 2 & 0 & | & 8\ \cancel{0} \\ 0 & 1 & 3 & | & 1 \\ 6 & 14 & 7 & | & 50 \end{bmatrix} \xrightarrow{-6\ [1]\ +\ [3]} \begin{bmatrix} 1 & 2 & 0 & | & 8\ \cancel{0} \\ 0 & 1 & 3 & | & 1 \\ 0 & 2 & 7 & | & 2 \end{bmatrix} \xrightarrow{-2[2]\ +\ [1]}$$

$$\begin{bmatrix} 1 & 0 & -6 & | & 6 \\ 0 & 1 & 3 & | & 1 \\ 0 & 2 & 7 & | & 2 \end{bmatrix} \xrightarrow{-2\ [2]\ +\ [3]} \begin{bmatrix} 1 & 0 & -6 & | & 6 \\ 0 & 1 & 3 & | & 1 \\ 0 & 0 & 1 & | & 0 \end{bmatrix} \xrightarrow{6\ [3]\ +\ [1]}$$

$$\begin{bmatrix} 1 & 0 & 0 & | & 6 \\ 0 & 1 & 3 & | & 1 \\ 0 & 0 & 1 & | & 0 \end{bmatrix} \xrightarrow{-3\ [3]\ +\ [2]} \begin{bmatrix} 1 & 0 & 0 & | & 6 \\ 0 & 1 & 0 & | & 1 \\ 0 & 0 & 1 & | & 0 \end{bmatrix}$$

$x = 6,\ y = 1,\ z = 0$

21. $$\begin{bmatrix} 2 & -2 & | & -4 \\ 3 & 4 & | & 1 \end{bmatrix} \xrightarrow{1/2\ [1]} \begin{bmatrix} 1 & -1 & | & -2 \\ 3 & 4 & | & 1 \end{bmatrix} \xrightarrow{-3\ [1]\ +\ [2]}$$

$$\begin{bmatrix} 1 & -1 & | & -2 \\ 0 & 7 & | & 7 \end{bmatrix} \xrightarrow{1/7\ [2]} \begin{bmatrix} 1 & -1 & | & -2 \\ 0 & 1 & | & 1 \end{bmatrix} \xrightarrow{[2]\ +\ [1]}$$

$$\begin{bmatrix} 1 & 0 & | & -1 \\ 0 & 1 & | & 1 \end{bmatrix} \qquad x = -1\ y = 1$$

22. $$\begin{bmatrix} 2 & 3 & | & 4 \\ -1 & 2 & | & -2 \end{bmatrix} \xrightarrow{1/2\ [1]} \begin{bmatrix} 1 & 3/2 & | & 2 \\ -1 & 2 & | & -2 \end{bmatrix} \xrightarrow{[1]\ +\ [2]}$$

$$\begin{bmatrix} 1 & 3/2 & | & 2 \\ 0 & 7/2 & | & 0 \end{bmatrix} \xrightarrow{2/7\ [2]} \begin{bmatrix} 1 & 3/2 & | & 2 \\ 0 & 1 & | & 0 \end{bmatrix} \xrightarrow{-3/2\ [2]\ +\ [1]}$$

$$\begin{bmatrix} 1 & 0 & | & 2 \\ 0 & 1 & | & 0 \end{bmatrix} \qquad x = 2,\ y = 0$$

23. $\begin{bmatrix} 4 & -4 & 4 & | & -8 \\ 1 & -2 & -2 & | & -1 \\ 2 & 1 & 3 & | & 1 \end{bmatrix} \xrightarrow{1/4\ [1]} \begin{bmatrix} 1 & -1 & 1 & | & -2 \\ 1 & -2 & -2 & | & -1 \\ 2 & 1 & 3 & | & 1 \end{bmatrix} \xrightarrow{-1[1]\ +\ [2]}$

$\begin{bmatrix} 1 & -1 & 1 & | & -2 \\ 0 & -1 & -3 & | & 1\ \cancel{8} \\ 2 & 1 & 3 & | & 1 \end{bmatrix} \xrightarrow{-2\ [1]\ +\ [3]} \begin{bmatrix} 1 & -1 & 1 & | & -2 \\ 0 & -1 & -3 & | & 3 \\ 0 & 3 & 1 & | & +5 \end{bmatrix} \xrightarrow{-1\ [2]}$

$\begin{bmatrix} 1 & -1 & 1 & | & -2 \\ 0 & 1 & 3 & | & \overset{-1}{\cancel{>}}3 \\ 0 & 3 & 1 & | & +5 \end{bmatrix} \xrightarrow{[2]\ +\ [1]} \begin{bmatrix} 1 & 0 & 4 & | & \overset{-3}{\cancel{>}}5 \\ 0 & 1 & 3 & | & \overset{-1}{\cancel{>}}3 \\ 0 & 3 & 1 & | & +5 \end{bmatrix} \xrightarrow{-3\ [2]\ +\ [3]}$

$\begin{bmatrix} 1 & 0 & 4 & | & \overset{-3}{\cancel{>}}5 \\ 0 & 1 & 3 & | & \overset{-1}{\cancel{>}}3 \\ 0 & 0 & -8 & | & 8\ \cancel{4} \end{bmatrix} \xrightarrow{-1/8\ [3]} \begin{bmatrix} 1 & 0 & 4 & | & \overset{-3}{\cancel{>}}5 \\ 0 & 1 & 3 & | & \cancel{>}3 \\ 0 & 0 & 1 & | & -1 \end{bmatrix} \xrightarrow{-4\ [3]\ +\ [1]}$

$\begin{bmatrix} 1 & 0 & 0 & | & 1 \\ 0 & 1 & 3 & | & -1 \\ 0 & 0 & 1 & | & -1 \end{bmatrix} \xrightarrow{-3\ [3]\ +\ [2]} \begin{bmatrix} 1 & 0 & 0 & | & 1 \\ 0 & 1 & 0 & | & 2 \\ 0 & 0 & 1 & | & -1 \end{bmatrix}$

$x = 1,\ y = 2,\ z = -1$

24. $\begin{bmatrix} 1 & 2 & 2 & | & 11 \\ 1 & -1 & -1 & | & -4 \\ 2 & 5 & 9 & | & 39 \end{bmatrix} \xrightarrow{-1[1]\ +\ [2]} \begin{bmatrix} 1 & 2 & 2 & | & 11 \\ 0 & -3 & -3 & | & -15 \\ 2 & 5 & 9 & | & 39 \end{bmatrix}$

$\xrightarrow{-2\ [1]\ +\ [3]}$

$\begin{bmatrix} 1 & 2 & 2 & | & 11 \\ 0 & -3 & -3 & | & -15 \\ 0 & 1 & 5 & | & 17 \end{bmatrix} \xrightarrow{-1/3\ [2]} \begin{bmatrix} 1 & 2 & 2 & | & 11 \\ 0 & 1 & 1 & | & 5 \\ 0 & 1 & 5 & | & 17 \end{bmatrix} \xrightarrow{-2[2]\ +\ [1]}$

$\begin{bmatrix} 1 & 0 & 0 & | & 1 \\ 0 & 1 & 1 & | & 5 \\ 0 & 1 & 5 & | & 17 \end{bmatrix} \xrightarrow{-1[2]\ +\ [3]} \begin{bmatrix} 1 & 0 & 0 & | & 1 \\ 0 & 1 & 1 & | & 5 \\ 0 & 0 & 4 & | & 12 \end{bmatrix} \xrightarrow{1/4\ [3]} \begin{bmatrix} 1 \\ 0 \\ 0 \end{bmatrix}$

$\begin{matrix} 0 & 0 & | & 1 \\ 1 & 1 & | & 5 \\ 0 & 1 & | & 3 \end{matrix} \xrightarrow{-1\ [3]\ +\ [2]} \begin{bmatrix} 1 & 0 & 0 & | & 1 \\ 0 & 1 & 0 & | & 2 \\ 0 & 0 & 1 & | & 3 \end{bmatrix}$

$x = 1,\ y = 2,\ z = 3$

25. $\begin{bmatrix} .2 & .3 & | & 4 \\ .6 & 1.1 & | & 5 \end{bmatrix} \xrightarrow{5\ [1]} \begin{bmatrix} 1 & 1.5 & | & 20 \\ .6 & 1.1 & | & 15 \end{bmatrix} \xrightarrow{-3/5\ [1]\ +\ [2]}$

$\begin{bmatrix} 1 & 1.5 & | & 20 \\ 0 & .2 & | & 3 \end{bmatrix} \xrightarrow{5\ [2]} \begin{bmatrix} 1 & 1.5 & | & 20 \\ 0 & 1 & | & 15 \end{bmatrix} \xrightarrow{-3/2\ [2]\ +\ [1]}$

$\begin{bmatrix} 1 & 0 & | & -2.5 \\ 0 & 1 & | & 15 \end{bmatrix}$ $x = -2.5, \ y = 15$

26. $\begin{bmatrix} 3/2 & 6 & | & 9 \\ 1/2 & -2/3 & | & 11 \end{bmatrix} \xrightarrow{2/3\ [1]} \begin{bmatrix} 1 & 4 & | & 6 \\ 1/2 & -2/3 & | & 11 \end{bmatrix} \xrightarrow{-1/2\ [1]\ +\ [2]}$

$\begin{bmatrix} 1 & 4 & | & 6 \\ 0 & -8/3 & | & 8 \end{bmatrix} \xrightarrow{-3/8\ [2]} \begin{bmatrix} 1 & 4 & | & 6 \\ 0 & 1 & | & -3 \end{bmatrix} \xrightarrow{-4\ [2]\ +\ [1]}$

$\begin{bmatrix} 1 & 0 & | & 18 \\ 0 & 1 & | & -3 \end{bmatrix}$ $x = 18, \ y = -3$

27. $\begin{bmatrix} 1 & 1 & 4 & | & 3 \\ 4 & 1 & -2 & | & -6 \\ -3 & 0 & 2 & | & 1 \end{bmatrix} \xrightarrow{-4\ [1]\ +\ [2]} \begin{bmatrix} 1 & 1 & 4 & | & 3 \\ 0 & -3 & -18 & | & -18 \\ -3 & 0 & 2 & | & 1 \end{bmatrix}$

$\xrightarrow{3[1]\ +\ [2]} \begin{bmatrix} 1 & 1 & 4 & | & 3 \\ 0 & -3 & -18 & | & -18 \\ 0 & 3 & 14 & | & 10 \end{bmatrix} \xrightarrow{-1/3\ [2]} \begin{bmatrix} 1 & 1 & 4 & | & 3 \\ 0 & 1 & 6 & | & 6 \\ 0 & 3 & 14 & | & 10 \end{bmatrix}$

$\xrightarrow{-1\ [2]\ +\ [1]} \begin{bmatrix} 1 & 0 & -2 & | & -3 \\ 0 & 1 & 6 & | & 6 \\ 0 & 3 & 14 & | & 10 \end{bmatrix} \xrightarrow{-3\ [2]\ +\ [3]}$

$\begin{bmatrix} 1 & 0 & -2 & | & -3 \\ 0 & 1 & 6 & | & 6 \\ 0 & 0 & -4 & | & -8 \end{bmatrix} \xrightarrow{-1/4\ [3]} \begin{bmatrix} 1 & 0 & -2 & | & -3 \\ 0 & 1 & 6 & | & 6 \\ 0 & 0 & 1 & | & 2 \end{bmatrix} \xrightarrow{2\ [3]\ +\ [1]}$

$\begin{bmatrix} 1 & 0 & 0 & | & 1 \\ 0 & 1 & 6 & | & 6 \\ 0 & 0 & 1 & | & 2 \end{bmatrix} \xrightarrow{-6\ [3]\ +\ [2]} \begin{bmatrix} 1 & 0 & 0 & | & 1 \\ 0 & 1 & 0 & | & -6 \\ 0 & 0 & 1 & | & 2 \end{bmatrix}$

$x = 1, \ y = -6, \ z = 2$

28. $\begin{bmatrix} -2 & -3 & 2 & | & -2 \\ 1 & 1 & 0 & | & 3 \\ -1 & -3 & 5 & | & 8 \end{bmatrix} \xrightarrow{-1/2\ [1]} \begin{bmatrix} 1 & 3/2 & -1 & | & 1 \\ 1 & 1 & 0 & | & 3 \\ -1 & -3 & 5 & | & 8 \end{bmatrix}$

$\xrightarrow{-1\ [1]\ +\ [2]} \begin{bmatrix} 1 & 3/2 & -1 & | & 1 \\ 0 & -1/2 & 1 & | & 2 \\ -1 & -3 & 5 & | & 8 \end{bmatrix} \xrightarrow{[1]\ +\ [3]}$

46

$$\begin{bmatrix} 1 & 3/2 & -1 & | & 1 \\ 0 & -1/2 & 1 & | & 2 \\ 0 & -3/2 & 4 & | & 9 \end{bmatrix} \xrightarrow{-2[2]} \begin{bmatrix} 1 & 3/2 & -1 & | & 1 \\ 0 & 1 & -2 & | & -4 \\ 0 & -3/2 & 4 & | & 9 \end{bmatrix}$$

$$\xrightarrow{-3/2\ [2]\ +\ [1]} \begin{bmatrix} 1 & 0 & 2 & | & 7 \\ 0 & 1 & -2 & | & -4 \\ 0 & -3/2 & 4 & | & 9 \end{bmatrix} \xrightarrow{3/2\ [2]\ +\ [3]}$$

$$\begin{bmatrix} 1 & 0 & 2 & | & 7 \\ 0 & 1 & -2 & | & -4 \\ 0 & 0 & 1 & | & 3 \end{bmatrix} \xrightarrow{-2\ [3]\ +\ [1]} \begin{bmatrix} 1 & 0 & 0 & | & 1 \\ 0 & 1 & -2 & | & -4 \\ 0 & 0 & 1 & | & 3 \end{bmatrix}$$

$$\xrightarrow{2\ [3]\ +\ [2]} \begin{bmatrix} 1 & 0 & 0 & | & 1 \\ 0 & 1 & 0 & | & 2 \\ 0 & 0 & 1 & | & 3 \end{bmatrix} \qquad x = 1,\ y = 2,\ z = 3$$

29. $$\begin{bmatrix} -1 & 1 & 0 & | & -1 \\ 1 & 0 & 1 & | & 4 \\ 6 & -3 & 2 & | & 10 \end{bmatrix} \xrightarrow{-1\ [1]} \begin{bmatrix} 1 & -1 & 0 & | & 1 \\ 1 & 0 & 1 & | & 4 \\ 6 & -3 & 2 & | & 10 \end{bmatrix} \xrightarrow{-1\ [1]\ +\ [2]}$$

$$\begin{bmatrix} 1 & -1 & 0 & | & 1 \\ 0 & 1 & 1 & | & 3 \\ 6 & -3 & 2 & | & 10 \end{bmatrix} \xrightarrow{-6\ [1]\ +\ [3]} \begin{bmatrix} 1 & -1 & 0 & | & 1 \\ 0 & 1 & 1 & | & 3 \\ 0 & 3 & 2 & | & 4 \end{bmatrix} \xrightarrow{[2]\ +\ [1]}$$

$$\begin{bmatrix} 1 & 0 & 1 & | & 4 \\ 0 & 1 & 1 & | & 3 \\ 0 & 3 & 2 & | & 4 \end{bmatrix} \xrightarrow{-3\ [2]\ +\ [3]} \begin{bmatrix} 1 & 0 & 1 & | & 4 \\ 0 & 1 & 1 & | & 3 \\ 0 & 0 & -1 & | & -5 \end{bmatrix} \xrightarrow{-1\ [3]}$$

$$\begin{bmatrix} 1 & 0 & 1 & | & 4 \\ 0 & 1 & 1 & | & 3 \\ 0 & 0 & 1 & | & 5 \end{bmatrix} \xrightarrow{-1[3]\ +\ [1]} \begin{bmatrix} 1 & 0 & 0 & | & -1 \\ 0 & 1 & 1 & | & 3 \\ 0 & 0 & 1 & | & 5 \end{bmatrix} \xrightarrow{-1\ [3]\ +\ [2]}$$

$$\begin{bmatrix} 1 & 0 & 0 & | & -1 \\ 0 & 1 & 0 & | & -2 \\ 0 & 0 & 1 & | & 5 \end{bmatrix} \qquad x = -1,\ y = -2,\ z = 5$$

30. $$\begin{bmatrix} 1 & 0 & 2 & | & 9 \\ 0 & 1 & 1 & | & 1 \\ 3 & -2 & 0 & | & 9 \end{bmatrix} \xrightarrow{-3\ [1]\ +\ [3]} \begin{bmatrix} 1 & 0 & 2 & | & 9 \\ 0 & 1 & 1 & | & 1 \\ 0 & -2 & -6 & | & -18 \end{bmatrix}$$

$$\xrightarrow{2\ [2]\ +\ [3]} \begin{bmatrix} 1 & 0 & 2 & | & 9 \\ 0 & 1 & 1 & | & 1 \\ 0 & 0 & -4 & | & -16 \end{bmatrix} \xrightarrow{-1/4\ [3]} \begin{bmatrix} 1 & 0 & 2 & | & 9 \\ 0 & 1 & 1 & | & 1 \\ 0 & 0 & 1 & | & 4 \end{bmatrix}$$

$$\xrightarrow{-2\ [3]\ +\ [1]}\begin{bmatrix} 1 & 0 & 0 & | & 1 \\ 0 & 1 & 1 & | & 1 \\ 0 & 0 & 1 & | & 4 \end{bmatrix}\xrightarrow{-1\ [3]\ +\ [2]}\begin{bmatrix} 1 & 0 & 0 & | & 1 \\ 0 & 1 & 0 & | & -3 \\ 0 & 0 & 1 & | & 4 \end{bmatrix}$$

$x = 1$, $y = -3$, $z = 4$

31. x = number of adults, y = number of children

$x + y = 600$

$5.5x + 2.5y = 1911$.

$$\begin{bmatrix} 1 & 1 & | & 600 \\ 5.5 & 2.5 & | & 1911 \end{bmatrix}\xrightarrow{[2]\ +\ -5.5\ [1]}\begin{bmatrix} 1 & 1 & | & 600 \\ 0 & -3 & | & -1389 \end{bmatrix}$$

$$\xrightarrow{-1/3\ [2]}\begin{bmatrix} 1 & 1 & | & 600 \\ 0 & 1 & | & 463 \end{bmatrix}\xrightarrow{-1\ [2]\ +\ [1]}\begin{bmatrix} 1 & 0 & | & 137 \\ 0 & 1 & | & 463 \end{bmatrix}$$

137 adults, 463 children

32. 15, 3, 200.

33. $x = \$25,000$, $y = \$50,000$, $z = \$25,000$

34. $x = 6$, $y = 3$, $z = 1$

39. $x = 3$, $y = -3$, $z = -2$, $w = -4$

40. $x = -1$, $y = 3$, $z = -1$, $w = 4$

2.2 Solving Systems of Linear Equations, II

1. $$\begin{bmatrix} 2 & -4 & 6 \\ 3 & 7 & 1 \end{bmatrix}\xrightarrow{1/2\ [1]}\begin{bmatrix} 1 & -2 & 3 \\ 3 & 7 & 1 \end{bmatrix}$$
$$\xrightarrow{-3\ [1]\ +\ [2]}\begin{bmatrix} 1 & -2 & 3 \\ 0 & 13 & -8 \end{bmatrix}$$

2. $$\begin{bmatrix} 1 & 2 & 3 \\ 4 & 8 & -12 \end{bmatrix}\xrightarrow{1/8\ [2]}\begin{bmatrix} 1 & 2 & 3 \\ 1/2 & 1 & -3/2 \end{bmatrix}$$
$$\xrightarrow[{[1]}]{-2\ [2]\ +\ [1]}\begin{bmatrix} 0 & 0 & 6 \\ 1/2 & 1 & -3/2 \end{bmatrix}$$

3. $$\begin{bmatrix} 9 & -1 & 0 & -7 \\ -\dfrac{1}{2} & \dfrac{1}{2} & 1 & 3 \\ 5 & -1 & 0 & -3 \end{bmatrix}$$

4. $$\begin{bmatrix} 15 & 0 & 0 & -28 \\ 7 & 0 & 9 & 0 \\ -1 & 1 & -1 & 4 \end{bmatrix}$$

5. $\begin{bmatrix} 1 & \frac{3}{2} \\ 0 & -9 \\ 0 & \frac{7}{2} \end{bmatrix}$

6. $\begin{bmatrix} 0 & 1 \\ 1 & 0 \end{bmatrix}$

7. $\left[\begin{array}{cc|c} 4 & 3 & 0 \\ \frac{2}{3} & 0 & -2 \\ 1 & 3 & 6 \end{array}\right] \xrightarrow{1/6\ [3]} \left[\begin{array}{cc|c} 4 & 3 & 0 \\ \frac{2}{3} & 0 & -2 \\ \frac{1}{6} & \frac{1}{2} & 1 \end{array}\right]$

$\xrightarrow{2\ [3]\ +\ [2]} \left[\begin{array}{cc|c} 4 & 3 & 0 \\ 1 & 1 & 0 \\ \frac{1}{6} & \frac{1}{2} & 1 \end{array}\right]$

8. $\left[\begin{array}{cc|c} 0 & 1 & 0 \\ \frac{1}{2} & -\frac{1}{2} & 1 \\ -2 & 5 & 0 \end{array}\right]$

9. $\left[\begin{array}{cc|c} 2 & -4 & 6 \\ -1 & 2 & -3 \end{array}\right] \xrightarrow{1/2\ [1]} \left[\begin{array}{cc|c} 1 & -2 & 3 \\ -1 & 2 & -3 \end{array}\right] \xrightarrow{[1]\ +\ [2]}$

$\left[\begin{array}{cc|c} 1 & -2 & 3 \\ 0 & 0 & 0 \end{array}\right]$ x = 2y + 3, y = any value

10. $\left[\begin{array}{cc|c} -1/2 & 1 & +3/2 \\ -3 & 6 & 10 \end{array}\right] \xrightarrow{-2\ [1]} \left[\begin{array}{cc|c} 1 & -2 & -3 \\ -3 & 6 & 10 \end{array}\right] \xrightarrow{3\ [1]\ +\ [2]}$

$\left[\begin{array}{cc|c} 1 & -2 & -3 \\ 0 & 0 & 1 \end{array}\right] \xrightarrow{3\ [2]\ +\ [1]} \left[\begin{array}{cc|c} 1 & -2 & 0 \\ 0 & 0 & 1 \end{array}\right]$ No Solution

11. $\left[\begin{array}{cc|c} 1 & 2 & 5 \\ 3 & -1 & 1 \\ -1 & 3 & 5 \end{array}\right] \xrightarrow{-3\ [1]\ +\ [2]} \left[\begin{array}{cc|c} 1 & 2 & 5 \\ 0 & -7 & -14 \\ -1 & 3 & 5 \end{array}\right] \xrightarrow{[1]\ +\ [2]}$

$\left[\begin{array}{cc|c} 1 & 2 & 5 \\ 0 & -7 & -14 \\ 0 & 5 & 10 \end{array}\right] \xrightarrow{-1/7\ [2]} \left[\begin{array}{cc|c} 1 & 2 & 5 \\ 0 & 1 & 2 \\ 0 & 5 & 10 \end{array}\right] \xrightarrow{-2[2]\ +\ [1]}$

$$\begin{bmatrix} 1 & 0 & | & 1 \\ 0 & 1 & | & 2 \\ 0 & 5 & | & 10 \end{bmatrix} \xrightarrow{-5[2] + [3]} \begin{bmatrix} 1 & 0 & | & 1 \\ 0 & 1 & | & 2 \\ 0 & 0 & | & 0 \end{bmatrix} \qquad x = 1, \ y = 2$$

12. $$\begin{bmatrix} 1 & -6 & | & 12 \\ -1/2 & 3 & | & -6 \\ 1/3 & -2 & | & 4 \end{bmatrix} \xrightarrow{1/2[1] + [2]} \begin{bmatrix} 1 & -6 & | & 12 \\ 0 & 0 & | & 0 \\ 1/3 & -2 & | & 4 \end{bmatrix}$$

$$\xrightarrow[\quad]{-1/3 \ [1] + [3]} \begin{bmatrix} 1 & -6 & | & 12 \\ 0 & 0 & | & 0 \\ 0 & 0 & | & 0 \end{bmatrix} \qquad x = 6y + 12, \ y = \text{any value}$$

13. $$\begin{bmatrix} 1 & -1 & 3 & | & 3 \\ -2 & 3 & -11 & | & -4 \\ 1 & -2 & 8 & | & 6 \end{bmatrix} \xrightarrow{2 \ [1] + [2]} \begin{bmatrix} 1 & -1 & 3 & | & 3 \\ 0 & 1 & -5 & | & 2 \\ 1 & -2 & 8 & | & 6 \end{bmatrix}$$

$$\xrightarrow{-1 \ [1] + [3]} \begin{bmatrix} 1 & -1 & 3 & | & 3 \\ 0 & 1 & -5 & | & 2 \\ 0 & -1 & 5 & | & 3 \end{bmatrix} \xrightarrow{[2] + [1]} \begin{bmatrix} 1 & 0 & -2 & | & 5 \\ 0 & 1 & -5 & | & 2 \\ 0 & -1 & 5 & | & 3 \end{bmatrix}$$

$$\xrightarrow{[2] + [3]} \begin{bmatrix} 1 & 0 & -2 & | & 5 \\ 0 & 1 & -5 & | & 2 \\ 0 & 0 & 0 & | & 5 \end{bmatrix}.$$

The system is inconsistent since the last line of the matrix
implies that 0x + 0y + 0z = 5.
There is no solution.

14. $$\begin{bmatrix} 1 & -3 & 1 & | & 5 \\ -2 & 7 & -6 & | & -9 \\ 1 & -2 & -3 & | & 6 \end{bmatrix} \xrightarrow{2 \ [1] + [2]} \begin{bmatrix} 1 & -3 & 1 & | & 5 \\ 0 & 1 & -4 & | & 1 \\ 1 & -2 & -3 & | & 6 \end{bmatrix}$$

$$\xrightarrow{-1 \ [1] + [3]} \begin{bmatrix} 1 & -3 & 1 & | & 5 \\ 0 & 1 & -4 & | & 1 \\ 0 & 1 & -4 & | & 1 \end{bmatrix} \xrightarrow{3 \ [2] + [1]}$$

$$\begin{bmatrix} 1 & 0 & -11 & | & 8 \\ 0 & 1 & -4 & | & 1 \\ 0 & 1 & -4 & | & 1 \end{bmatrix} \xrightarrow{-1 \ [2] + [3]} \begin{bmatrix} 1 & 0 & -11 & | & 8 \\ 0 & 1 & -4 & | & 1 \\ 0 & 0 & 0 & | & 0 \end{bmatrix}$$

x = 11z + 8, y = 4z + 1, z = any value

15. $\begin{bmatrix} 1 & 1 & 1 & | & -1 \\ 2 & 3 & 2 & | & 3 \\ 2 & 1 & 2 & | & -7 \end{bmatrix} \xrightarrow{-2\ [1]\ +\ [2]} \begin{bmatrix} 1 & 1 & 1 & | & -1 \\ 0 & 1 & 0 & | & 5 \\ 2 & 1 & 2 & | & -7 \end{bmatrix}$

$\xrightarrow{-2\ [1]\ +\ [3]} \begin{bmatrix} 1 & 1 & 1 & | & -1 \\ 0 & 1 & 0 & | & 5 \\ 0 & -1 & 0 & | & -5 \end{bmatrix} \xrightarrow{-1\ [2]\ +\ [1]}$

$\begin{bmatrix} 1 & 0 & 1 & | & -6 \\ 0 & 1 & 0 & | & 5 \\ 0 & -1 & 0 & | & -5 \end{bmatrix} \xrightarrow{[2]\ +\ [3]} \begin{bmatrix} 1 & 0 & 1 & | & -6 \\ 0 & 1 & 0 & | & 5 \\ 0 & 0 & 0 & | & 0 \end{bmatrix}$

x = -z - 6, y = 5, z = any value

16. $\begin{bmatrix} 1 & -3 & 2 & | & 10 \\ -1 & 3 & -1 & | & -6 \\ -1 & 3 & 2 & | & 6 \end{bmatrix} \xrightarrow{[1]\ +\ [2]} \begin{bmatrix} 1 & -3 & 2 & | & 10 \\ 0 & 0 & 1 & | & 4 \\ -1 & 3 & 2 & | & 6 \end{bmatrix} \xrightarrow{[1]\ +\ [3]}$

$\begin{bmatrix} 1 & -3 & 2 & | & 10 \\ 0 & 0 & 1 & | & 4 \\ 0 & 0 & 4 & | & 16 \end{bmatrix} \xrightarrow{-2\ [2]\ +\ [1]} \begin{bmatrix} 1 & -3 & 0 & | & 2 \\ 0 & 0 & 1 & | & 4 \\ 0 & 0 & 4 & | & 16 \end{bmatrix}$

$\xrightarrow{-4\ [2]\ +\ [3]} \begin{bmatrix} 1 & -3 & 0 & | & 2 \\ 0 & 0 & 1 & | & 4 \\ 0 & 0 & 0 & | & 0 \end{bmatrix},$ x = 3y + 2, z = 4,
                       y = any value

17. $\begin{bmatrix} 1 & 2 & 3 & | & 4 \\ 5 & 6 & 7 & | & 8 \\ 1 & 2 & 3 & | & 5 \end{bmatrix} \xrightarrow{-5\ [1]\ +\ [2]} \begin{bmatrix} 1 & 2 & 3 & | & 4 \\ 0 & -4 & -8 & | & -12 \\ 1 & 2 & 3 & | & 5 \end{bmatrix}$

$\xrightarrow{-1\ [1]\ +\ [3]} \begin{bmatrix} 1 & 2 & 3 & | & 4 \\ 0 & -4 & -8 & | & -12 \\ 0 & 0 & 0 & | & 1 \end{bmatrix} \xrightarrow{-1/4\ [2]} \begin{bmatrix} 1 & 2 & 3 & | & 4 \\ 0 & 1 & 2 & | & 3 \\ 0 & 0 & 0 & | & 1 \end{bmatrix}$

$\xrightarrow{-2[2]\ +\ [1]} \begin{bmatrix} 1 & 0 & -1 & | & -2 \\ 0 & 1 & 2 & | & 3 \\ 0 & 0 & 0 & | & 1 \end{bmatrix} \xrightarrow{2[3]\ +\ [1]} \begin{bmatrix} 1 & 0 & -1 & | & 0 \\ 0 & 1 & 2 & | & 3 \\ 0 & 0 & 0 & | & 1 \end{bmatrix}$

$\xrightarrow{-3\ [3]\ +\ [2]} \begin{bmatrix} 1 & 0 & -1 & | & 0 \\ 0 & 1 & 2 & | & 0 \\ 0 & 0 & 0 & | & 1 \end{bmatrix}$ No solution

18.
$\begin{bmatrix} 1 & 3 & | & 7 \\ 1 & 2 & | & 5 \\ -1 & 1 & | & 2 \end{bmatrix} \xrightarrow{-1\ [1]\ +\ [2]} \begin{bmatrix} 1 & 3 & | & 7 \\ 0 & -1 & | & -2 \\ -1 & 1 & | & 2 \end{bmatrix} \xrightarrow{[1]\ +\ [3]}$

$\begin{bmatrix} 1 & 3 & | & 7 \\ 0 & -1 & | & -2 \\ 0 & 4 & | & 9 \end{bmatrix} \xrightarrow{-1\ [2]} \begin{bmatrix} 1 & 3 & | & 7 \\ 0 & 1 & | & 2 \\ 0 & 4 & | & 9 \end{bmatrix} \xrightarrow{-3\ [2]\ +\ [1]}$

$\begin{bmatrix} 1 & 0 & | & 1 \\ 0 & 1 & | & 2 \\ 0 & 4 & | & 9 \end{bmatrix} \xrightarrow{-4\ [2]\ +\ [3]} \begin{bmatrix} 1 & 0 & | & 1 \\ 0 & 1 & | & 2 \\ 0 & 0 & | & 1 \end{bmatrix} \xrightarrow{-1\ [3]\ +\ [1]}$

$\begin{bmatrix} 1 & 0 & | & 0 \\ 0 & 1 & | & 2 \\ 0 & 0 & | & 1 \end{bmatrix} \xrightarrow{-2\ [3]\ +\ [2]} \begin{bmatrix} 1 & 0 & | & 0 \\ 0 & 1 & | & 0 \\ 0 & 0 & | & 1 \end{bmatrix}$ No solution.

19.
$\begin{bmatrix} 1 & 1 & -2 & 2 & | & 5 \\ 2 & 1 & -4 & 1 & | & 5 \\ 3 & 4 & -6 & 9 & | & 20 \\ 4 & 4 & -8 & 8 & | & 20 \end{bmatrix} \xrightarrow{-2\ [1]\ +\ [2]} \begin{bmatrix} 1 & 1 & -2 & 2 & | & 5 \\ 0 & -1 & 0 & -3 & | & -5 \\ 3 & 4 & -6 & 9 & | & 20 \\ 4 & 4 & -8 & 8 & | & 20 \end{bmatrix}$

$\xrightarrow{-3\ [1]\ +\ [3]} \begin{bmatrix} 1 & 1 & -2 & 2 & | & 5 \\ 0 & -1 & 0 & -3 & | & -5 \\ 0 & 1 & 0 & 3 & | & 5 \\ 4 & 4 & -8 & 8 & | & 20 \end{bmatrix} \xrightarrow{-4\ [1]\ +\ [4]}$

$\begin{bmatrix} 1 & 1 & -2 & 2 & | & 5 \\ 0 & -1 & 0 & -3 & | & -5 \\ 0 & 1 & 0 & 3 & | & 5 \\ 0 & 0 & 0 & 0 & | & 0 \end{bmatrix} \xrightarrow{-1[2]} \begin{bmatrix} 1 & 1 & -2 & 2 & | & 5 \\ 0 & 1 & 0 & 3 & | & 5 \\ 0 & 1 & 0 & 3 & | & 5 \\ 0 & 0 & 0 & 0 & | & 0 \end{bmatrix}$

$\xrightarrow{-1\ [2]\ +\ [1]} \begin{bmatrix} 1 & 0 & -2 & -1 & | & 0 \\ 0 & 1 & 0 & 3 & | & 5 \\ 0 & 1 & 0 & 3 & | & 5 \\ 0 & 0 & 0 & 0 & | & 0 \end{bmatrix} \xrightarrow{-1\ [2]\ +\ [3]}$

$$\begin{bmatrix} 1 & 0 & -2 & -1 & \bigg| & 0 \\ 0 & 1 & 0 & 3 & \bigg| & 5 \\ 0 & 0 & 0 & 0 & \bigg| & 0 \\ 0 & 0 & 0 & 0 & \bigg| & 0 \end{bmatrix} \qquad \begin{array}{l} x = 2z + w, \ y = 5 - 3w, \\ z = \text{any value}; \ w = \text{any value} \end{array}$$

20. $\begin{bmatrix} 0 & 2 & 1 & -1 & \bigg| & 1 \\ 1 & -1 & 1 & 1 & \bigg| & 14 \\ -1 & -9 & -1 & 4 & \bigg| & 11 \\ 1 & 1 & 1 & 0 & \bigg| & 9 \end{bmatrix}$ $\begin{array}{c}\text{Exchange} \\ \text{[1] \& [4]}\end{array}$ $\begin{bmatrix} 1 & 1 & 1 & 0 & \bigg| & 9 \\ 1 & -1 & 1 & 1 & \bigg| & 14 \\ -1 & -9 & -1 & 4 & \bigg| & 11 \\ 0 & 2 & 1 & -1 & \bigg| & 1 \end{bmatrix}$

$\xrightarrow{-1 \ [1] \ + \ [2]}$ $\begin{bmatrix} 1 & 1 & 1 & 0 & \bigg| & 9 \\ 0 & -2 & 0 & 1 & \bigg| & 5 \\ -1 & -9 & -1 & 4 & \bigg| & 11 \\ 0 & 2 & 1 & -1 & \bigg| & 1 \end{bmatrix}$ $\xrightarrow{[1] \ + \ [3]}$

$\begin{bmatrix} 1 & 1 & 1 & 0 & \bigg| & 9 \\ 0 & -2 & 0 & 1 & \bigg| & 5 \\ 0 & -8 & 0 & 4 & \bigg| & 20 \\ 0 & 2 & 1 & -1 & \bigg| & 1 \end{bmatrix}$ $\xrightarrow{-1/2 \ [2]}$ $\begin{bmatrix} 1 & 1 & 1 & 0 & \bigg| & 9 \\ 0 & 1 & 0 & -\frac{1}{2} & \bigg| & -\frac{5}{2} \\ 0 & -8 & 0 & 4 & \bigg| & 20 \\ 0 & 2 & 1 & -1 & \bigg| & 1 \end{bmatrix}$

$\xrightarrow{-1 \ [2] \ + \ [1]}$ $\begin{bmatrix} 1 & 0 & 1 & \frac{1}{2} & \bigg| & \frac{23}{2} \\ 0 & 1 & 0 & -\frac{1}{2} & \bigg| & -\frac{5}{2} \\ 0 & -8 & 0 & 4 & \bigg| & 20 \\ 0 & 2 & 1 & -1 & \bigg| & 1 \end{bmatrix}$ $\xrightarrow{8 \ [2] \ + \ [3]}$

$\begin{bmatrix} 1 & 0 & 1 & \frac{1}{2} & \bigg| & \frac{23}{2} \\ 0 & 1 & 0 & -\frac{1}{2} & \bigg| & -\frac{5}{2} \\ 0 & 0 & 0 & 0 & \bigg| & 0 \\ 0 & 2 & 1 & -1 & \bigg| & 1 \end{bmatrix}$ $\xrightarrow{-2 \ [2] \ + \ [4]}$ $\begin{bmatrix} 1 & 0 & 1 & \frac{1}{2} & \bigg| & \frac{23}{2} \\ 0 & 1 & 0 & -\frac{1}{2} & \bigg| & -\frac{5}{2} \\ 0 & 0 & 0 & 0 & \bigg| & 0 \\ 0 & 0 & 1 & 0 & \bigg| & 6 \end{bmatrix}$

$\begin{array}{c}\text{Exchange} \\ \text{[3] \& [4]}\end{array}$ $\begin{bmatrix} 1 & 0 & 1 & \frac{1}{2} & \bigg| & \frac{23}{2} \\ 0 & 1 & 0 & -\frac{1}{2} & \bigg| & -\frac{5}{2} \\ 0 & 0 & 1 & 0 & \bigg| & 6 \\ 0 & 0 & 0 & 0 & \bigg| & 0 \end{bmatrix}$ $\xrightarrow{-1 \ [3] \ + \ [1]}$

$$\begin{bmatrix} 1 & 0 & 0 & \frac{1}{2} & \Big| & \frac{11}{2} \\ 0 & 1 & 0 & -\frac{1}{2} & \Big| & -\frac{5}{2} \\ 0 & 0 & 1 & 0 & \Big| & 6 \\ 0 & 0 & 0 & 0 & \Big| & 0 \end{bmatrix}$$

w = any value,

$x = \frac{11}{2} - \frac{1}{2}w, \ y = -\frac{5}{2} + \frac{1}{2}w, \ z = 6$

21. $\begin{bmatrix} 6 & -4 & \Big| & 2 \\ -3 & 3 & \Big| & 6 \\ 5 & 2 & \Big| & 39 \end{bmatrix} \xrightarrow{1/6 \ [1]} \begin{bmatrix} 1 & -\frac{2}{3} & \Big| & \frac{1}{3} \\ -3 & 3 & \Big| & 6 \\ 5 & 2 & \Big| & 39 \end{bmatrix} \xrightarrow{3 \ [1] + [2]}$

$\begin{bmatrix} 1 & -\frac{2}{3} & \Big| & \frac{1}{3} \\ 0 & 1 & \Big| & 7 \\ 5 & 2 & \Big| & 39 \end{bmatrix} \xrightarrow{-5 \ [1] + [3]} \begin{bmatrix} 1 & -\frac{2}{3} & \Big| & \frac{1}{3} \\ 0 & 1 & \Big| & 7 \\ 0 & \frac{16}{3} & \Big| & \frac{112}{3} \end{bmatrix} \xrightarrow{2/3 \ [2] + [1]}$

$\begin{bmatrix} 1 & 0 & \Big| & 5 \\ 0 & 1 & \Big| & 7 \\ 0 & \frac{16}{3} & \Big| & \frac{112}{3} \end{bmatrix} \xrightarrow{-16/3 \ [2] + [3]} \begin{bmatrix} 1 & 0 & \Big| & 5 \\ 0 & 1 & \Big| & 7 \\ 0 & 0 & \Big| & 0 \end{bmatrix} \ x = 5, \ y = 7$

22. $\begin{bmatrix} 3 & 2 & \Big| & 5 \\ -1 & 3 & \Big| & 2 \\ 5 & 2 & \Big| & 6 \\ 6 & 1 & \Big| & 39 \end{bmatrix} \xrightarrow{1/3 \ [1]} \begin{bmatrix} 1 & 2/3 & \Big| & 5/3 \\ -1 & 3 & \Big| & 2 \\ 5 & 2 & \Big| & 6 \\ 6 & 1 & \Big| & 39 \end{bmatrix} \xrightarrow{[1] + [2]}$

$\begin{bmatrix} 1 & 2/3 & \Big| & 5/3 \\ 0 & 11/3 & \Big| & 11/3 \\ 5 & 2 & \Big| & 6 \\ 6 & 1 & \Big| & 39 \end{bmatrix} \xrightarrow{-5 \ [1] + [3]} \begin{bmatrix} 1 & 2/3 & \Big| & 5/3 \\ 0 & 11/3 & \Big| & 11/3 \\ 0 & -4/3 & \Big| & -7/3 \\ 6 & 1 & \Big| & 39 \end{bmatrix}$

$\xrightarrow{-6 \ [1] + [4]} \begin{bmatrix} 1 & 2/3 & \Big| & 5/3 \\ 0 & 11/3 & \Big| & 11/3 \\ 0 & -4/3 & \Big| & -7/3 \\ 0 & -3 & \Big| & 29 \end{bmatrix} \xrightarrow{3/11 \ [2]}$

$\begin{bmatrix} 1 & 2/3 & \Big| & 5/3 \\ 0 & 1 & \Big| & 1 \\ 0 & -4/3 & \Big| & -7/3 \\ 0 & -3 & \Big| & 29 \end{bmatrix} \xrightarrow{-2/3 \ [2] + [1]} \begin{bmatrix} 1 & 0 & \Big| & 1 \\ 0 & 1 & \Big| & 1 \\ 0 & -4/3 & \Big| & -7/3 \\ 0 & -3 & \Big| & 29 \end{bmatrix}$

$$\xrightarrow{4/3\ [2]\ +\ [3]} \begin{bmatrix} 1 & 0 & 1 \\ 0 & 1 & 1 \\ 0 & 0 & -1 \\ 0 & -3 & 29 \end{bmatrix} \xrightarrow{3\ [2]\ +\ [4]} \begin{bmatrix} 1 & 0 & 1 \\ 0 & 1 & 1 \\ 0 & 0 & -1 \\ 0 & 0 & 32 \end{bmatrix}$$

$$\xrightarrow{-1\ [3]} \begin{bmatrix} 1 & 0 & 1 \\ 0 & 1 & 1 \\ 0 & 0 & 1 \\ 0 & 0 & 32 \end{bmatrix} \xrightarrow{-1\ [3]\ +\ [1]} \begin{bmatrix} 1 & 0 & 0 \\ 0 & 1 & 1 \\ 0 & 0 & 1 \\ 0 & 0 & 32 \end{bmatrix}$$

$$\xrightarrow{-1\ [3]\ +\ [2]} \begin{bmatrix} 1 & 0 & 0 \\ 0 & 1 & 0 \\ 0 & 0 & 1 \\ 0 & 0 & 32 \end{bmatrix} \xrightarrow{-32\ [3]\ +\ [4]} \begin{bmatrix} 1 & 0 & 0 \\ 0 & 1 & 0 \\ 0 & 0 & 1 \\ 0 & 0 & 0 \end{bmatrix}$$

No solution

23. $\begin{bmatrix} 1 & 2 & 1 & 5 \\ 0 & 1 & 3 & 9 \end{bmatrix} \xrightarrow{-2[2]\ +\ [1]} \begin{bmatrix} 1 & 0 & -5 & -13 \\ 0 & 1 & 3 & 9 \end{bmatrix}$

pick any value for z and calculate x and y using the formulas:

   x = 5z - 13   and   y = -3z + 9

24. $\begin{bmatrix} 1 & 5 & 3 & 9 \\ 2 & 9 & 7 & 5 \end{bmatrix} \xrightarrow{-2[1]\ +\ [2]} \begin{bmatrix} 1 & 5 & 3 & 9 \\ 0 & -1 & 1 & -13 \end{bmatrix}$

$\xrightarrow{-1[2]} \begin{bmatrix} 1 & 5 & 3 & 9 \\ 0 & 1 & -1 & 13 \end{bmatrix} \xrightarrow{-5[2]\ +\ [1]} \begin{bmatrix} 1 & 0 & 8 & -56 \\ 0 & 1 & -1 & 13 \end{bmatrix}$

pick any value for z and calculate x and y using the formulas:

   x = -8z - 56   and   y = z + 13

25. $\begin{bmatrix} 1 & 7 & -3 & 8 \\ 0 & 0 & 1 & 5 \end{bmatrix} \xrightarrow{3[2]\ +\ [1]} \begin{bmatrix} 1 & 7 & 0 & 23 \\ 0 & 0 & 1 & 5 \end{bmatrix}$

z = 5, pick any value for y and calculate x using the formula

x = -7y + 23

26. 10, 2, 20 miles

27. z = any value, x = 300 - z, y = 100 - z
Of course, to be realistic, we must have 0 ≤ z ≤ 100.

28. Not possible.

29. $\begin{bmatrix} 1 & 1 & 1 & | & 96 \\ -1 & -1 & 15 & | & 0 \\ 3 & 3 & 5 & | & 300 \end{bmatrix}$ $\xrightarrow{[2] + [1]}$ $\begin{bmatrix} 1 & 1 & 1 & | & 96 \\ 0 & 0 & 16 & | & 96 \\ 3 & 3 & 5 & | & 300 \end{bmatrix}$ $\xrightarrow{-3\,[1] + [3]}$

$\begin{bmatrix} 1 & 1 & 1 & | & 96 \\ 0 & 0 & 16 & | & 96 \\ 0 & 0 & 2 & | & 12 \end{bmatrix}$ $\xrightarrow{\frac{1}{16}\,[2]}$ $\begin{bmatrix} 1 & 1 & 1 & | & 96 \\ 0 & 0 & 1 & | & 6 \\ 0 & 0 & 2 & | & 12 \end{bmatrix}$ $\xrightarrow{-1[2] + [1]}$ $\begin{bmatrix} 1 & 1 & 0 & | & 90 \\ 0 & 0 & 1 & | & 6 \\ 0 & 0 & 2 & | & 12 \end{bmatrix}$

$\xrightarrow{-2[2] + [3]}$ $\begin{bmatrix} 1 & 1 & 0 & | & 90 \\ 0 & 0 & 1 & | & 6 \\ 0 & 0 & 0 & | & 0 \end{bmatrix}$

We then have z = 6 so they will use 6 floral squares. Also x + y = 90 so they will use 90 solids in any combination of blue and green.

30. $\begin{bmatrix} 1 & 1 & 1 & | & 15 \\ 7 & 10 & 13 & | & 150 \end{bmatrix}$ $\xrightarrow{-7[1] + 2}$ $\begin{bmatrix} 1 & 1 & 1 & | & 15 \\ 0 & 3 & 6 & | & 45 \end{bmatrix}$ $\xrightarrow{\frac{1}{3}[2]}$ $\begin{bmatrix} 1 & 1 & 1 & | & 15 \\ 0 & 1 & 2 & | & 15 \end{bmatrix}$

$\xrightarrow{-1[2] + [1]}$ $\begin{bmatrix} 1 & 0 & -1 & | & 0 \\ 0 & 1 & -2 & | & 15 \end{bmatrix}$

Therefore z = anything; however, logically z ≥ 0 and z ≤ 7.5 (since y ≥ 0 and y = -2z + 15). Once z has been chosen from a number between and including 0 and 7 then x and y can be calculated from the formulas x = z and y = -2z + 15.

31. $\begin{bmatrix} 1 & 1 & 1 & | & 14 \\ 1 & -1 & 2 & | & 15 \\ 1 & 2 & 3 & | & 36 \end{bmatrix}$ $\xrightarrow{-1\,[1] + [2]}$ $\begin{bmatrix} 1 & 1 & 1 & | & 14 \\ 0 & -2 & 1 & | & 1 \\ 1 & 2 & 3 & | & 36 \end{bmatrix}$

$\xrightarrow{-1\,[1] + [3]}$ $\begin{bmatrix} 1 & 1 & 1 & | & 14 \\ 0 & -2 & 1 & | & 1 \\ 0 & 1 & 2 & | & 22 \end{bmatrix}$ $\xrightarrow{-1/2\,[2]}$ $\begin{bmatrix} 1 & 1 & 1 & | & 14 \\ 0 & 1 & -\frac{1}{2} & | & -\frac{1}{2} \\ 0 & 1 & 2 & | & 22 \end{bmatrix}$

$\xrightarrow{-1\,[2] + [1]}$ $\begin{bmatrix} 1 & 0 & \frac{3}{2} & | & \frac{29}{2} \\ 0 & 1 & -\frac{1}{2} & | & -\frac{1}{2} \\ 0 & 1 & 2 & | & 22 \end{bmatrix}$ $\xrightarrow{-1\,[2] + [3]}$

$$\begin{bmatrix} 1 & 0 & \frac{3}{2} & \Big| & \frac{29}{2} \\ 0 & 1 & -\frac{1}{2} & \Big| & -\frac{1}{2} \\ 0 & 0 & \frac{5}{2} & \Big| & \frac{45}{2} \end{bmatrix} \xrightarrow{2/5\ [3]} \begin{bmatrix} 1 & 0 & \frac{3}{2} & \Big| & \frac{29}{2} \\ 0 & 1 & -\frac{1}{2} & \Big| & -\frac{1}{2} \\ 0 & 0 & 1 & \Big| & 9 \end{bmatrix} \xrightarrow{-3/2\ [3]\ +\ [1]}$$

$$\begin{bmatrix} 1 & 0 & 0 & \Big| & 1 \\ 0 & 1 & -\frac{1}{2} & \Big| & -\frac{1}{2} \\ 0 & 0 & 1 & \Big| & 9 \end{bmatrix} \xrightarrow{1/2\ [3]\ +\ [2]} \begin{bmatrix} 1 & 0 & 0 & \Big| & 1 \\ 0 & 1 & 0 & \Big| & 4 \\ 0 & 0 & 1 & \Big| & 9 \end{bmatrix}$$

$x^2 = 1$, $y^2 = 4$ and $z^2 = 9$ therefore $x = \pm 1$, $y = \pm 2$ and $z = \pm 3$.

32. $$\begin{bmatrix} 2 & 6 & \Big| & 4 \\ 1 & 7 & \Big| & 10 \\ k & 8 & \Big| & 4 \end{bmatrix} \xrightarrow{\frac{1}{2}[1]} \begin{bmatrix} 1 & 3 & \Big| & 2 \\ 1 & 7 & \Big| & 10 \\ k & 8 & \Big| & 4 \end{bmatrix} \xrightarrow{-1[1]\ +\ [2]} \begin{bmatrix} 1 & 3 & \Big| & 2 \\ 0 & 4 & \Big| & 8 \\ k & 8 & \Big| & 4 \end{bmatrix} \xrightarrow{-k[1]\ +[3]}$$

$$\begin{bmatrix} 1 & 3 & \Big| & 2 \\ 0 & 4 & \Big| & 8 \\ 0 & 8-3k & \Big| & 4-2k \end{bmatrix} \xrightarrow{\frac{1}{4}[2]} \begin{bmatrix} 1 & 3 & \Big| & 2 \\ 0 & 1 & \Big| & 2 \\ 0 & 8-3k & \Big| & 4-2k \end{bmatrix} \xrightarrow{-3[2]\ +\ [1]}$$

$$\begin{bmatrix} 1 & 0 & \Big| & -4 \\ 0 & 1 & \Big| & 2 \\ 0 & 8-3k & \Big| & 4-2k \end{bmatrix} \xrightarrow{-(8-3k)[2]\ +\ [3]} \begin{bmatrix} 1 & 0 & \Big| & -4 \\ 0 & 1 & \Big| & 2 \\ 0 & 0 & \Big| & -12+4k \end{bmatrix}$$

For there to be a solution the last row must be all zeros. Therefore $-12 + 4k = 0$ or $k = 3$.

33. $$\begin{bmatrix} 2 & -3 & \Big| & 4 \\ -6 & 9 & \Big| & k \end{bmatrix} \xrightarrow{-3[1]} \begin{bmatrix} -6 & 9 & \Big| & -12 \\ -6 & 9 & \Big| & k \end{bmatrix} \xrightarrow{-1[1]\ +\ [2]} \begin{bmatrix} -6 & 9 & \Big| & -12 \\ 0 & 0 & \Big| & k+12 \end{bmatrix}$$

If $k + 12 \neq 0$ ($k \neq -12$) then there will not be any solutions since the last row would not be all zeros. If $k = -12$ then there will be infinitely many solutions since the last row would be all zeros.

34. (7, 3)   35. None   36. None   37. (5, 6)   38. No solution.

39. Infinitely many   40. Infinitely many   41. None

2.3 Arithmetic Operations on Matrices

1.   2 x 3

2.   2 × 1, column matrix

57

3. 1 x 3, row matrix

4. 2 × 2, identity matrix, square matrix

5. 1 x 1, square matrix, row matrix, column matrix

6. 2 × 4, zero matrix

7. $\begin{bmatrix} 9 & 3 \\ 7 & -1 \end{bmatrix}$

8. $\begin{bmatrix} 13 \\ 3 \end{bmatrix}$

9. $\begin{bmatrix} 1 & 3 \\ 1 & 2 \\ 4 & -2 \end{bmatrix}$

10. $\begin{bmatrix} .2 & -.5 \\ -.2 & .5 \end{bmatrix}$

11. [11]

12. $\begin{bmatrix} \frac{1}{2} \end{bmatrix}$

13. 6(1/2) + 1(-3) + 5(2) = [10]

14. [0]

15. 3 x 5

16. 3 × 4

17. Not defined

18. 1 × 1

19. 3 x 1

20. Not defined

21. $\begin{bmatrix} 6 & 17 \\ 6 & 10 \end{bmatrix}$

22. $\begin{bmatrix} 10 \\ 7 \end{bmatrix}$

23. $\begin{bmatrix} 21 \\ -4 \\ 8 \end{bmatrix}$

24. $\begin{bmatrix} 0 & 0 \\ 0 & 0 \\ 0 & 0 \end{bmatrix}$

25. $\begin{bmatrix} 5 & 6 \\ 7 & 8 \end{bmatrix}$

26. $\begin{bmatrix} 1 & 0 \\ 0 & 1 \end{bmatrix}$

27. $\begin{bmatrix} .48 & .39 \\ .52 & .61 \end{bmatrix}$

28. $\begin{bmatrix} 8 & -10 & 2 \\ -1 & 6 & 3 \\ 3 & 5 & 11 \end{bmatrix}$

29. $\begin{bmatrix} 25 & 17 & 2 \\ 3 & -1 & 2 \\ 1 & 1 & 4 \end{bmatrix}$

30. $\begin{bmatrix} 1 \\ 2 \\ 3 \end{bmatrix}$

31. $\begin{cases} 2x + 3y = 6 \\ 4x + 5y = 7 \end{cases}$

32. $\begin{cases} -3x + 4y = 1 \\ \phantom{-3x + {}} y = 1 \end{cases}$

33. $\begin{cases} x + 2y + 3z = 10 \\ 4x + 5y + 6z = 11 \\ 7x + 8y + 9z = 12 \end{cases}$

34. $\begin{cases} x \phantom{{}+y+z} = 1 \\ \phantom{x+{}} y \phantom{{}+z} = 2 \\ \phantom{x+y+{}} z = 3 \end{cases}$

35. $\begin{bmatrix} 3 & 2 \\ 7 & -1 \end{bmatrix} \begin{bmatrix} x \\ y \end{bmatrix} = \begin{bmatrix} -1 \\ 2 \end{bmatrix}$

36. $\begin{bmatrix} 5 & -2 \\ -3 & 4 \end{bmatrix} \begin{bmatrix} x \\ y \end{bmatrix} = \begin{bmatrix} 6 \\ 0 \end{bmatrix}$
${}_{-2}$

37. $\begin{bmatrix} 1 & -2 & 3 \\ 0 & 1 & 1 \\ 0 & 0 & 1 \end{bmatrix} \begin{bmatrix} x \\ y \\ z \end{bmatrix} = \begin{bmatrix} 5 \\ 6 \\ 2 \end{bmatrix}$

38. $\begin{bmatrix} -2 & 4 & -1 \\ 1 & 6 & 3 \\ 7 & 0 & 4 \end{bmatrix} \begin{bmatrix} x \\ y \\ z \end{bmatrix} = \begin{bmatrix} 5 \\ -1 \\ 8 \end{bmatrix}$

39. $\begin{bmatrix} 4 & 24 \\ 20 & 24 \end{bmatrix}$

40. $\begin{bmatrix} -9 \\ 22 \\ 14 \end{bmatrix}$

41. $\begin{bmatrix} 3 & -1 \\ -1 & \frac{1}{2} \end{bmatrix} \cdot \begin{bmatrix} 1 & 2 \\ 2 & 6 \end{bmatrix} = \begin{bmatrix} 3 \cdot 1 + -1 \cdot 2 & 3 \cdot 2 + -1 \cdot 6 \\ -1 \cdot 1 + \frac{1}{2} \cdot 2 & -1 \cdot 2 + \frac{1}{2} \cdot 6 \end{bmatrix} = \begin{bmatrix} 1 & 0 \\ 0 & 1 \end{bmatrix}$

42. $\begin{bmatrix} 2 & 8 & -11 \\ -1 & -5 & 7 \\ 1 & 2 & -3 \end{bmatrix} \cdot \begin{bmatrix} 1 & 2 & 1 \\ 4 & 5 & -3 \\ 3 & 4 & -2 \end{bmatrix} = \begin{bmatrix} 24+32-33 & 4+40-44 & 2-24+22 \\ -1-20+21 & -2-25+28 & -1+15-14 \\ 1+8-9 & 2+10-12 & 1-6+6 \end{bmatrix}$

$= \begin{bmatrix} 1 & 0 & 0 \\ 0 & 1 & 0 \\ 0 & 0 & 1 \end{bmatrix}$

43. (a) $\begin{bmatrix} 6 & 8 & 2 \\ 2 & 5 & 3 \end{bmatrix} \cdot \begin{bmatrix} 20 \\ 15 \\ 50 \end{bmatrix} = \begin{bmatrix} 120 + 120 + 100 \\ 40 + 75 + 150 \end{bmatrix} = \begin{bmatrix} 340 \\ 265 \end{bmatrix}$

(b) Mike's clothes cost $340.
Don's clothes cost $265.

44. (a) [18,500   21,750   24,250]. September wholesale costs for each of the three stores.

(b) [18,000   26,500   27,500]. October wholesale costs for each of the three stores.

(c) [31,500   37,250   40,750]. September revenue for each of the three stores.

(d) [31,000   44,500   46,500]. October revenue for each of the three stores.

(e) [200   200   300]. Profits for each of the three appliances.

(f) [13,000 15,500 16,500], September profits for each of the three stores.

(g) [13,000 18,000 19,000], October profits for each of the three stores.

(h) $\begin{bmatrix} 50 & 90 & 50 \\ 50 & 40 & 30 \\ 20 & 25 & 65 \end{bmatrix}$, quantities of each of the appliances sold during September and October.

(i) [26,000 33,500 35,500], combined September and October profits for each of the three stores.

45. (a) $\begin{bmatrix} .25 & .35 & .30 & .10 & 0 \\ .10 & .20 & .40 & .20 & .10 \\ .5 & .10 & .20 & .40 & .25 \end{bmatrix} \begin{bmatrix} 4 \\ 3 \\ 2 \\ 1 \\ 0 \end{bmatrix} = \begin{bmatrix} 2.75 \\ 2.00 \\ 1.30 \end{bmatrix}$

I: 2.75, II: 2, III: 1.3

(b) $\begin{bmatrix} 240 & 120 & 40 \end{bmatrix} \begin{bmatrix} .25 & .35 & .30 & .10 & 0 \\ .10 & .20 & .40 & .20 & .10 \\ .5 & .10 & .20 & .40 & .25 \end{bmatrix} = \begin{bmatrix} 74 & 112 & 128 & 64 & 22 \end{bmatrix}$

A: 74, B: 112, C: 128, D: 64, F:22.

46. $\begin{bmatrix} .10 & .10 & .30 & .50 \\ .10 & .20 & .30 & .40 \\ .15 & .15 & .35 & .35 \end{bmatrix} \begin{bmatrix} 97 \\ 72 \\ 83 \\ 75 \end{bmatrix} = \begin{bmatrix} 79.3 \\ 79 \\ 80.65 \end{bmatrix}$

Scheme III (80.65) is the most advantageous.

47. $[6000 \quad 8000 \quad 4000] \begin{bmatrix} .65 & .35 \\ .55 & .45 \\ .45 & .55 \end{bmatrix} =$

[(3900 + 4400 + 1800) (2100 + 3600 + 2200)] = [10,100 7,900]
Number voting Democratic = 10,100·
Number voting Republican = 7,900.

48. (a) Democratic victory with $\dfrac{10100}{10100+7900} \cdot 100 \approx 56.1\%$ of the vote.

(b) $\begin{bmatrix} 2000 & 4000 & 12000 \end{bmatrix} \begin{bmatrix} .65 & .35 \\ .55 & .45 \\ .45 & .55 \end{bmatrix} = \begin{bmatrix} 8900 & 9100 \end{bmatrix}$

Republican victory with $\dfrac{9100}{9100+8900} \cdot 100 \approx 50.6\%$ of the vote.

49. $\begin{bmatrix} 50 & 20 & 10 \\ 30 & 30 & 15 \\ 20 & 20 & 5 \end{bmatrix} \begin{bmatrix} 10 \\ 15 \\ 20 \end{bmatrix} = \begin{bmatrix} 1000 \\ 1050 \\ 600 \end{bmatrix}$

Carpenters: $1000, Bricklayers: $1050, Plumbers: $600.

50. (a) $AB = \begin{bmatrix} 232{,}000 & 260{,}500 \\ 86{,}000 & 97{,}500 \\ 42{,}000 & 47{,}000 \end{bmatrix}$

(b) 86,000 sick males

(c) 47,000 carrier females

51. (a) $BN = \begin{bmatrix} 162 & 150 & 143 \end{bmatrix}$ For breakfast he gets 162 units of nutrient 1, 150 units of nutrient 2 and 143 units of nutrient 3.

(b) $LN = \begin{bmatrix} 186 & 200 & 239 \end{bmatrix}$ For lunch he gets 186 units of nutrient 1, 200 units of nutrient 2 and 239 units of nutrient 3.

(c) $DN = \begin{bmatrix} 288 & 300 & 344 \end{bmatrix}$ For dinner he gets 288 units of nutrient 1, 300 units of nutrient 2 and 344 units of nutrient 3.

(d) $B + L + D = \begin{bmatrix} 5 & 8 \end{bmatrix}$ In a day he gets 5oz of food X and 8oz of food Y.

(e) $(B + L + D)N = \begin{bmatrix} 636 & 650 & 726 \end{bmatrix}$ In a day Mikey gets 636 units of nutrient 1, 650 units of nutrient 2 and 726 units of nutrient 3.

52. (a) $RM = \begin{bmatrix} 100 & 115 & 85 & 75 \end{bmatrix}$ To make the cookies that were ordered the bakery needs 100 units of ingredient A, 115 units of ingredient B, 85 units of ingredient C and 75 units of ingredient D.

(b) $MN = \begin{bmatrix} 108 \\ 102 \\ 182 \end{bmatrix}$ The cost of making type I cookies is $1.80, type II cookies is $1.02 and type III cookies is $1.82.

(c) $RMN = \begin{bmatrix} 5850 \end{bmatrix}$ The total cost for ingredients is $58.50.

(d) $S - MN = \begin{bmatrix} 67 \\ 48 \\ 43 \end{bmatrix}$ The profit is $.67 for cookie I, $.48 for cookie II and $.43 for cookie III.

(e) $R(S-MN) = \begin{bmatrix} 2275 \end{bmatrix}$ The total profit from the sale of the order is $22.75.

(f) $RS = \begin{bmatrix} 8125 \end{bmatrix}$ The total revenue from the sale of the order is $81.25.

53. (a) $AP = \begin{bmatrix} 720 \\ 646 \end{bmatrix}$

(b) the pool brings in $720 per day on average.

54. (a) $T = \begin{bmatrix} 3 & 5 \\ \frac{1}{2} & 1 \end{bmatrix}$

(b) $S = \begin{bmatrix} 30 \\ 20 \end{bmatrix}$ $TS = \begin{bmatrix} 119 \\ 35 \end{bmatrix}$ The total assembly time is 119 hrs and the total packing time is 35 hrs.

55. $x = 3$, $y = 4$, $z = 5$

56. $a = 1$, $b = -2$

57. $\begin{bmatrix} 27.9 & 130.6 & -69.88 \\ 106.75 & -149.44 & 26.1 \\ -47.5 & 336.2 & -18.7 \end{bmatrix}$ 58. $\begin{bmatrix} -171.3 & 40.8 & -31.8 \\ 454.6 & -22.5 & 22.7 \\ -2.6 & 122.3 & 53.56 \end{bmatrix}$

59. $\begin{bmatrix} -69.14 & 147.9 & -43.26 \\ 158.05 & -3.69 & 33.46 \\ -176.1 & 259.5 & 59.3 \end{bmatrix}$ 60. $\begin{bmatrix} -69.14 & 147.9 & -43.26 \\ 158.05 & -3.69 & 33.46 \\ -176.1 & 259.5 & 59.3 \end{bmatrix}$

61. $\begin{bmatrix} 160.16 & -26.7 & 4 \\ 2.7 & 150.85 & -53 \\ 187.4 & -35.5 & 48.6 \end{bmatrix}$ 62. $\begin{bmatrix} -479.236 & 1151.77 & -515.2 \\ 3344.23 & -488.675 & 127.26 \\ -1036.94 & 1828.65 & -521.8 \end{bmatrix}$

2.4 The Inverse of a Matrix

1. $\begin{bmatrix} 1 & -2 \\ -1/2 & 2 \end{bmatrix} \begin{bmatrix} 2 & 2 \\ 1/2 & 1 \end{bmatrix} \begin{bmatrix} x \\ y \end{bmatrix} = \begin{bmatrix} 1 & -2 \\ -1/2 & 2 \end{bmatrix} \begin{bmatrix} 4 \\ 1 \end{bmatrix}$

$\begin{bmatrix} 1 & 0 \\ 0 & 1 \end{bmatrix} \begin{bmatrix} x \\ y \end{bmatrix} = \begin{bmatrix} 2 \\ 0 \end{bmatrix}$ $x = 2$, $y = 0$

2. $\begin{bmatrix} 1 & -2 \\ -1/2 & 2 \end{bmatrix} \begin{bmatrix} 2 & 2 \\ 1/2 & 1 \end{bmatrix} \begin{bmatrix} x \\ y \end{bmatrix} = \begin{bmatrix} 1 & -2 \\ -1/2 & 2 \end{bmatrix} \begin{bmatrix} 14 \\ 4 \end{bmatrix}$

$\begin{bmatrix} 1 & 0 \\ 0 & 1 \end{bmatrix} \begin{bmatrix} x \\ y \end{bmatrix} = \begin{bmatrix} 6 \\ 1 \end{bmatrix}$ $x = 6$, $y = 1$

3. $\Delta = 1$ $A^{-1} = \begin{bmatrix} 1 & -2 \\ -3 & 7 \end{bmatrix}$

4. $\Delta = -1$ $\quad A^{-1} = \begin{bmatrix} 7/-1 & -3/-1 \\ -5/-1 & 3/-1 \end{bmatrix} = \begin{bmatrix} -7 & 3 \\ 5 & -2 \end{bmatrix}$

5. $\Delta = 2$ $\quad A^{-1} = \begin{bmatrix} 2/2 & -2/2 \\ -5/2 & 6/2 \end{bmatrix} = \begin{bmatrix} 1 & -1 \\ -5/2 & 3 \end{bmatrix}$

6. $\Delta = .5$ $\quad A^{-1} = \begin{bmatrix} .5/.5 & -.5/.5 \\ -0/.5 & 1/.5 \end{bmatrix} = \begin{bmatrix} 1 & -1 \\ 0 & 2 \end{bmatrix}$

7. $\Delta = .5$ $\quad A^{-1} = \begin{bmatrix} .8/.5 & -.2/.5 \\ -.3/.5 & .7/.5 \end{bmatrix} = \begin{bmatrix} 1.6 & -.4 \\ -.6 & 1.4 \end{bmatrix}$

8. $\Delta = -1$ $\quad A^{-1} = \begin{bmatrix} 0/-1 & -1/-1 \\ -1/-1 & 0/-1 \end{bmatrix} = \begin{bmatrix} 0 & 1 \\ 1 & 0 \end{bmatrix}$

$\qquad\qquad\qquad A \quad A^{-1} \quad I_1$

9. $[1/3]$ $\quad [3][x] = [1]$ $\quad 3x = 1$ $\quad x = 1/3$

10. $[5]$

11. Coefficient matrix $A = \begin{bmatrix} 1 & 2 \\ 2 & 6 \end{bmatrix}$ and $\Delta = 1 \cdot 6 - 2 \cdot 2 = 2.$

$A^{-1} = \begin{bmatrix} 3 & -1 \\ -1 & 1/2 \end{bmatrix}$

$\begin{bmatrix} 3 & -1 \\ -1 & 1/2 \end{bmatrix} \begin{bmatrix} 1 & 2 \\ 2 & 6 \end{bmatrix} \begin{bmatrix} x \\ y \end{bmatrix} = \begin{bmatrix} 3 & -1 \\ -1 & 1/2 \end{bmatrix} \begin{bmatrix} 3 \\ 5 \end{bmatrix}$

$\begin{bmatrix} x \\ y \end{bmatrix} = \begin{bmatrix} 4 \\ 1/2 \end{bmatrix}$ Therefore $x = 4$, $y = -\dfrac{1}{2}$.

12. Coefficient matrix $A = \begin{bmatrix} 5 & 3 \\ 7 & 4 \end{bmatrix}$ and $\Delta = 5 \cdot 4 - 3 \cdot 7 = -1$

$A^{-1} = \begin{bmatrix} -4 & 3 \\ 7 & -5 \end{bmatrix}$

$\begin{bmatrix} -4 & 3 \\ 7 & -5 \end{bmatrix} \begin{bmatrix} 5 & 3 \\ 7 & 4 \end{bmatrix} \begin{bmatrix} x \\ y \end{bmatrix} = \begin{bmatrix} -4 & 3 \\ 7 & -5 \end{bmatrix} \begin{bmatrix} 1 \\ 2 \end{bmatrix}$

$\begin{bmatrix} x \\ y \end{bmatrix} = \begin{bmatrix} 2 \\ -3 \end{bmatrix}$ Therefore $x = 2$, $y = -3$.

13. Coefficient matrix $A = \begin{bmatrix} 1/2 & 2 \\ 3 & 16 \end{bmatrix}$ $\Delta = 1/2 \cdot 16 - 2 \cdot 3 = 2$

$A^{-1} = \begin{bmatrix} 8 & -1 \\ -3/2 & 1/4 \end{bmatrix}$

$\begin{bmatrix} 8 & -1 \\ -3/2 & 1/4 \end{bmatrix} \begin{bmatrix} 1/2 & 2 \\ 3 & 16 \end{bmatrix} \begin{bmatrix} x \\ y \end{bmatrix} = \begin{bmatrix} 8 & -1 \\ -3/2 & 1/4 \end{bmatrix} \begin{bmatrix} 4 \\ 0 \end{bmatrix}$

$$\begin{bmatrix} x \\ y \end{bmatrix} = \begin{bmatrix} 32 \\ -6 \end{bmatrix} \qquad \text{Therefore} \quad x = 32, \ y = -6.$$

14. Coefficient matrix $A = \begin{bmatrix} .8 & .6 \\ .2 & .4 \end{bmatrix}$ and $\Delta = .8 \cdot .4 - .6 \cdot .2 = .2$

$$A^{-1} = \begin{bmatrix} 2 & -3 \\ -1 & 4 \end{bmatrix}$$

$$\begin{bmatrix} 2 & -3 \\ -1 & 4 \end{bmatrix} \begin{bmatrix} .8 & .6 \\ .2 & .4 \end{bmatrix} \begin{bmatrix} x \\ y \end{bmatrix} = \begin{bmatrix} 2 & -3 \\ -1 & 4 \end{bmatrix} \begin{bmatrix} 2 \\ 1 \end{bmatrix}$$

$$\begin{bmatrix} x \\ y \end{bmatrix} = \begin{bmatrix} 1 \\ 2 \end{bmatrix} \qquad \text{Therefore} \quad x = 1, \ y = 2.$$

15. (a) $\begin{bmatrix} .8 & .3 \\ .2 & .7 \end{bmatrix} \begin{bmatrix} x \\ y \end{bmatrix} = \begin{bmatrix} m \\ s \end{bmatrix}$

   (b) $\begin{bmatrix} x \\ y \end{bmatrix} = \begin{bmatrix} 1.4 & -.6 \\ -.4 & 1.6 \end{bmatrix} \begin{bmatrix} m \\ s \end{bmatrix}$

   (c) $\begin{bmatrix} x \\ y \end{bmatrix} = \begin{bmatrix} 1.4 & -.6 \\ -.4 & 1.6 \end{bmatrix} \begin{bmatrix} 100000 \\ 50000 \end{bmatrix} = \begin{bmatrix} 110000 \\ 40000 \end{bmatrix}$ There were
   110000 married adults and 40000 single adults one year ago.

   (d) $\begin{bmatrix} x \\ y \end{bmatrix} = \begin{bmatrix} 1.4 & -.6 \\ -.4 & 1.6 \end{bmatrix} \begin{bmatrix} 110000 \\ 40000 \end{bmatrix} = \begin{bmatrix} 130000 \\ 20000 \end{bmatrix}$ There were
   130000 married adults and 20000 single adults two years ago.

16. (a) $\begin{bmatrix} \frac{1}{3} & \frac{1}{4} \\ \frac{2}{3} & \frac{3}{4} \end{bmatrix} \begin{bmatrix} x \\ y \end{bmatrix} = \begin{bmatrix} s \\ w \end{bmatrix}$

   (b) $\begin{bmatrix} x \\ y \end{bmatrix} = \begin{bmatrix} 9 & -3 \\ -8 & 4 \end{bmatrix} \begin{bmatrix} s \\ w \end{bmatrix}$

   (c) 12,000
   (d) 24,000

17. (a) $\begin{bmatrix} .7 & .1 \\ .3 & .9 \end{bmatrix} \begin{bmatrix} x \\ y \end{bmatrix} = \begin{bmatrix} u \\ v \end{bmatrix}$

   (b) $\begin{bmatrix} x \\ y \end{bmatrix} = \begin{bmatrix} 3/2 & -1/6 \\ -1/2 & 7/6 \end{bmatrix} \begin{bmatrix} u \\ v \end{bmatrix}$

   (c) $\begin{bmatrix} x \\ y \end{bmatrix} = \begin{bmatrix} 3/2 & -1/6 \\ -1/2 & 7/6 \end{bmatrix} \begin{bmatrix} 6000 \\ 3000 \end{bmatrix} = \begin{bmatrix} 8500 \\ 500 \end{bmatrix}$ Therefore 8500
   students lived on campus last semester.
   $\begin{bmatrix} .7 & .1 \\ .3 & .9 \end{bmatrix} \begin{bmatrix} x \\ y \end{bmatrix} = \begin{bmatrix} 6000 \\ 3000 \end{bmatrix} = \begin{bmatrix} 4500 \\ 4500 \end{bmatrix}$ Therefore 4500 students
   will live off campus next semester.

18. (a) $\begin{bmatrix} .8 & .5 \\ .2 & .5 \end{bmatrix} \begin{bmatrix} x \\ y \end{bmatrix} = \begin{bmatrix} u \\ v \end{bmatrix}$

(b) $\begin{bmatrix} .8 & .5 \\ .2 & .5 \end{bmatrix} \begin{bmatrix} 25 \\ 8 \end{bmatrix} = \begin{bmatrix} 24 \\ 9 \end{bmatrix}$ Therefore 24 students will pass the

4th test.

$\begin{bmatrix} 5/3 & -5/3 \\ -2/3 & 8/3 \end{bmatrix} \begin{bmatrix} 25 \\ 8 \end{bmatrix} = \begin{bmatrix} 85/3 \\ 14/3 \end{bmatrix}$ Therefore approximately 28

passed the 2nd test.

19. $\begin{bmatrix} 1 & 2 & 2 \\ 1 & 3 & 2 \\ 1 & 2 & 3 \end{bmatrix} \begin{bmatrix} x \\ y \\ z \end{bmatrix} = \begin{bmatrix} 1 \\ -1 \\ -1 \end{bmatrix}$

$\begin{bmatrix} x \\ y \\ z \end{bmatrix} = \begin{bmatrix} 5 & -2 & -2 \\ -1 & 1 & 0 \\ -1 & 0 & 1 \end{bmatrix} \begin{bmatrix} 1 \\ -1 \\ -1 \end{bmatrix} = \begin{bmatrix} 9 \\ -2 \\ -2 \end{bmatrix}$ $x = 9, \ y = -2, \ z = -2$

20. $\begin{bmatrix} 1 & 2 & 2 \\ 1 & 3 & 2 \\ 1 & 2 & 3 \end{bmatrix} \begin{bmatrix} x \\ y \\ z \end{bmatrix} = \begin{bmatrix} 1 \\ 0 \\ 0 \end{bmatrix}$

$\begin{bmatrix} x \\ y \\ z \end{bmatrix} = \begin{bmatrix} 5 & -2 & -2 \\ -1 & 1 & 0 \\ -1 & 0 & 1 \end{bmatrix} \begin{bmatrix} 1 \\ 0 \\ 0 \end{bmatrix} = \begin{bmatrix} 5 \\ -1 \\ -1 \end{bmatrix}$ $x = 5, \ y = -1, \ z = -1$

21. $\begin{bmatrix} 9 & 0 & 2 & 0 \\ -20 & -9 & 5 & 5 \\ 4 & 0 & 1 & 0 \\ -4 & -2 & -1 & 1 \end{bmatrix} \begin{bmatrix} x \\ y \\ z \\ w \end{bmatrix} = \begin{bmatrix} 1 \\ 0 \\ 0 \\ -1 \end{bmatrix}$

$\begin{bmatrix} x \\ y \\ z \\ w \end{bmatrix} = \begin{bmatrix} 1 & 0 & -2 & 0 \\ 0 & 1 & 0 & -5 \\ -4 & 0 & 9 & 0 \\ 0 & 2 & 1 & -9 \end{bmatrix} \begin{bmatrix} 1 \\ 0 \\ 0 \\ -1 \end{bmatrix} = \begin{bmatrix} 1 \\ 5 \\ -4 \\ 9 \end{bmatrix}$

$x = 1, \ y = 5, \ z = -4, \ w = 9$

22. $\begin{bmatrix} 9 & 0 & 2 & 0 \\ -20 & -9 & 5 & 5 \\ 4 & 0 & 1 & 0 \\ -4 & -2 & -1 & 1 \end{bmatrix} \begin{bmatrix} x \\ y \\ z \\ w \end{bmatrix} = \begin{bmatrix} 2 \\ 1 \\ 3 \\ 0 \end{bmatrix}$

$$\begin{bmatrix} x \\ y \\ z \\ w \end{bmatrix} = \begin{bmatrix} 1 & 0 & -2 & 0 \\ 0 & 1 & 0 & -5 \\ -4 & 0 & 9 & 0 \\ 0 & 2 & 1 & -9 \end{bmatrix} \begin{bmatrix} 2 \\ 1 \\ 3 \\ 0 \end{bmatrix} = \begin{bmatrix} -4 \\ 1 \\ 19 \\ 5 \end{bmatrix}$$

$x = -4$, $y = 1$, $z = 19$, $w = 5$

23. This matrix does not have an inverse since the two rows represent equivalent equations (Row 1 = (Row 2)·3).

24. $A = \begin{bmatrix} \frac{3}{13} & \frac{7}{13} \\ \frac{1}{13} & \frac{-2}{13} \end{bmatrix}$ since $(A^{-1})^{-1} = A$

25. (a) $\begin{bmatrix} 1 & 2 \\ .9 & 0 \end{bmatrix} \begin{bmatrix} x \\ y \end{bmatrix} = \begin{bmatrix} a \\ b \end{bmatrix}$

(b) $\begin{bmatrix} 1 & 2 \\ .9 & 0 \end{bmatrix} \begin{bmatrix} 450000 \\ 360000 \end{bmatrix} = \begin{bmatrix} 1170000 \\ 405000 \end{bmatrix}$ After 1 year there will be 1,170,000 in group I and 405,000 in group II.

$\begin{bmatrix} 1 & 2 \\ .9 & 0 \end{bmatrix} \begin{bmatrix} 1170000 \\ 405000 \end{bmatrix} = \begin{bmatrix} 1980000 \\ 1053000 \end{bmatrix}$ After 2 years there will be 1,980,000 in group I and 1,053,000 in group II.

(c) $A^{-1}B = \begin{bmatrix} 0 & 10/9 \\ 1/2 & -5/9 \end{bmatrix} \begin{bmatrix} 810000 \\ 630000 \end{bmatrix} = \begin{bmatrix} 700000 \\ 55000 \end{bmatrix}$ So one year earlier there were 700,000 in group I, 55,000 in II.

26. $A = A^{-2} \cdot A^3$ where $A^{-2} = \begin{bmatrix} -2 & -1 \\ 2 & -1 \end{bmatrix}^{-1} = \begin{bmatrix} -1/4 & 1/4 \\ -1/2 & -1/2 \end{bmatrix}$

$A = \begin{bmatrix} -1/4 & 1/4 \\ -1/2 & -1/2 \end{bmatrix} \begin{bmatrix} -2 & 1 \\ -2 & -3 \end{bmatrix} = \begin{bmatrix} 0 & -1 \\ 2 & 1 \end{bmatrix}$

27. $\begin{bmatrix} -.14 & .26 \\ .34 & -.02 \end{bmatrix}$ 28. $\begin{bmatrix} -.02 & .13 \\ .24 & .49 \end{bmatrix}$ 29. $\begin{bmatrix} .11 & .33 & -.06 \\ .34 & .10 & .22 \\ .01 & .07 & .09 \end{bmatrix}$ 30. $\begin{bmatrix} .04 & -.34 & -.40 \\ .12 & .44 & .39 \\ .09 & .11 & .19 \end{bmatrix}$

31. $x = -.8$, $y = 5.6$, $z = 5$ 32. $x = 11.5$, $y = 128.5$, $z = 104.5$

33. $x = 0$, $y = 2$, $z = 0$, $w = 2$ 34. $x = -.04$, $y = 2.28$, $z = 4.14$, $w = 2.03$

2.5 The Gauss-Jordan Method for Calculating Inverses

1. $\begin{bmatrix} 7 & 3 & | & 1 & 0 \\ 5 & 2 & | & 0 & 1 \end{bmatrix} \xrightarrow{1/7\ [1]} \begin{bmatrix} 1 & 3/7 & | & 1/7 & 0 \\ 5 & 2 & | & 0 & 1 \end{bmatrix} \xrightarrow{-5\ [1]\ +\ [2]}$

$\begin{bmatrix} 1 & 3/7 & | & 1/7 & 0 \\ 0 & -1/7 & | & -5/7 & 1 \end{bmatrix} \xrightarrow{-7\ [2]} \begin{bmatrix} 1 & 3/7 & | & 1/7 & 0 \\ 0 & 1 & | & 5 & -7 \end{bmatrix}$

$\xrightarrow{-3/7\ [2]\ +\ [1]} \begin{bmatrix} 1 & 0 & | & -2 & 3 \\ 0 & 1 & | & 5 & -7 \end{bmatrix}$

So the inverse is $\begin{bmatrix} -2 & 3 \\ 5 & -7 \end{bmatrix}$.

2. $\begin{bmatrix} 5 & -2 & | & 1 & 0 \\ 6 & 2 & | & 0 & 1 \end{bmatrix} \xrightarrow{1/5\ [1]} \begin{bmatrix} 1 & -2/5 & | & 1/5 & 0 \\ 6 & 2 & | & 0 & 1 \end{bmatrix} \xrightarrow{-6\ [1]\ +\ [2]}$

$\begin{bmatrix} 1 & -2/5 & | & 1/5 & 0 \\ 0 & 22/5 & | & -3/5 & 1 \end{bmatrix} \xrightarrow{5/22\ [2]} \begin{bmatrix} 1 & -2/5 & | & 1/5 & 0 \\ 0 & 1 & | & -3/11 & 5/22 \end{bmatrix}$

$\xrightarrow{-2/5\ [2]\ +\ [1]} \begin{bmatrix} 1 & 0 & | & 1/11 & 1/11 \\ 0 & 1 & | & -3/11 & 5/22 \end{bmatrix}$

So the inverse is $\begin{bmatrix} 1/11 & 1/11 \\ -3/11 & 5/22 \end{bmatrix}$.

3. $\begin{bmatrix} 10 & 12 & | & 1 & 0 \\ 3 & -4 & | & 0 & 1 \end{bmatrix} \xrightarrow{1/10\ [1]} \begin{bmatrix} 1 & 6/5 & | & 1/10 & 0 \\ 3 & -4 & | & 0 & 1 \end{bmatrix}$

$\xrightarrow{-3\ [1]\ +\ [2]} \begin{bmatrix} 1 & 6/5 & | & 1/10 & 0 \\ 0 & -38/5 & | & -3/10 & 1 \end{bmatrix} \xrightarrow{-5/38\ [2]}$

$\begin{bmatrix} 1 & 6/5 & | & 1/10 & 0 \\ 0 & 1 & | & 3/76 & -5/38 \end{bmatrix} \xrightarrow{-6/5\ [2]\ +\ [1]}$

$\begin{bmatrix} 1 & 0 & | & 1/19 & 3/19 \\ 0 & 1 & | & 3/76 & -5/38 \end{bmatrix}$ So the inverse is $\begin{bmatrix} 1/19 & 3/19 \\ 3/76 & -5/38 \end{bmatrix}$.

4. $\begin{bmatrix} 1 & -3 & | & 1 & 0 \\ 0 & 1 & | & 0 & 1 \end{bmatrix} \xrightarrow[3\ [1]\ +\ [2]]{3\ [2] \quad [1]} \begin{bmatrix} 1 & 0 & | & 1 & 3 \\ 0 & 1 & | & 0 & 1 \end{bmatrix}$

So the inverse is $\begin{bmatrix} 1 & 3 \\ 0 & 1 \end{bmatrix}$.

5. $\begin{bmatrix} 2 & -4 & | & 1 & 0 \\ -1 & 2 & | & 0 & 1 \end{bmatrix} \xrightarrow{1/2\ [1]} \begin{bmatrix} 1 & -2 & | & 1/2 & 0 \\ -1 & 2 & | & 0 & 1 \end{bmatrix} \xrightarrow{1\ [1]\ +\ [2]}$

$\begin{bmatrix} 1 & -2 & | & 1/2 & 0 \\ 0 & 0 & | & 1/2 & 1 \end{bmatrix}$ There is no inverse.

6. $\begin{bmatrix} 1 & 3 & 1 & | & 1 & 0 & 0 \\ -1 & 2 & 0 & | & 0 & 1 & 0 \\ 2 & 11 & 3 & | & 0 & 0 & 1 \end{bmatrix} \xrightarrow{[1]\ +\ [2]} \begin{bmatrix} 1 & 3 & 1 & | & 1 & 0 & 0 \\ 0 & 5 & 1 & | & 1 & 1 & 0 \\ 2 & 11 & 3 & | & 0 & 0 & 1 \end{bmatrix}$

$\xrightarrow{-2\ [1]\ +\ [3]} \begin{bmatrix} 1 & 3 & 1 & | & 1 & 0 & 0 \\ 0 & 5 & 1 & | & 1 & 1 & 0 \\ 0 & 5 & 1 & | & -2 & 0 & 1 \end{bmatrix} \xrightarrow{1/5\ [2]}$

$$\begin{bmatrix} 1 & 3 & 1 & | & 1 & 0 & 0 \\ 0 & 1 & 1/5 & | & 1/5 & 1/5 & 0 \\ 0 & 5 & 1 & | & -2 & 0 & 1 \end{bmatrix} \xrightarrow{-3\ [2]\ +\ [1]}$$

$$\begin{bmatrix} 1 & 0 & 2/5 & | & 2/5 & -3/5 & 0 \\ 0 & 1 & 1/5 & | & 1/5 & 1/5 & 0 \\ 0 & 5 & 1 & | & -2 & 0 & 1 \end{bmatrix} \xrightarrow{-5\ [2]\ +\ [3]}$$

$$\begin{bmatrix} 1 & 0 & 2/5 & | & 2/5 & -3/5 & 0 \\ 0 & 1 & 1/5 & | & 1/5 & 1/5 & 0 \\ 0 & 0 & 0 & | & -3 & -1 & 1 \end{bmatrix} \quad \text{There is no inverse.}$$

7. $$\begin{bmatrix} 1 & 2 & -2 & | & 1 & 0 & 0 \\ 1 & 1 & 1 & | & 0 & 1 & 0 \\ 0 & 0 & 1 & | & 0 & 0 & 1 \end{bmatrix} \xrightarrow{-1\ [1]\ +\ [2]}$$

$$\begin{bmatrix} 1 & 2 & -2 & | & 1 & 0 & 0 \\ 0 & -1 & 3 & | & -1 & 1 & 0 \\ 0 & 0 & 1 & | & 0 & 0 & 1 \end{bmatrix} \xrightarrow{-1\ [2]} \begin{bmatrix} 1 & 2 & -2 & | & 1 & 0 & 0 \\ 0 & 1 & -3 & | & 1 & -1 & 0 \\ 0 & 0 & 1 & | & 0 & 0 & 1 \end{bmatrix}$$

$$\xrightarrow{-2\ [2]\ +\ [1]} \begin{bmatrix} 1 & 0 & 4 & | & -1 & 2 & 0 \\ 0 & 1 & -3 & | & 1 & -1 & 0 \\ 0 & 0 & 1 & | & 0 & 0 & 1 \end{bmatrix} \xrightarrow{-4\ [3]\ +\ [1]}$$

$$\begin{bmatrix} 1 & 0 & 0 & | & -1 & 2 & -4 \\ 0 & 1 & -3 & | & 1 & -1 & 0 \\ 0 & 0 & 1 & | & 0 & 0 & 1 \end{bmatrix} \xrightarrow{3\ [3]\ +\ [2]}$$

$$\begin{bmatrix} 1 & 0 & 0 & | & -1 & 2 & -4 \\ 0 & 1 & 0 & | & 1 & -1 & 3 \\ 0 & 0 & 1 & | & 0 & 0 & 1 \end{bmatrix} \quad \text{So the inverse is } \begin{bmatrix} -1 & 2 & -4 \\ 1 & -1 & 3 \\ 0 & 0 & 1 \end{bmatrix}.$$

8. $$\begin{bmatrix} 2 & 2 & 0 & | & 1 & 0 & 0 \\ 0 & -2 & 0 & | & 0 & 1 & 0 \\ 3 & 0 & 1 & | & 0 & 0 & 1 \end{bmatrix} \xrightarrow{1/2\ [1]} \begin{bmatrix} 1 & 1 & 0 & | & 1/2 & 0 & 0 \\ 0 & -2 & 0 & | & 0 & 1 & 0 \\ 3 & 0 & 1 & | & 0 & 0 & 1 \end{bmatrix}$$

$$\xrightarrow{-3\ [1]\ +\ [3]} \begin{bmatrix} 1 & 1 & 0 & | & 1/2 & 0 & 0 \\ 0 & -2 & 0 & | & 0 & 1 & 0 \\ 0 & -3 & 1 & | & -3/2 & 0 & 1 \end{bmatrix} \xrightarrow{-1/2\ [2]}$$

$$\begin{bmatrix} 1 & 1 & 0 & | & 1/2 & 0 & 0 \\ 0 & 1 & 0 & | & 0 & -1/2 & 0 \\ 0 & -3 & 1 & | & -3/2 & 0 & 1 \end{bmatrix} \xrightarrow{-1\ [2]\ +\ [1]}$$

$$\begin{bmatrix} 1 & 0 & 0 & | & 1/2 & 1/2 & 0 \\ 0 & 1 & 0 & | & 0 & -1/2 & 0 \\ 0 & -3 & 1 & | & -3/2 & 0 & 1 \end{bmatrix} \xrightarrow{3\ [2]\ +\ [3]}$$

$$\begin{bmatrix} 1 & 0 & 0 & | & 1/2 & 1/2 & 0 \\ 0 & 1 & 0 & | & 0 & -1/2 & 0 \\ 0 & 0 & 1 & | & -3/2 & -3/2 & 1 \end{bmatrix}$$

So the inverse is $$\begin{bmatrix} 1/2 & 1/2 & 0 \\ 0 & -1/2 & 0 \\ -3/2 & -3/2 & 1 \end{bmatrix}.$$

9. $$\begin{bmatrix} -2 & 5 & 2 & | & 1 & 0 & 0 \\ 1 & -3 & -1 & | & 0 & 1 & 0 \\ -1 & 2 & 1 & | & 0 & 0 & 1 \end{bmatrix} \xrightarrow{-1/2[1]} \begin{bmatrix} 1 & -5/2 & -1 & | & -1/2 & 0 & 0 \\ 1 & -3 & -1 & | & 0 & 1 & 0 \\ -1 & 2 & 1 & | & 0 & 0 & 1 \end{bmatrix}$$

69

$$\xrightarrow{-1\ [1]\ +\ [2]} \begin{bmatrix} 1 & -5/2 & -1 & | & -1/2 & 0 & 0 \\ 0 & -1/2 & 0 & | & 1/2 & 1 & 0 \\ -1 & 2 & 1 & | & 0 & 0 & 1 \end{bmatrix} \xrightarrow{[1]\ +\ [3]}$$

$$\begin{bmatrix} 1 & -5/2 & -1 & | & -1/2 & 0 & 0 \\ 0 & -1/2 & 0 & | & 1/2 & 1 & 0 \\ 0 & -1/2 & 0 & | & -1/2 & 0 & 1 \end{bmatrix} \xrightarrow{-2\ [2]} \begin{bmatrix} 1 & 5/2 & -1 & | & -1/2 & 0 & 0 \\ 0 & 1 & 0 & | & -1 & -2 & 0 \\ 0 & -1/2 & 0 & | & -1/2 & 0 & 1 \end{bmatrix}$$

$$\xrightarrow{5/2\ [2]\ +\ [1]} \begin{bmatrix} 1 & 0 & -1 & | & -3 & -5 & 0 \\ 0 & 1 & 0 & | & -1 & -2 & 0 \\ 0 & -1/2 & 0 & | & -1/2 & 0 & 1 \end{bmatrix} \xrightarrow{1/2\ [2]\ +\ [3]}$$

$$\begin{bmatrix} 1 & 0 & -1 & | & -3 & -5 & 0 \\ 0 & 1 & 0 & | & -1 & -2 & 0 \\ 0 & 0 & 0 & | & -1 & -1 & 1 \end{bmatrix}$$ There is no inverse.

10. $$\begin{bmatrix} 1 & 0 & 0 & | & 1 & 0 & 0 \\ 2 & 1 & -2 & | & 0 & 1 & 0 \\ -1 & 2 & 1 & | & 0 & 0 & 1 \end{bmatrix} \xrightarrow{-2[1]\ +\ [2]} \begin{bmatrix} 1 & 0 & 0 & | & 1 & 0 & 0 \\ 0 & 1 & -2 & | & -2 & 1 & 0 \\ -1 & 2 & 1 & | & 0 & 0 & 1 \end{bmatrix}$$

$$\xrightarrow{[1]\ +\ [3]} \begin{bmatrix} 1 & 0 & 0 & | & 1 & 0 & 0 \\ 0 & 1 & -2 & | & -2 & 1 & 0 \\ 0 & 2 & 1 & | & 1 & 0 & 1 \end{bmatrix} \xrightarrow{-2\ [2]\ +\ [2]}$$

$$\begin{bmatrix} 1 & 0 & 0 & | & 1 & 0 & 0 \\ 0 & 1 & -2 & | & -2 & 1 & 0 \\ 0 & 0 & 5 & | & 5 & -2 & 1 \end{bmatrix} \xrightarrow{1/5\ [3]} \begin{bmatrix} 1 & 0 & 0 & | & 1 & 0 & 0 \\ 0 & 1 & -2 & | & -2 & 1 & 0 \\ 0 & 0 & 1 & | & 1 & -2/5 & 1/5 \end{bmatrix}$$

$$\xrightarrow{-2\ [3]\ +\ [2]} \begin{bmatrix} 1 & 0 & 0 & | & 1 & 0 & 0 \\ 0 & 1 & 0 & | & 0 & 1/5 & 2/5 \\ 0 & 0 & 1 & | & 1 & -2/5 & 1/5 \end{bmatrix}$$

So the inverse is $\begin{bmatrix} 1 & 0 & 0 \\ 0 & 1/5 & 2/5 \\ 1 & -2/5 & 1/5 \end{bmatrix}$.

11. $$\begin{bmatrix} 1 & 6 & 0 & 0 & | & 1 & 0 & 0 & 0 \\ 1 & 5 & 0 & 0 & | & 0 & 1 & 0 & 0 \\ 0 & 0 & 4 & 2 & | & 0 & 0 & 1 & 0 \\ 0 & 0 & 50 & 2 & | & 0 & 0 & 0 & 1 \end{bmatrix} \xrightarrow{-1\ [1]\ +\ [2]}$$

$$\begin{bmatrix} 1 & 6 & 0 & 0 & | & 1 & 0 & 0 & 0 \\ 0 & -1 & 0 & 0 & | & -1 & 1 & 0 & 0 \\ 0 & 0 & 4 & 2 & | & 0 & 0 & 1 & 0 \\ 0 & 0 & 50 & 2 & | & 0 & 0 & 0 & 1 \end{bmatrix} \xrightarrow{-1\ [2]}$$

$$\begin{bmatrix} 1 & 6 & 0 & 0 & | & 1 & 0 & 0 & 0 \\ 0 & 1 & 0 & 0 & | & 1 & -1 & 0 & 0 \\ 0 & 0 & 4 & 2 & | & 0 & 0 & 1 & 0 \\ 0 & 0 & 50 & 2 & | & 0 & 0 & 0 & 1 \end{bmatrix} \xrightarrow{-6\ [2]\ +\ [1]}$$

$$\begin{bmatrix} 1 & 0 & 0 & 0 & | & -5 & 6 & 0 & 0 \\ 0 & 1 & 0 & 0 & | & 1 & -1 & 0 & 0 \\ 0 & 0 & 4 & 2 & | & 0 & 0 & 1 & 0 \\ 0 & 0 & 50 & 2 & | & 0 & 0 & 0 & 1 \end{bmatrix} \quad \xrightarrow{1/4 \ [3]}$$

$$\begin{bmatrix} 1 & 0 & 0 & 0 & | & -5 & 6 & 0 & 0 \\ 0 & 1 & 0 & 0 & | & 1 & -1 & 0 & 0 \\ 0 & 0 & 1 & 1/2 & | & 0 & 0 & 1/4 & 0 \\ 0 & 0 & 50 & 2 & | & 0 & 0 & 0 & 1 \end{bmatrix} \quad \xrightarrow{-50 \ [3] \ + \ [4]}$$

$$\begin{bmatrix} 1 & 0 & 0 & 0 & | & -5 & 6 & 0 & 0 \\ 0 & 1 & 0 & 0 & | & 1 & -1 & 0 & 0 \\ 0 & 0 & 1 & 1/2 & | & 0 & 0 & 1/4 & 0 \\ 0 & 0 & 0 & -23 & | & 0 & 0 & -25/2 & 1 \end{bmatrix} \quad \xrightarrow{-1/23 \ [4]}$$

$$\begin{bmatrix} 1 & 0 & 0 & 0 & | & -5 & 6 & 0 & 0 \\ 0 & 1 & 0 & 0 & | & 1 & -1 & 0 & 0 \\ 0 & 0 & 1 & 1/2 & | & 0 & 0 & 1/4 & 0 \\ 0 & 0 & 0 & 1 & | & 0 & 0 & 25/46 & -1/23 \end{bmatrix} \quad \xrightarrow{-1/2 \ [4] \ + \ [3]}$$

$$\begin{bmatrix} 1 & 0 & 0 & 0 & | & -5 & 6 & 0 & 0 \\ 0 & 1 & 0 & 0 & | & 1 & -1 & 0 & 0 \\ 0 & 0 & 1 & 1/2 & | & 0 & 0 & -1/46 & 1/46 \\ 0 & 0 & 0 & 1 & | & 0 & 0 & 25/46 & -1/23 \end{bmatrix}$$

So the inverse is $\begin{bmatrix} -5 & 6 & 0 & 0 \\ 1 & -1 & 0 & 0 \\ 0 & 0 & -1/46 & 1/46 \\ 0 & 0 & 25/46 & -1/23 \end{bmatrix}.$

12. $\begin{bmatrix} 6 & 0 & 2 & 0 & | & 1 & 0 & 0 & 0 \\ -6 & 1 & 0 & 1 & | & 0 & 1 & 0 & 0 \\ 1 & 0 & 1 & 0 & | & 0 & 0 & 1 & 0 \\ -9 & 0 & -1 & 1 & | & 0 & 0 & 0 & 1 \end{bmatrix} \quad \xrightarrow{1/6 \ [1]}$

$$\begin{bmatrix} 1 & 0 & 1/3 & 0 & | & 1/6 & 0 & 0 & 0 \\ -6 & 1 & 0 & 1 & | & 0 & 1 & 0 & 0 \\ 1 & 0 & 1 & 0 & | & 0 & 0 & 1 & 0 \\ -9 & 0 & -1 & 1 & | & 0 & 0 & 0 & 1 \end{bmatrix} \quad \xrightarrow{6 \ [1] \ + \ [2]}$$

71

$$\begin{bmatrix} 1 & 0 & 1/3 & 0 & | & 1/6 & 0 & 0 & 0 \\ 0 & 1 & 2 & 1 & | & 1 & 1 & 0 & 0 \\ 1 & 0 & 1 & 0 & | & 0 & 0 & 1 & 0 \\ -9 & 0 & -1 & 1 & | & 0 & 0 & 0 & 1 \end{bmatrix} \xrightarrow{\;-1\;[1]\;+\;[3]\;}$$

$$\begin{bmatrix} 1 & 0 & 1/3 & 0 & | & 1/6 & 0 & 0 & 0 \\ 0 & 1 & 2 & 1 & | & 1 & 1 & 0 & 0 \\ 0 & 0 & 2/3 & 0 & | & -1/6 & 0 & 1 & 0 \\ -9 & 0 & -1 & 1 & | & 0 & 0 & 0 & 1 \end{bmatrix} \xrightarrow{\;9\;[1]\;+\;[4]\;}$$

$$\begin{bmatrix} 1 & 0 & 1/3 & 0 & | & 1/6 & 0 & 0 & 0 \\ 0 & 1 & 2 & 1 & | & 1 & 1 & 0 & 0 \\ 0 & 0 & 2/3 & 0 & | & -1/6 & 0 & 1 & 0 \\ 0 & 0 & 2 & 1 & | & 3/2 & 0 & 0 & 1 \end{bmatrix} \xrightarrow{\;3/2\;[3]\;}$$

$$\begin{bmatrix} 1 & 0 & 1/3 & 0 & | & 1/6 & 0 & 0 & 0 \\ 0 & 1 & 2 & 1 & | & 1 & 1 & 0 & 0 \\ 0 & 0 & 1 & 0 & | & -1/4 & 0 & 3/2 & 0 \\ 0 & 0 & 2 & 1 & | & 3/2 & 0 & 0 & 1 \end{bmatrix} \xrightarrow{\;-1/3\;[3]\;+\;[1]\;}$$

$$\begin{bmatrix} 1 & 0 & 0 & 0 & | & 1/4 & 0 & -1/2 & 0 \\ 0 & 1 & 2 & 1 & | & 1 & 1 & 0 & 0 \\ 0 & 0 & 1 & 0 & | & -1/4 & 0 & 3/2 & 0 \\ 0 & 0 & 2 & 1 & | & 3/2 & 0 & 0 & 1 \end{bmatrix} \xrightarrow{\;-2\;[3]\;+\;[2]\;}$$

$$\begin{bmatrix} 1 & 0 & 0 & 0 & | & 1/4 & 0 & -1/2 & 0 \\ 0 & 1 & 0 & 1 & | & 3/2 & 1 & -3 & 0 \\ 0 & 0 & 1 & 0 & | & -1/4 & 0 & 3/2 & 0 \\ 0 & 0 & 2 & 1 & | & 3/2 & 0 & 0 & 1 \end{bmatrix} \xrightarrow{\;-2\;[3]\;+\;[4]\;}$$

$$\begin{bmatrix} 1 & 0 & 0 & 0 & | & 1/4 & 0 & -1/2 & 0 \\ 0 & 1 & 0 & 1 & | & 3/2 & 1 & -3 & 0 \\ 0 & 0 & 1 & 0 & | & -1/4 & 0 & 3/2 & 0 \\ 0 & 0 & 0 & 1 & | & 2 & 0 & -3 & 1 \end{bmatrix} \xrightarrow{\;-1\;[4]\;+\;[2]\;}$$

$$\begin{bmatrix} 1 & 0 & 0 & 0 & | & 1/4 & 0 & -1/2 & 0 \\ 0 & 1 & 0 & 0 & | & -1/2 & 1 & 0 & -1 \\ 0 & 0 & 1 & 0 & | & -1/4 & 0 & 3/2 & 0 \\ 0 & 0 & 0 & 1 & | & 2 & 0 & -3 & 1 \end{bmatrix}$$

So the inverse is $\begin{bmatrix} 1/4 & 0 & -1/2 & 0 \\ -1/2 & 1 & 0 & -1 \\ -1/4 & 0 & 3/2 & 0 \\ 2 & 0 & -3 & 1 \end{bmatrix}$.

13. $\begin{bmatrix} 1 & 1 & 2 \\ 3 & 2 & 2 \\ 1 & 1 & 3 \end{bmatrix} \begin{bmatrix} x \\ y \\ z \end{bmatrix} = \begin{bmatrix} 3 \\ 4 \\ 5 \end{bmatrix}$

$\begin{bmatrix} x \\ y \\ z \end{bmatrix} = \begin{bmatrix} -4 & 1 & 2 \\ 7 & -1 & -4 \\ -1 & 0 & 1 \end{bmatrix} \begin{bmatrix} 3 \\ 4 \\ 5 \end{bmatrix} = \begin{bmatrix} 2 \\ -3 \\ 2 \end{bmatrix}$ Therefore x = 2, y = -3, z = 2.

14. $\begin{bmatrix} 1 & 2 & 3 \\ 3 & 5 & 5 \\ 2 & 4 & 2 \end{bmatrix} \begin{bmatrix} x \\ y \\ z \end{bmatrix} = \begin{bmatrix} 4 \\ 3 \\ 4 \end{bmatrix}$

$\begin{bmatrix} x \\ y \\ x \end{bmatrix} = \begin{bmatrix} -5/2 & 2 & -5/4 \\ 1 & -1 & 1 \\ 1/2 & 0 & -1/4 \end{bmatrix} \begin{bmatrix} 4 \\ 3 \\ 4 \end{bmatrix} = \begin{bmatrix} -9 \\ 5 \\ 1 \end{bmatrix}$ Therefore x =-9, y = 5, z = 1.

15. $\begin{bmatrix} 1 & 0 & -2 & -2 \\ 0 & 1 & 0 & -5 \\ -4 & 0 & 9 & 9 \\ 0 & 2 & 1 & -8 \end{bmatrix} \begin{bmatrix} x \\ y \\ z \\ w \end{bmatrix} = \begin{bmatrix} 0 \\ 1 \\ 2 \\ 3 \end{bmatrix}$

$\begin{bmatrix} x \\ y \\ z \\ w \end{bmatrix} = \begin{bmatrix} 9 & 0 & 2 & 0 \\ -20 & -9 & -5 & 5 \\ 8 & 2 & 2 & -1 \\ -4 & -2 & -1 & 1 \end{bmatrix} \begin{bmatrix} 0 \\ 1 \\ 2 \\ 3 \end{bmatrix} = \begin{bmatrix} 4 \\ -4 \\ 3 \\ -1 \end{bmatrix}$ Therefore x = 4, y = -4, z = 3, w = -1.

16. $\begin{bmatrix} 0 & 1 & 2 \\ 2 & 1 & 3 \\ 1 & 1 & 2 \end{bmatrix} \begin{bmatrix} x \\ y \\ z \end{bmatrix} = \begin{bmatrix} 1 \\ 2 \\ 3 \end{bmatrix}$

$\begin{bmatrix} x \\ y \\ z \end{bmatrix} = \begin{bmatrix} -1 & 0 & 1 \\ -1 & -2 & 4 \\ 1 & 1 & -2 \end{bmatrix} \begin{bmatrix} 1 \\ 2 \\ 3 \end{bmatrix} = \begin{bmatrix} 2 \\ 7 \\ -3 \end{bmatrix}$ Therefore x = 2, y = 7, z = -3.

17. Either no solution or infinitely many solutions.

18. $A^{-1} = \begin{bmatrix} 3 & -2 \\ -4 & 3 \end{bmatrix}$ $C = A^{-1}B = \begin{bmatrix} 13 & 4 \\ -17 & -3 \end{bmatrix}$

19. $\begin{bmatrix} -3 & 5 \\ 10 & -16 \end{bmatrix}$

73

20. AX = B has solution $X = \begin{bmatrix} 7 & -3 \\ -12 & 6.5 \end{bmatrix}$, XA = B has solution

$X = \begin{bmatrix} -6.5 & 15.5 \\ -9 & 20 \end{bmatrix}$. The answers differ since matrix

multiplication is not commutative.

21. $\begin{bmatrix} 2 & -1 \\ -7 & 4 \end{bmatrix}$ **22.** $\begin{bmatrix} 5 & -3 \\ -13 & 8 \end{bmatrix}$ **23.** $\begin{bmatrix} -2.4 & 2.2 & 1.8 \\ .8 & -.4 & -.6 \\ .6 & -.8 & -.2 \end{bmatrix}$ **24.** $\begin{bmatrix} -3 & -6 & -1 \\ -16.5 & -32 & -6 \\ 2.5 & 5 & 1 \end{bmatrix}$

2.6 Input-Output Analysis

1. $X = (I - A)^{-1} \cdot D = \begin{bmatrix} 1.01 & .2 & .5 \\ .02 & 1.05 & .23 \\ .01 & .09 & 1.08 \end{bmatrix} \begin{bmatrix} 4 \\ 1.5 \\ 9 \end{bmatrix} = \begin{bmatrix} 8.84 \\ 3.73 \\ 9.9 \end{bmatrix}$

   To satisfy demand production should be: Coal: $8.84 billion;
   Steel: $3.73 billion; Electricity: $9.90 billion

2. $X = (I - A)^{-1} \cdot D = \begin{bmatrix} 1.04 & .02 & .1 \\ .21 & 1.01 & .02 \\ .11 & .02 & 1.02 \end{bmatrix} \begin{bmatrix} 4.5 \\ 2 \\ 1 \end{bmatrix} = \begin{bmatrix} 4.82 \\ 2.99 \\ 1.56 \end{bmatrix}$ To satisfy

   demand production should be: Computers: $482 million; semi-
   conductors: $299 million; business forms $156 million.

3. $X = (I - A)^{-1} \cdot D = \begin{bmatrix} 1.04 & .02 & .1 \\ .21 & 1.01 & .02 \\ .11 & .02 & 1.02 \end{bmatrix} \begin{bmatrix} 3 \\ 1 \\ 4 \end{bmatrix} = \begin{bmatrix} 3.54 \\ 1.72 \\ 4.43 \end{bmatrix}$ To satisfy

   this new demand the Computers should produce $354 million
   and the Semi-conductors should produce $172 million.

4. $X = (I - A)^{-1} \cdot D = \begin{bmatrix} 1.02 & 0 & .02 \\ .01 & 1.03 & .01 \\ .03 & 0 & .01 \end{bmatrix} \begin{bmatrix} 8 \\ 3 \\ 14 \end{bmatrix} = \begin{bmatrix} 8.44 \\ 3.31 \\ 14.52 \end{bmatrix}$

   To satisfy demand production should be: U.S.: $844 million;
   Canada: $331 million; England: $1.452 billion.

5. Use a calculator to multiply the two matrices $(A \cdot A^{-1})$ and
   the answer will be the identity matrix if all the elements
   are rounded to two decimal places.

6. Use a calculator to multiply the two matrices $(A \cdot A^{-1})$ and
   the answer will be the identity matrix if all the elements
   are rounded to two decimal places.

7.　$X = (I - A)^{-1} \cdot D = \begin{bmatrix} 1.02 & .01 \\ .11 & 1.05 \end{bmatrix} \begin{bmatrix} 9.3 \\ 4.65 \end{bmatrix} = \begin{bmatrix} 9.5 \\ 5.9 \end{bmatrix}$

To satisfy demand production should be: Plastics: $955,000; industrial equipment:$590,000.

8.　$X = (I - A)^{-1} \cdot D = \begin{bmatrix} 1.02 & .01 \\ .11 & 1.05 \end{bmatrix} \begin{bmatrix} 18.6 \\ 27.9 \end{bmatrix} = \begin{bmatrix} 19.25 \\ 31.34 \end{bmatrix}$

To satisfy demand production should be Plastics: $1,930,000; industrial equipment: $3,140,000.

9.　$X = (I - A)^{-1} \cdot D = \begin{bmatrix} 2.05 & .85 & .63 \\ .63 & 1.56 & .63 \\ .45 & .4 & 1.88 \end{bmatrix} \begin{bmatrix} 100 \\ 80 \\ 200 \end{bmatrix} = \begin{bmatrix} 399 \\ 313.8 \\ 453 \end{bmatrix}$

To satisfy demand production should be: Manufacturing goods: $399 million; Transportation: $314 million; agriculture: $453 million.

10.　$X = (I - A)^{-1} \cdot D = \begin{bmatrix} 1.97 & 1.52 & 1.28 \\ 1 & 2 & 1 \\ 1.55 & 1.72 & 2.59 \end{bmatrix} \begin{bmatrix} 20 \\ 15 \\ 18 \end{bmatrix} = \begin{bmatrix} 85.24 \\ 68 \\ 103.42 \end{bmatrix}$

To satisfy demand production should be: Merchant: $85,000 ; Baker: $68,000; Farmer: $103,000.

11. $\begin{bmatrix} 10.25 \\ 13.82 \\ 8.65 \end{bmatrix}$　　12. $\begin{bmatrix} 11.61 \\ 8.17 \\ 5.09 \\ 13.32 \end{bmatrix}$

SUPPLEMENTARY EXERCISES

1. $\begin{bmatrix} 1 & -2 & \frac{1}{3} \\ 0 & 8 & \frac{16}{3} \end{bmatrix}$

2. $\begin{bmatrix} 1 & 0 & 1 \\ 2 & 1 & 0 \\ -12 & 0 & 7 \end{bmatrix}$

3.　$x = 4, \; y = 5$

4.　$x = 50 \; , \; y = 2, \; z = -12$

5.　$x = -1, \; y = \frac{2}{3}, \; z = \frac{1}{3}$

6.　No solution.

7. z = any value, x = 1 - 3z, y = 4z, w = 5.

8. x = 7, y = 3.

9. $\begin{bmatrix} 5 \\ 3 \\ 7 \end{bmatrix}$

10. $\begin{bmatrix} 6 & 17 \\ 12 & 26 \end{bmatrix}$

11. x = -2, y = 3.

12. (a) x = 13, y = 23, z = 19.
    (b) x = -4, y = 13, z = 14.

13. $\begin{bmatrix} 2 & 6 & | & 1 & 0 \\ 1 & 2 & | & 0 & 1 \end{bmatrix} \xrightarrow{1/2 \ [1]} \begin{bmatrix} 1 & 3 & | & 1/2 & 0 \\ 1 & 2 & | & 0 & 1 \end{bmatrix} \xrightarrow{-1 \ [1] + [2]}$

    $\begin{bmatrix} 1 & 3 & | & 1/2 & 0 \\ 0 & -1 & | & -1/2 & 1 \end{bmatrix} \xrightarrow{-1 \ [2]} \begin{bmatrix} 1 & 3 & | & 1/2 & 0 \\ 0 & 1 & | & 1/2 & -1 \end{bmatrix} \xrightarrow{-3 \ [2] + [1]}$

    $\begin{bmatrix} 1 & 0 & | & -1 & 3 \\ 0 & 1 & | & 1/2 & -1 \end{bmatrix}$ The inverse is $\begin{bmatrix} -1 & 3 \\ 1/2 & -1 \end{bmatrix}$ or $\begin{bmatrix} -1 & 3 \\ .5 & -1 \end{bmatrix}$.

14. $\begin{bmatrix} 1 & 1 & 1 & | & 1 & 0 & 0 \\ 3 & 4 & 3 & | & 0 & 1 & 0 \\ 1 & 1 & 2 & | & 0 & 0 & 1 \end{bmatrix} \xrightarrow{-3 \ [1] + [2]} \begin{bmatrix} 1 & 1 & 1 & | & 1 & 0 & 0 \\ 0 & 1 & 0 & | & -3 & 1 & 0 \\ 1 & 1 & 2 & | & 0 & 0 & 1 \end{bmatrix}$

    $\xrightarrow{-1 \ [1] + [3]} \begin{bmatrix} 1 & 1 & 1 & | & 1 & 0 & 0 \\ 0 & 1 & 0 & | & -3 & 1 & 0 \\ 0 & 0 & 1 & | & -1 & 0 & 1 \end{bmatrix} \xrightarrow{-1 \ [2] + [1]}$

    $\begin{bmatrix} 1 & 0 & 1 & | & 4 & -1 & 0 \\ 0 & 1 & 0 & | & -3 & 1 & 0 \\ 0 & 0 & 1 & | & -1 & 0 & 1 \end{bmatrix} \xrightarrow{-1 \ [3] + [1]} \begin{bmatrix} 1 & 0 & 0 & | & 5 & -1 & -1 \\ 0 & 1 & 0 & | & -3 & 1 & 0 \\ 0 & 0 & 1 & | & -1 & 0 & 1 \end{bmatrix}$

    The inverse is $\begin{bmatrix} 5 & -1 & -1 \\ -3 & 1 & 0 \\ -1 & 0 & 1 \end{bmatrix}$.

15. Farmer Brown should plant 500 acres of corn, no acres of wheat, and 500 acres of soy beans.

16. (a) A: 9400, 8980; B: 7300, 7510
    (b) A: 10,857, 12,082; B: 6571, 5959

    (c) $\begin{bmatrix} .8 & .2 \\ .1 & .9 \end{bmatrix} \begin{bmatrix} x \\ y \end{bmatrix} = \begin{bmatrix} .8x + .2y \\ .1x + .9y \end{bmatrix}$,

    The gap is A - B or (.8x + .2y) - (.1x + .9y) = .7(x - y) Since x - y is the gap in one year we have here that 70% of that gap is the next year's gap. Therefore the gap decreases by 30%.

The difference between the number of weapons from one year to the next is

$$[(.8x + .2y) + (.1x + .9y)] - (x + y) = .1(y - x)$$

If $.1(y - x)$ is positive then there were more weapons the second year than the first. This occurs when $y > x$ or when Nation B has more weapons than Nation A.

If $.1(y - x)$ is negative then there were more weapons the first year than the second. This occurs when $y < x$ or when Nation A has more weapons than Nation B.

17. Industry I: 20 units, Industry II: 20 units.

3
LINEAR PROGRAMMING: A GEOMETRIC APPROACH

3.1. A Linear Programming Problem

1. (8,7)   6·8 + 3·7   =   69 ≤ 96
            8 + 7   =   15 ≤ 18
         2·8 + 6·7   =   58 ≤ 72
             7≥0,   8≥0
   (8,7) is in the feasible set.

2. (14,3)   6·14 + 3·3   =   93 ≤ 96
           14 + 3   =   17 ≤ 18
       2·14 + 6·3   =   46 ≤ 72
          14≥0,   3≥0
   (14,3) is in the feasible set.

3. (9,10)   6·9 + 3·10   =   94 ≤ 96
         9 + 10   =   19 > 18
   (9,10) is <u>not</u> in the feasible set.

4. (16,0)   6·16 + 3·0   =   96 ≤ 96
         16 + 0   =   16 ≤ 18
       2·16 + 6·0   =   32 ≤ 72
         16≥0,   0≥0
   (16,0) is in the feasible set.

5. (a)

	Truck A	Truck B	Truck capacity
Volume	4	3	300
Weight	100	200	10,000
Earnings	13	9	

(b) $4x + 3y \le 300$
    $100x + 200y \le 10,000$
(c) $x \ge 0$, $y \ge 0$, $y \le 2x$
(d) Earnings = $13x + 9y$
(e)

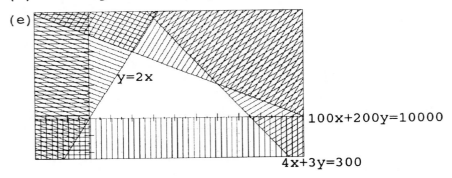

6. (a)

	Mine 1	Mine 2	Ordered
Anthracite	4	10	80
Ordinary	4	5	60
Bituminous	7	5	75
Daily Cost	150	200	

(b) $4x + 10y \geq 80$ (1)
    $4x + 5y \geq 60$ (2)
    $7x + 5y \geq 75$ (3)
    (the mine must meet or exceed the amount of the order)
(c) $x \geq 0$, $y \geq 0$
(d) Cost $= 150x + 200y$

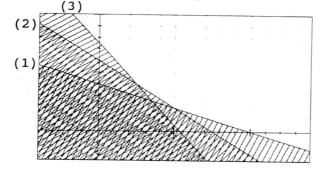

7.   (a)

	Essay Questions	Short-Answer Questions	Available
Time	10	2	90
Quantity	10	50	
Required	3	10	
Worth	20	5	

(b) $10x + 2y \leq 90$
(c) $3 \leq x \leq 10$, $10 \leq y \leq 50$
(d) Score $= 20x + 5y$

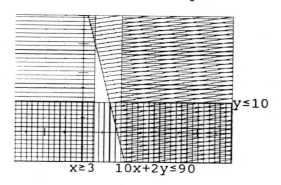

$y \leq 10$

$x \geq 3$ $10x + 2y \leq 90$

8.   (a)

	1 min. T.V. Add	1 min Radio Add	Available
Cost	8000	2000	80000
Audience reached	20000	4000	

(b) $8000x + 2000y \leq 80000$ (1)
(c) $8000x \leq .9(80000)$ or $x \leq 9$ (2)
    $x \geq 0$, $y \geq 0$
(d) Audience reached $= 20000x + 4000y$

(e)

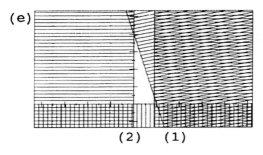

           (2)   (1)

9.   (a)

	Alfalfa	Corn	Requirements
Protein	.13	.065	4550
TDN	.48	.96	26,880
Vitamin A	2.16	0.00	43,200
Cost	.01	.016	

(b) $.13x + .065y \geq 4550$ (1)
          $.48x + .96y \geq 26880$ (2)
              $2.16x \geq 43200$ (3)
                 $x \geq 0,$ $y \geq 0$

(c)

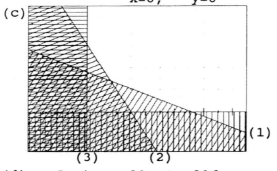

                (3)   (2)

(d)   Cost $= .01x + .016y$

3.2   Linear Programming, I

1.   (0,20) $4 \cdot 0 + 3 \cdot 20 = 60$
     (0,0) $4 \cdot 0 + 3 \cdot 0 = 0$
     (20,0) $4 \cdot 20 + 0 \cdot 0 = 80$
     $4x + 3y$ is maximized at the point (20,0); $x = 20$, $y = 0$.

2.   (0,0) $4 \cdot 0 + 3 \cdot 0 = 0$ (0,5) $4 \cdot 0 + 3 \cdot 5 = 15$
     (4,10) $4 \cdot 4 + 3 \cdot 10 = 46$ (10,12) $4 \cdot 10 + 3 \cdot 12 = 76$
     (15,8) $4 \cdot 15 + 3 \cdot 8 = 84$ (18,5) $4 \cdot 18 + 3 \cdot 5 = 87$
     (20,0) $4 \cdot 20 + 3 \cdot 0 = 80$
     $4x + 3y$ is maximized at the point (18,5); $x = 18$, $y = 5$.

3.   First determine the vertices of the feasible set.

     $y = \frac{1}{2}x + 4$ intersects $y = -x + 6$ at (4,2) and intersects the

     y-axis at (0,4); $y = -x + 6$ intersects the x-axis at (6,0).
     The fourth vertex is the origin.
     (0,0) $4 \cdot 0 + 3 \cdot 0 = 0$ (0,4) $4 \cdot 0 + 3 \cdot 4 = 12$
     (4,2) $4 \cdot 4 + 3 \cdot 2 = 22$ (6,0) $4 \cdot 6 + 3 \cdot 0 = 24$
     $4x + 3y$ is maximized at the point (6,0); $x = 6$, $y = 0$.

4.   The first vertex is the origin (0,0). The intersections of

     $y = 3x$ and $y = -\frac{1}{4}x + 2$ and $y = -\frac{1}{4}x + 2$ and $y = \frac{1}{2}x$ are

     $\left(\frac{8}{13}, \frac{24}{13}\right)$ and $\left(\frac{8}{3}, \frac{4}{3}\right)$ respectively.

     (0,0); $4 \cdot 0 + 3 \cdot 0 = 0$

     $\left(\frac{8}{13}, \frac{24}{13}\right)$; $4 \cdot \frac{8}{13} + 3 \cdot \frac{24}{13} = \frac{104}{13} = 8$

     $\left(\frac{8}{3}, \frac{4}{3}\right)$; $4 \cdot \frac{8}{3} + 3 \cdot \frac{4}{3} = \frac{44}{3} > 8$.

     $4x + 3y$ is maximized at the point $\left(\frac{8}{3}, \frac{4}{3}\right)$; $x = \frac{8}{3}$ and $y = \frac{4}{3}$.

5.   Maximize $x + 2y$
     (0,5) $0 + 2 \cdot 5 = 10*$
     (3,3) $3 + 2 \cdot 3 = 9$
     (4,0) $4 + 0 = 4$
     (0,0) $0 + 0 = 0$ $x + 2y$ is maximized at the point (0,5)

6.   Maximize $x + y$
     (0,5) $0 + 5 = 5$
     (3,3) $3 + 3 = 6*$
     (4,0) $4 + 0 = 4$
     (0,0) $0 + 0 = 0$ $x + y$ is maximized at the point (3,3)

7. Maximize 2x + y
    (0,5)   2·0 + 5 = 5
    (3,3)   2·3 + 3 = 9*
    (4,0)   2·4 + 0 = 8
    (0,0)   2·0 + 0 = 0   2x + y is maximized at the point (3,3).

8. Maximize 3 - x - y
    (0,5)   3 - 0 - 5 = -2
    (3,3)   3 - 3 - 3 = -3
    (4,0)   3 - 4 - 0 = -1
    (0,0)   3 - 0 - 0 = 3*   3-x-y is maximized at the point (0,0).

9. Minimize 8x + y
    (0,7)   8·0 + 7 = 7*
    (1,2)   8·1 + 2 = 10
    (2,1)   8·2 + 1 = 17
    (6,0)   8·6 + 0 = 48   8x + y is minimized at the point (0,7).

10. Minimize 3x + 2y
    (0,7)   3·0 + 2·7 = 14
    (1,2)   3·1 + 2·2 = 7*
    (2,1)   3·2 + 2·1 = 8
    (6,0)   3·6 + 2·0 = 18   3x+2y is minimized at the point (1,2).

11. Minimize 2x + 3y
    (0,7)   2·0 + 3·7 = 21
    (1,2)   2·1 + 3·2 = 8
    (2,1)   2·2 + 3·1 = 7*
    (6,0)   2·6 + 3·0 = 12   2x+3y is minimized at the point (2,1).

12. Minimize x + 8y
    (0,7)   0 + 8·7 = 56
    (1,2)   1 + 8·2 = 17
    (2,1)   2 + 8·1 = 10
    (6,0)   6 + 8·0 = 6*   x+8y is minimized at the point (6,0).

13. Let x = number of crates of A, y = number of crates of B.
    The first vertex is the origin (0,0).

    The intersection of y = 2x and y = $-\frac{1}{2}x$ + 50 is (20,40).

    The intersection of y = $-\frac{1}{2}x$ + 50 and y = $-\frac{4}{3}x$ + 100 is (60,20).

    The intersection of y = $-\frac{4}{3}x$ + 100 and y = 0 is (75,0).

    Earnings = 13x + 9y is to be maximized.
    (0,0)   0   + 0   = 0
    (20,40) 13·20 + 9·40 = 620
    (60,20) 13·60 + 9·20 = 960
    (75,0) 13·75 + 9·0 = 975*
    To receive the maximum earnings of $975, sip 75 crates of A
    and no crates of B.

14. x = number of days for mine I,
    y = number of days for mine II.
    The vertices are (0,15),(5,8),(10,4),and (20,0).
    Cost = 150x + 200y is to be minimized.
    (0,15) 150·0 + 200·15 = 3000
    (5,8) 150·5 + 200·8 = 2350
    (10,4) 150·10 + 200·4 = 2300*
    (20,0) 150·20 + 200·0 = 3000
    To obtain the minimum cost of $2,300, operate mine I for 10
    days and mine II for 4 days.

15. Maximize total score = 20x + 5y.
    (3,10) 20·3 + 5·10 = 110
    (3,30) 20·3 + 5·30 = 210
    (7,10) 20·7 + 5·10 = 190
    To obtain the maximum score of 210 points, the student
    should do 3 essay questions and 30 short answer questions.

16. Maximize total audience = 8000x + 2000y
    (0,40) 8000·0 +2000·40 = 80000*
    (9,4)   8000·9 +2000·4 = 80000*
    (9,0)   8000·9 +2000·0 = 72000
    (0,0)   8000·0 +2000·0 = 0
    There are many combinations that give a maximum audience of
    80000 people.   They are the points on the feasible set
    between (0,40) and (9,4). For example, the politician could
    allocate 5 minutes to T.V. ads and 20 minutes to Radio.

17. Objective equation is 150x + 70y = profit to be maximized.
    (14,4) 150·14 + 70·4 = 2380   (9,9) 150·9 + 70·9 = 1980
    (0,12) 150·0 + 70·12 = 840   (0,0) 150·0 + 70·0 =   0
    (16,0) 150·16 + 70·0 = 2400*
    150x + 70y is maximized at (16,0). Produce 16 chairs and 0
    sofas for a profit of $2400.

18. Objective equation is 60x + 70y = profit to be maximized.
    (14,4) 60·14 + 70·4 = 1120   (9,9) 60·9 + 70·9 = 1170*
    (0,12) 60·0 + 70·12 = 840   (0,0) 60·0 + 70·0 =   0
    (16,0) 60·16 + 70·0 = 960
    60x + 70y is maximized at (9,9). Produce 9 chairs and 9
    sofas for a profit of $1170.

19.

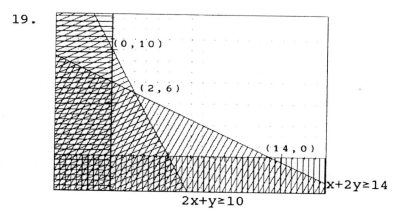

83

vertex	3x + 4y
(0,10)	40
(2,6)	30*
(14,0)	42

The minimum value is 30 and occurs at the point (2,6).

20.

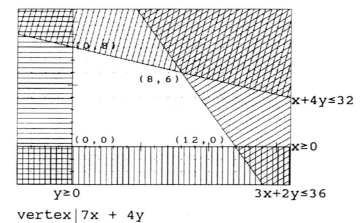

(0,8)
(8,6)
x+4y≤32
(0,0)   (12,0)
x≥0
y≥0   3x+2y≤36

vertex	7x + 4y
(0,8)	32
(8,6)	80
(12,0)	84*

The maximum value is 84 and occurs at the point (12,0)

21.

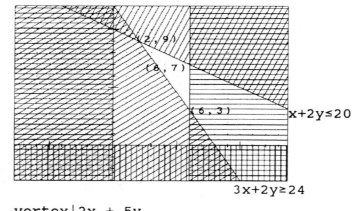

(2,9)
(6,7)
(6,3)
x+2y≤20
3x+2y≥24

vertex	2x + 5y
(6,3)	27
(6,7)	47
(2,6)	49*

The maximum value is 49 and it occurs at the point (2,6).

22.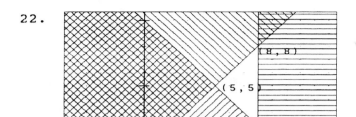

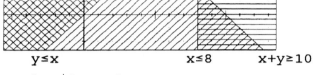

y≤x   x≤8   x+y≥10

vertex	2x + 3y
(8,2)	22*
(8,8)	40
(5,5)	25

The minimum value is 22 and it occurs at the point (8,2).

23.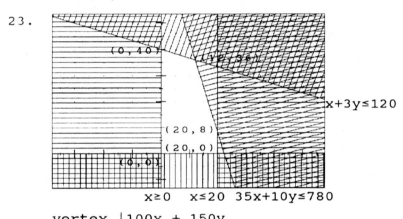

x≥0   x≤20   35x+10y≤780

vertex	100x + 150y
(0,0)	0
(20,0)	2000
(20,8)	3200
(12,36)	6600
(0,40)	6000

The maximum value is 6600 and it occurs at the point (12,36).

24.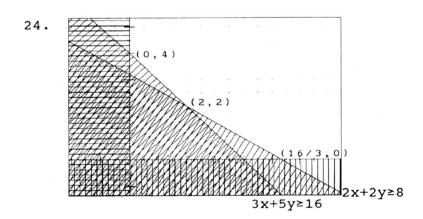

3x+5y≥16

vertex	$\frac{1}{2}x + \frac{3}{4}y$
$(2,2)$	$\frac{5}{2}$*
$(0,4)$	3
$\left(\frac{16}{3},0\right)$	$\frac{8}{3}$

The minimum value is 5/2 and it occurs at the point (2,2).

25.

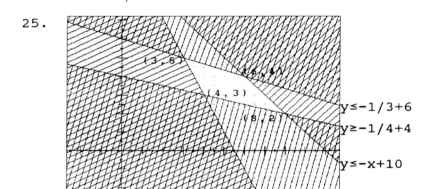

$y \le -1/3+6$

$y \ge -1/4+4$

$y \le -x+10$

$y \ge -2x+11$

vertex	7x + 4y
$(8,2)$	64
$(6,4)$	58
$(4,3)$	40*
$(3,5)$	41

The minimum value is 40 and it occurs at the point (4,3).

26.

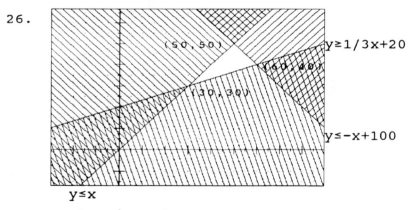

$y \ge 1/3x+20$

$y \le -x+100$

$y \le x$

vertex	x + 2y
$(30,30)$	90
$(60,40)$	140
$(50,50)$	150*

The maximum value is 150 and it occurs at the point (50,50).

27.

	Hockey	Soccer	Total
Assembly	2	3	42
Testing	2	1	26

x = # of hockey games
y = # of soccer games

86

$$\begin{cases} 2x + 3y \le 42 & (1) \\ 2x + y \le 26 & (2) \\ x \ge 0 \quad y \ge 0 \end{cases} \quad \text{Maximize, Output} = x + y$$

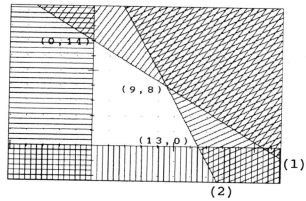

vertex	x + y
(13,0)	13
(9,8)	17*
(0,14)	14

To maximize daily output Infotron should produce 9 hockey games and 8 soccer games for a daily output of 17 games.

28.

	Cleveland	Toledo	Order
3-head	500	300	25,000
4-head	300	300	21,000
Cost	18,000	15,000	

x = # of 3-heads in Clev
y = # of 4-heads in Tol

$$\begin{cases} 500x + 300y \ge 25000 & (1) \\ 300x + 300y \ge 21000 & (2) \\ x \ge 0, \quad y \ge 0 \end{cases} \quad \text{Minimize, Cost} = 18x + 15y$$

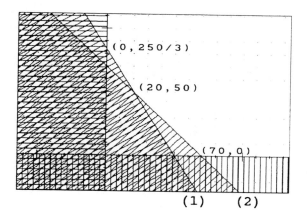

vertex	18x + 15y
(70,0)	1260
(20,50)	1110*
$\left(0, \dfrac{250}{3}\right)$	1250

To minimize cost, the Cleveland plant should operate for 20 days and the Toledo plant should operate for 50 days.

29.

	Type one	Type two	Restriction
Capital	12000	32000	2880000
Labor	150	200	24000
Profit	2400	3400	

x = # type-one houses
y = # type-two houses
total # lots is 150

$$\begin{cases} 12000x + 32000y \leq 2880000 & (1) \\ 150x + 200y \leq 24000 & (2) \\ x + y \leq 150 & (3) \\ x \geq 0, \quad y \geq 0 \end{cases}$$

Minimize,   Profit = 2400x + 3400y

(0,90)

(80,60)

(120,30)

(150,0)

(1)

(2)

(3)   Note: At (0,0), profit = 0.

vertex	2400x + 3400y
(150,0)	360,000
(80,60)	396,000*
(120,30)	390,000
(0,90)	306,000

To achieve a maximum profit of $396,000 the contractor must build 80 type-1 and 60 type-2 homes.

30.

	Food A	Food B	Requirements
Protein	4	3	42
Carbohydrate	2	6	30
Fat	2	1	18
Weight	3	2	

x = # tubes of A
y = # tubes of B

$$\begin{cases} 4x + 3y \geq 42 & (1) \\ 2x + 6y \geq 30 & (2) \\ 2x + y \geq 18 & (3) \\ x \geq 0, \ y \geq 0 \end{cases}$$

Minimize,   Weight = 3x + 2y

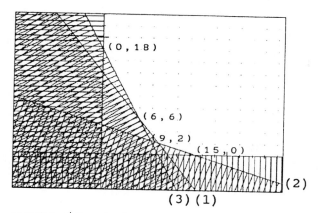

vertex	3x + 2y
(15,0)	45
(9,2)	31
(6,6)	30*
(0,18)	36

To minimize the weight the nutritionist should supply 6 tubes of each food.

31.

	F D	H P	Restrictions
Pineapple	10	10	9000
Orange	3	2	2400
Apricot	1	2	1400
Profit	20	30	

$x = \#$ cans F.D.
$y = \#$ cans H.P.

$$\begin{cases} 10x + 10y \leq 9000 & (1) \\ 3x + 2y \leq 2400 & (2) \\ x + 2y \leq 1400 & (3) \\ x \geq 0, \quad y \geq 0 \end{cases}$$

Maximize, Profit = 20x + 30y

vertex	20x + 30y
(800,0)	16000
(600,300)	21000
(400,500)	23000*
(0,700)	21000

Note: At (0,0), profit = 0.

To achieve a maximum profit of $230, the company must produce 400 cans of FD and 500 cans of HP.

32.

	Type A	Type B	Restrictions
Cutting	2	1	120
Stringing	1	3	150
Finishing	2	2	140
Profit	8	10	

$x = \#$ Type A Sticks
$y = \#$ Type B Sticks

$$\begin{cases} 2x + y \le 120 & (1) \\ x + 3y \le 150 & (2) \\ 2x + 2y \le 140 & (3) \\ x \ge 0, \ y \ge 0 \end{cases}$$

Maximize,   Profit = 8x + 10y

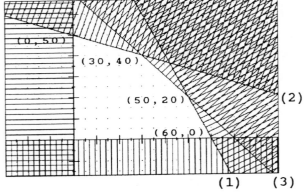

vertex	8x + 10y
(60,0)	480
(50,20)	600
(30,40)	640*
(0,50)	500

To achieve maximum profit of $640, manufacture 30 lacrosse sticks of Type A and 40 of Type B.

33.

	Oats	Corn	Restrictions
Capital	18	36	2100
Labor·Cost	2·8	6·8	2400
Revenue	55	125	

x = # acres of oats
y = # acres of corn
total # acres = 100

$$\begin{cases} 18x + 36y \le 2100 & (1) \\ 16x + 48y \le 2400 & (2) \\ x + y \le 100 & (3) \\ x \ge 0, \quad y \ge 0 \end{cases}$$

Profit = 55x + 125y + 2400 - 16x - 48y + 2100 - 18x - 36y
         = 21x + 41y + 4500

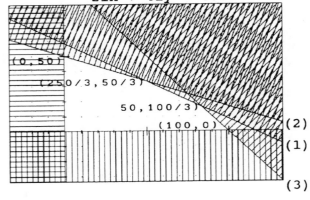

vertex	$21x + 41y + 4500$
$(100, 0)$	6600
$\left(\dfrac{250}{3}, \dfrac{50}{3}\right)$	$\dfrac{20800}{3}$ *
$\left(50, \dfrac{100}{3}\right)$	$\dfrac{20750}{3}$
$(0, 50)$	6500

To achieve the maximum profit of $6,933.33 (20800/3), plant 250/3 acres of oats and 50/3 acres of corn.

34. (a) Note that $2100 + $2400 = $4500. The solution for exercise 17 assumed conditions that also satisfy the demands for the current situation, so the point of the feasible set that gave the solution for 17 is also a feasible point for the current problem. For that reason, the optimal solution for the current problem has to give a profit that is at least as big as the profit given by the solution for 17.

(b) x and y are as defined in exercise 17

Money $18x + 16x + 36y + 48y = 34x + 84y \le 4500$ (1)
Acres $x + y \le 100$ (2)
Profit$= 55x + 125y + 4500 - 34x - 84y = 21x + 41y + 4500$.

$$\begin{cases} 34x + 84y \le 4500 & (1) \\ x + y \le 100 & (2) \\ x \ge 0, \quad y \ge 0 \end{cases}$$ Maximize Profit $= 21x + 41y + 4500$.

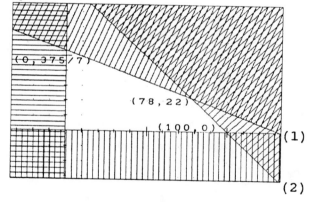

vertex	$21x + 41y + 4500$
$(100, 0)$	6600
$(78, 22)$	7040 *
$\left(0, \dfrac{375}{7}\right)$	$\dfrac{46875}{7}$

To achieve the maximum profit of $7040, plant 78 acres of oats and 22 acres of corn.

35.

	I_1	I_2	Restrictions
M_1	3	4	40
M_2	2	1	20
M_3	2	3	60
Profit	8	6	

x = # items of I_1

y = # items of I_2

$$\begin{cases} 3x + 4y \le 40 & (1) \\ 2x + y \le 20 & (2) \\ 2x + 3y \le 60 & (3) \\ x \ge 0, \quad y \ge 0 \end{cases}$$

Maximize, Profit = $8x + 6y$.

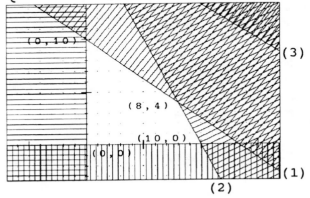

vertex	$8x + 6y$
(10,0)	80
(8,4)	88*
(0,10)	60
(0,0)	0

(a) To maximize profit, the company should make 8 of I_1 and 4 of I_2.

(b) The maximum profit is $88.

(c) $3 \cdot 8 + 4 \cdot 4 = 40$ ounces of M_1

$2 \cdot 8 + 4 = 20$ ounces of M_2

$2 \cdot 8 + 3 \cdot 4 = 28$ ounces of M_3.

(d) Profit = $13x + 6y$

Vertex	$13x + 6y$
(0,10)	60
(8,4)	128
(10,0)	130*
(0,0)	0

To maximize profit, the company should now make 10 of I_1 and 0 of I_2.

(36) (a)

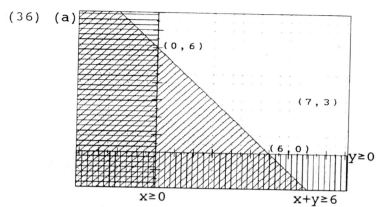

(0,6)

(7,3)

(6,0)

y≥0

x≥0

x+y≥6

(b)

vertex	10x + 6y
(6,0)	60
(0,6)	36
(7,3)	88

(c) The maximum value would need to be attained by one of
the vertices of the feasible set. The vertices of the
feasible set are (6,0) and (0,6) and corresponding
values of M are 60 and 36 respectively. From part (b),
it is clear that a vertex of the feasible set does not
give the equation M = 10x + 6y its greatest value.

37. (a)

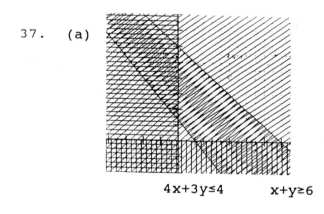

4x+3y≤4   x+y≥6

(b) The feasible set
contains no points.

3.3 Linear Programming, II

1. (a) Cost function is 21x + 14y, so c = 21x + 14y or
   $y = -\frac{3}{2}x + \frac{c}{14}$.

   (b) As c increases, the y-intercept $\frac{c}{14}$ increases, so the line moves up.

   (c) By inspection, the vertex of the feasible set that gives the optimum solution is B (cost line intersects feasible set here first).

2. (a) Cost function is 375 - 2x - 3y, so c = 375 - 2x -3y or
   $y = -\frac{2}{3}x + 125 - \frac{c}{3}$.

   (b) As c increases, the y-intercept $125 - \frac{c}{3}$ decreases, so the line moves down.

   (c) By inspection, the vertex of the feasible set that gives the optimum solution is D.

3. If $\frac{a}{b} > 3$ the answer is correct. For example M = 4x + y.

4. If $\frac{1}{3} < \frac{a}{b} < 1$ the answer is correct. For example M = x + 2y.

5. If $1 < \frac{a}{b} < 3$ the answer is correct. For example M = 2x + y.

6. If $\frac{a}{b} < \frac{1}{3}$ the answer is correct. For example M = x + 4y.

7. If $\frac{a}{b} < \frac{1}{3}$ the answer is correct. For example M = x + 4y.

8. If $1 < \frac{a}{b} < 3$ the answer is correct. For example M = 2x + y.

9. If $\frac{1}{3} < \frac{a}{b} < 1$ the answer is correct. For example M = x +2 y.

10. If $3 < \frac{a}{b}$ the answer is correct. For example M = 4x + y.

For 11 - 18 the slope of the equation M = ax + by is $-\frac{a}{b}$ and must be compared to the slopes given on the graph to determine which point gives the least or greatest value for M.

94

11. B, since the slope is $-\frac{3}{2}$ and $-4 < -\frac{3}{2} < -1$.

12. D, since the slope is $-\frac{1}{5}$ and $-\frac{1}{5} > -\frac{1}{4}$.

13. C, since the slope is -5 and $-5 < -4$.

14. C, since the slope is $-\frac{2}{3}$ and $-1 < -\frac{2}{3} < -\frac{1}{4}$.

15. A, since the slope is $-\frac{1}{5}$ and $-\frac{1}{5} > -\frac{1}{4}$.

16. D, since the slope is -5 and $-5 < -4$.

17. B, since the slope is $-\frac{2}{3}$ and $-1 < -\frac{2}{3} < -\frac{1}{4}$.

18. C, since the slope is $-\frac{3}{2}$ and $-4 < -\frac{3}{2} < -1$.

19. The slope between $(0,5)$ and $(3,4)$ is $-\frac{1}{3}$.

The slope between $(3,4)$ and $(4,0)$ is -4.
Therefore for $M = x + ky$ to be maximized at $(3,4)$ its slope $-\frac{1}{k}$ must satisfy the inequalities $-4 \le -\frac{1}{k}$ and $-\frac{1}{k} \le -\frac{1}{3}$

$$k \ge \frac{1}{4} \quad \text{and} \quad 3 \ge k$$

$$\frac{1}{4} \le k \le 3$$

20. Each coordinate of E is greater than the coordinates of any other vertex of the feasible set. Since a and b are positive, $ax + by$ will have its greatest value at E.

21.

x = cans of Brand A
y = cans of Brand B

	A	B	Requirements
Protein	3	1	6
Carbohydrates	1	1	4
Fat	2	6	12
Cost	80	50	

$$\begin{cases} 3x + y \ge 6 & (1) \\ x + y \ge 4 & (2) \\ 2x + 6y \ge 12 & (3) \\ x \ge 0, \quad y \ge 0 \end{cases}$$ Minimize, Cost $= 80x + 50y$

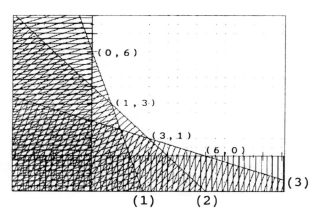

vertex	80x + 50y
(0,6)	300
(1,3)	230*
(3,1)	290
(6,0)	480

To satisfy the minimum requirements and obtain a minimum cost of $230, Mr. Smith should feed the dogs 1 can of Brand A and 3 cans of Brand B.

22.

x = # days operating I
y = # days operating II

	I	II	Requirements
High	100	200	1000
Medium	200	100	1000
Low	300	200	1800
Cost	10000	9000	

$$\begin{cases} 100x + 200y \geq 1000 \quad (1) \\ 200x + 100y \geq 1000 \quad (2) \\ 300x + 200y \geq 1800 \quad (3) \\ x \geq 0, \quad y \geq 0 \end{cases}$$

Minimize, Cost = 10000x + 9000y

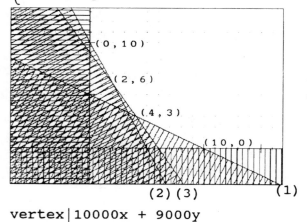

vertex	10000x + 9000y
(0,10)	90000
(2,6)	74000
(4,3)	67000*
(10,0)	100000

To fill the order at the least cost of $67,000, Refinery I should be operated for 4 days and Refinery II should be operated for 3 days.

23. x = # crates of oranges
    y = # crates of grapefruit
    100 - x - y = # crates of avocados

$$\begin{cases} x \geq 20 & (1) \\ y \geq 10 & (2) \\ 100 - x - y \geq 30 \text{ or } x + y \leq 70 & (3) \\ x \geq y & (4) \end{cases}$$

Maximize, Profit = 5x + 6y + 4(100 - x - y) = x + 2y + 400

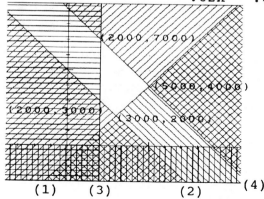

(35,35)
(20,20)
(20,10)
(60,10) (2)
(3)
(4)   (1)

vertex	x + 2y + 400
(20,20)	460
(35,35)	505*
(60,10)	480
(20,10)	440

To obtain a maximum profit of $505, 35 crates of oranges, 35 crates of grapefruit, and 30 crates of avocados should be shipped.

24. x = amount of money invested in low risk stocks
    y = amount of money invested in medium risk stocks
    9000 - x - y = amount of money invested in high risk stocks

$$\begin{cases} x \leq y + 1000 & (1) \\ x + y \geq 5000 & (2) \\ y + 9000 - x - y \leq 7000 \text{ or } x \geq 2000 & (3) \\ 9000 - x - y \geq 0 \text{ or } x + y \leq 9000 & (4) \end{cases}$$

Maximize, Profit = .06x + .07y + .08(9000 + x - y)
                 = -.02x - .01y + 720

(2000,7000)
(5000,4000)
(2000,3000)
(3000,2000)
(1)   (3)   (2)   (4)

vertex	-.02 - .01 + 720
(2000,7000)	610
(5000,4000)	580
(3000,2000)	640
(2000,3000)	650

To obtain a maximum yield of $650, Mr. Jones should invest $2000 in low risk stock, $3000 in medium risk stock and $4000 in high risk stocks.

25. x = # of cars produced in Detroit
y = # of trucks produced in Detroit
600 - x = # of cars produced in Cleveland
300 - y = # of trucks produced in Cleveland

$$\begin{cases} x + y \leq 800 \quad (1) \\ 600 - x + 300 - y \leq 500 \text{ or } x + y \geq 400 \quad (2) \\ x \leq 600 \qquad (3) \\ y \leq 300 \qquad (4) \\ x \geq 0, \quad y \geq 0 \end{cases}$$

Minimize, Cost = 1200x + 2100y + 1000(600 - x) + 2000(300 - y)
= 200x + 100y + 1200000

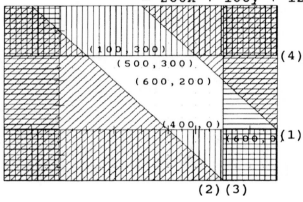

(100,300)
(500,300)
(600,200)
(4)
(400,0)
(600,0) (1)
(2) (3)

vertex	200x + 100y + 1200000
(100,300)	1250000*
(500,300)	1330000
(600,200)	1340000
(400,0)	1280000
(600,0)	1320000

To obtain the mimimum cost of $1,250,000, 100 cars and 300 trucks should be made in Detroit and 500,(600-100) cars and 0,(300-300) trucks should be made in Cleveland.

26. x = # of cars sent from Baltimore to Philadelphia
y = # of cars sent from Baltimore to Trenton
4 - x = # of cars sent from New York to Philadelphia
7 - y = # of cars sent from New York to Trenton

$$\begin{cases} x + y \leq 8 \quad (1) \\ 4 - x + 7 - y \leq 6 \text{ or } x + y \geq 5 \quad (2) \\ x \leq 4, \qquad (3) \\ y \leq 7 \qquad (4) \\ x \geq 0, \quad y \geq 0 \end{cases}$$

Minimize, Cost = 120x + 90y + 100(4-x) + 70(7-y)
= 20x + 20y + 890

y Baltimore x
Trenton ← 8 ↘ Philadelphia
7 ← ↗ New York ↗ 4-x 4
7-y 6

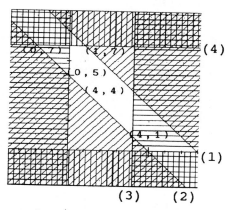

vertex	20x + 20y + 890
(0,7)	1030
(1,7)	1050
(4,4)	1050
(4,1)	990*
(0,5)	990*

There are five solutions, both corner points (4,1) and (0,5) and the points (1,4), (2,3), and (3,2) which lie on line (2), that give a minimum cost of $990. For example, send 2 cars from Baltimore to Philadelphia, 3 cars from Baltimore to Trenton, 2, (4-2), cars from New York to Philadelphia, and 4, (7-3), cars from New York to Trenton. In all cases, 5 cars will be shipped from Baltimore and 6 cars from New York.

27. x = number of gallons of gasoline
y = number of gallons of jet fuel
100000 - x - y = number of gallons of diesel fuel

$$\begin{cases} x + y \geq 20000 \ (1) \\ x + 100000 - x - y \geq 50000 \ \text{or} \ y \leq 50000 \ (2) \\ x \geq 5000 \ (3) \\ y \geq 5000 \ (4) \\ 100000 - x - y \geq 5000 \ \text{or} \ x + y \leq 95000 \ (5) \end{cases}$$

Maximize, Profit = .15x + .12y + .10(100000 - x - y)
                  = .05x + .02y + 10000

99

vertex	.05x + .02y + 10000
(5000,50000)	11250
(45000,50000)	13250
(90000,5000)	14600*
(15000,5000)	10850
(5000,15000)	10550

To achieve a maximum profit of $14,600, the oil refinery must produce 90,000 gal of gasoline, 5,000 gal of jet fuel and 5,000 gal of diesel fuel.

28. This problem has the same constraints as problem #9, so it will have the same corner points. The only thing that changes is the profit equation.

Maximize, Profit = .05x + .12y + .10(100000 - x - y)
$$= -.05x + .02y + 10000$$

Vertex	-.05x + .02y + 10000
(5000,50000)	10750*
(45000,50000)	8750
(90000,5000)	5600
(15000,5000)	9350
(5000,15000)	10050

To achieve a maximum profit of $10,750, the oil refinery should produce 5,000 gallons of gasoline, $50,000 gallons of jet fuel, and (100000 - 5000 - 50000 = 45000) 45,000 gallons of diesel fuel.

29.

	high capacity	low capacity	requirements
cases	320	200	
cost	50000	30000	1,080,000

x = # of high cap trucks
y = # of low cap trucks

$$\begin{cases} 50000x + 30000y \leq 1080000 \quad (1) \\ x + y \leq 30 \quad (2) \\ x \leq 15 \quad (3) \\ x \geq 0, \quad y \geq 0 \end{cases}$$

Maximize, Capacity = 320x + 200y

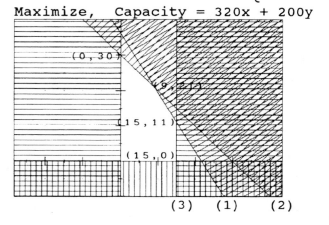

vertex	320x + 200y
(0,30)	6000
(9,21)	7080*
(15,11)	7000
(15,0)	4800

To be able to ship the maximum value of 7080 cases, the company must buy 9 high-cap trucks and 21 low-cap trucks.

30.

	high capacity	low capacity	requirements
cases	320	200	11200
cost	50000	30000	

x = # of high-cap trucks
y = # of low-cap trucks

$$\begin{cases} 320x + 200y \geq 11200 \quad (1) \\ x + y \leq 30 \quad (2) \\ x \leq 15 \quad (3) \\ x \geq 0, \quad y \geq 0 \end{cases}$$

(a)

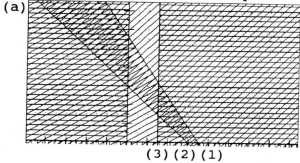

(3) (2) (1)

There is no feasible set so the company will not be able to ship 11,200 cases under these restrictions.

(b)
$$\begin{cases} 320x + 200y \geq 11200 \quad (1) \\ x + y \leq 30 + 23 = 53 \quad (2) \\ x \leq 15 \quad (3) \\ x \geq 0, \quad y \geq 0 \end{cases}$$

Minimize, Cost = 50000x + 30000y

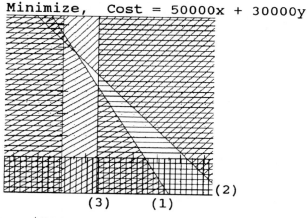

(3)   (1)   (2)

vertex	50000x + 30000y
(5,48)	1,690,000*
(15,38)	1,890,000
(15,32)	1,710,000

To have the minimum cost of $1,690,000, the company must buy 5 high-capacity and 48 low-capacity trucks.

Supplementary Exercises

1. x = # Type A planes
    y = # Type B planes

	Type A	Type B	Restrictions
Passengers	50	300	1400
Stewards	3	4	42
Cost	14000	90000	

$$\begin{cases} 50x + 300y \geq 1400 & (1) \\ 3x + 4y \leq 43 & (2) \\ x \geq y & (3) \\ x \geq 0, \quad y \geq 0 \end{cases}$$

Minimize Cost = 14000x + 90000y

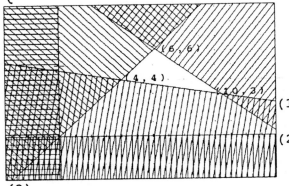

vertex	14000x + 90000y
(6,6)	624,000
(10,3)	410,000
(4,4)	416,000

To obtain a minimum cost of $410,000, 10 planes of Type A and 3 planes of Type B should be used.

2. x = # ounces of wheat germ
    y = # ounces of oat flour

	Wheat	Oat	Requirements
Niacin	2	3	7
Iron	3	3	9
Thiamin	.5	.25	1
Cost	.03	.04	

$$\begin{cases} 2x + 3y \geq 7 & (1) \\ 3x + 3y \geq 9 & (2) \\ .5x + .25y \geq 1 & (3) \\ x \geq 0, \quad y \geq 0 \end{cases}$$

Minimize   Cost = 3x + 4y   in cents

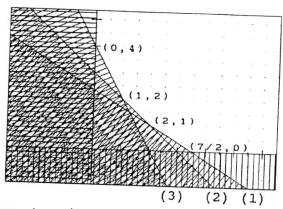

vertex	3x + 4y
(0,4)	16
(1,2)	11
(2,1)	10*
(7/2,0)	10.5

To obtain the minimum cost of 10 cents 2 oz of wheat germ and 1 oz of enriched oat flour should be used in each serving.

3. x = # of hardtop cars
    y = # of sports cars

	Hardtop	Sport	Restrictions
assemble	8	18	360
paint	2	2	50
upholster	2	1	40
profit	90	100	

$$\begin{cases} 8x + 18y \le 360 & (1) \\ 2x + 2y \le 50 & (2) \\ 2x + y \le 40 & (3) \\ x \ge 0, \quad y \ge 0 \end{cases}$$

Maximize Profit = 90x + 100y

vertex	90x + 100y
(0,20)	2000
(9,16)	2410*
(15,10)	2350
(20,0)	1800

To obtain a maximum profit of $2,410, 9 hardtops and 16 sports cars should be produced each day.

4. x = # boxes Mix A
    y = # boxes Mix B

	Mix A	Mix B	Restrictions
peanuts	6	12	5400
raisins	1	3	1200
cashews	4	2	2400
revenue	.50	.90	

$$\begin{cases} 6x + 12y \leq 5400 & (1) \\ x + 3y \leq 1200 & (2) \\ 4x + 2y \leq 2400 & (3) \\ x \geq 0, \quad y \geq 0 \end{cases}$$

Maximize Revenue = .5x + .9y

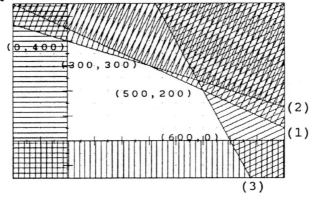

vertex	.5x + .9y
(0,400)	360
(300,300)	420
(500,200)	430
(600,0)	300

To obtain a maximum profit of $430, 500 boxes of Mixture A and 200 boxes of Mixture B should be made.

5. x = # of elementary textbooks
    y = # intermediate textbooks
    72 - x - y = # of advanced textbooks

$$\begin{cases} x \geq y & (1) \\ 72 - x - y \geq 4 \text{ or } x + y \leq 68 & (2) \\ y \geq 2(72 - x - y) \text{ or } 2x + 3y \geq 144 & (3) \\ x \geq 0, \quad y \geq 0 \end{cases}$$

Maximize Profit = 8000x + 7000y + 1000(72 - x - y)
                  = 7000x + 6000y + 72000

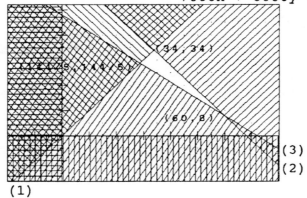

vertex	7000x + 6000y + 72000
(34,34)	514000
(60,8)	548000*
$\left(\dfrac{144}{5}, \dfrac{144}{5}\right)$	446400

To obtain a maximum profit of $548,000, the publisher should print 60 elementary, 8 intermediate, and 4 advanced texts.

6.

x = # of computers from Rochester
y = # of computers from Queens

	Rochester	Queens
Time	15	20
Cost	15	30
Available	80	120
Profit	40	30

$$\begin{cases} 15x + 20y \leq 2100 \quad (1) \\ 15x + 30y \leq 3000 \quad (2) \\ x \leq 80 \quad (3) \quad y \leq 120 \quad (4) \\ x \geq 0, \quad y \geq 0 \end{cases}$$

Maximize Profit = 40x + 30y

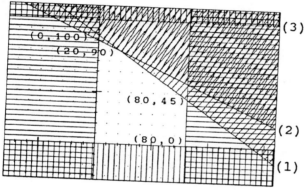

vertex	40x + 30y
(0,100)	3000
(20,90)	3500
(80,45)	4550*
(80,0)	3200
(0,0)	0

To obtain the maximum profit of $4,550, the company should send 80 computers from Rochester and 45 computers from Queens.

7. x = # of refrigerators sent from A to I
y = # of refrigerators sent from A to II
200 - x = # of refrigerators sent from B to I
300 - y = # of refrigerators sent from B to II

$$\begin{cases} x + y \leq 400 \quad (1) \\ 200 - x + 300 - y \leq 300 \text{ or } x + y \geq 200 \quad (2) \\ 200 - x \geq 0 \text{ or } x \leq 200 \quad (3) \\ 300 - y \geq 0 \text{ or } y \leq 300 \quad (4) \\ x \geq 0, \quad y \geq 0 \end{cases}$$

Minimize Cost = 36x + 30y + (200 - x)·30 + (300 - y)·25
                = 6x + 5y + 13500

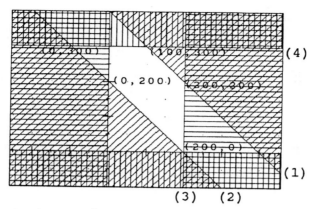

vertex	6x + 5y + 13500
(0,200)	14500*
(0,300)	15000
(100,300)	15600
(200,200)	15700
(200,0)	14700

To obtain the minimum cost of $14,500, the company should ship 0 fridges from A to I,200 from A to II, 200 (200-0) from B to I, and 100 (300-200) from B to II.

4
SIMPLEX METHOD

4.1 Slack Variables and the Simplex Tableau

1.
$$\begin{cases} 20x + 30y + u & = 3500 \\ 50x + 10y \quad\quad + v & = 5000 \\ -8x - 13y \quad\quad\quad\quad + M = 0 \end{cases}$$

Find a solution to the linear system for which $x \geq 0$, $y \geq 0$, $u \geq 0$, $v \geq 0$, and M is as large as possible.

2.
$$\begin{cases} 3x + 2y + u & = 10 \\ x \quad\quad\quad + v & = 15 \\ y \quad\quad\quad + w & = 3 \\ x + y \quad\quad\quad\quad + t & = 5 \\ -x - 15y \quad\quad\quad\quad\quad + M = 0 \end{cases}$$

Find a solution to the linear system for which $x \geq 0$, $y \geq 0$, $u \geq 0$, $v \geq 0$, $w \geq 0$, $t \geq 0$ and M is as large as possible.

3.
$$\begin{cases} x + y + z + u & = 100 \\ 3x \quad\quad + z \quad\quad + v & = 200 \\ 5x + 10y \quad\quad\quad\quad + w & = 100 \\ -x - 2y + 3z \quad\quad\quad\quad + M = 0 \end{cases}$$

Find a solution to the linear system for which $x \geq 0$, $y \geq 0$, $z \geq 0$, $u \geq 0$, $v \geq 0$, $w \geq 0$ and M is as large as possible.

4.
$$\begin{cases} x + 3y + u & = 24 \\ y \quad\quad + v & = 5 \\ x + 7y \quad\quad\quad + w & = 10 \\ -2x - y \quad\quad\quad\quad + M = 50 \end{cases}$$

Find a solution of the linear system for which $x \geq 0$, $y \geq 0$, $u \geq 0$, $v \geq 0$, $w \geq 0$, and M is as large as possible.

5.
$$\begin{bmatrix} x & y & u & v & M & \\ 20 & 30 & 1 & 0 & 0 & 3000 \\ 50 & 10 & 0 & 1 & 0 & 5000 \\ -8 & -13 & 0 & 0 & 1 & 0 \end{bmatrix}$$

$x = 0$, $y = 0$, $u = 3500$, $v = 5000$, $M = 0$

6.
$$\begin{bmatrix} x & y & u & v & w & z & M & \\ 3 & 2 & 1 & 0 & 0 & 0 & 0 & 10 \\ 1 & 0 & 0 & 1 & 0 & 0 & 0 & 15 \\ 0 & 1 & 0 & 0 & 1 & 0 & 0 & 3 \\ 1 & 1 & 0 & 0 & 0 & 1 & 0 & 5 \\ -1 & -15 & 0 & 0 & 0 & 0 & 1 & 0 \end{bmatrix}$$

$x = 0$, $y = 0$, $u = 10$, $v = 15$, $w = 3$, $z = 5$, $M = 0$

7.
$$\begin{bmatrix} x & y & z & u & v & w & M & \\ 1 & 1 & 1 & 1 & 0 & 0 & 0 & 100 \\ 3 & 0 & 1 & 0 & 1 & 0 & 0 & 200 \\ 5 & 10 & 0 & 0 & 0 & 1 & 0 & 100 \\ -1 & -2 & 3 & 0 & 0 & 0 & 1 & 0 \end{bmatrix}$$
$x = 0, \ y = 0, \ z = 0, \ u = 100, \ v = 200, \ w = 100, \ M = 0$

8.
$$\begin{bmatrix} x & y & u & v & w & M & \\ 1 & 3 & 1 & 0 & 0 & 0 & 24 \\ 0 & 1 & 0 & 1 & 0 & 0 & 5 \\ 1 & 7 & 0 & 0 & 1 & 0 & 10 \\ -2 & -1 & 0 & 0 & 0 & 1 & 50 \end{bmatrix}$$
$x = 0, \ y = 0, \ u = 24, \ v = 5, \ w = 10, \ M = 50$

9. $x = 15, \ y = 0, \ u = 10, \ v = 0, \ M = 20$

10. $x = 6, \ y = 16, \ u = 0, \ v = 0, \ M = 3$

11. $x = 10, \ y = 0, \ z = 15, \ u = 23, \ v = 0, \ w = 0, \ M = -11$

12. $x = 0, \ y = 100, \ z = \frac{1}{4}, \ u = 11, \ v = 0, \ w = 0, \ M = -\frac{1}{2}$

13. (a)
$$\begin{bmatrix} x & y & u & v & M & \\ 1 & \frac{3}{2} & \frac{1}{2} & 0 & 0 & 6 \\ 0 & -\frac{1}{2} & -\frac{1}{2} & 1 & 0 & 4 \\ 0 & -5 & 5 & 0 & 1 & 60 \end{bmatrix}$$

Row operations:
1. $\frac{1}{2} \cdot$ Row 1
2. $-1 \cdot$ Row 1 + Row 2
3. $10 \cdot$ Row 1 (+ Row 3)

$x = 6, \ y = 0, \ u = 0, \ v = 4, \ M = 60$

(b)
$$\begin{bmatrix} x & y & u & v & M & \\ \frac{2}{3} & 1 & \frac{1}{3} & 0 & 0 & 4 \\ \frac{1}{3} & 0 & -\frac{1}{3} & 1 & 0 & 6 \\ \frac{10}{3} & 0 & \frac{20}{3} & 0 & 1 & 80 \end{bmatrix}$$

Row operations:
1. $\frac{1}{3} \cdot$ Row 1
2. $-1 \cdot$ Row 1 + Row 2
3. $20 \cdot$ Row 1 + Row 3

$x = 0, \ y = 4, \ u = 0, \ v = 6, \ M = 80$

(c)
$$\begin{bmatrix} x & y & u & v & M & \\ 0 & 1 & 1 & -2 & 0 & -8 \\ 1 & 1 & 0 & 1 & 0 & 10 \\ 0 & -10 & 0 & 10 & 1 & 100 \end{bmatrix}$$

Row operations:
1. $-2 \cdot$ Row 2 + Row 1
3. $10 \cdot$ Row 2 + Row 3

$x = 10, \ y = 0, \ u = -8, \ v = 0, \ M = 100$

(d)
$$\begin{bmatrix} x & y & u & v & M & \\ -1 & 0 & 1 & -3 & 0 & -18 \\ 1 & 1 & 0 & 1 & 0 & 10 \\ 10 & 0 & 0 & 20 & 1 & 200 \end{bmatrix}$$

Row operations:
1. $-3 \cdot$ Row 2 + Row1
3. $20 \cdot$ Row 2 + Row3

$x = 0, \ y = 10, \ u = -18, \ v = 0, \ M = 200$

14. (a)

$$\begin{bmatrix} x & y & u & v & M & \\ 1 & \frac{4}{5} & \frac{1}{5} & 0 & 0 & 20 \\ 0 & -2 & -2 & 1 & 0 & 1000 \\ 0 & \frac{14}{5} & \frac{1}{5} & 0 & 1 & 20 \end{bmatrix}$$

Rowoperations:

1. $\frac{1}{5} \cdot$ Row 1

2. $-10 \cdot$ Row 1 + Row 2

3. Row 1 + Row 3

$x = 20, \ y = 0, \ u = 0, \ v = 1000, \ M = 20$

(b)

$$\begin{bmatrix} x & y & u & v & M & \\ \frac{5}{4} & 1 & \frac{1}{4} & 0 & 0 & 25 \\ \frac{5}{2} & 0 & -\frac{3}{2} & 1 & 0 & 1050 \\ -\frac{7}{2} & 0 & -\frac{1}{2} & 0 & 1 & -50 \end{bmatrix}$$

Row operations:

1. $\frac{1}{4} \cdot$ Row 1

2. $-6 \cdot$ Row 1 + Row 2

3. $-2 \cdot$ Row 1 + Row 3

$x = 0, \ y = 25, \ u = 0, \ v = 1050, \ M = -50$

(c)

$$\begin{bmatrix} x & y & u & v & M & \\ 0 & 1 & 1 & -\frac{1}{2} & 0 & -500 \\ 1 & \frac{3}{5} & 0 & \frac{1}{10} & 0 & 120 \\ 0 & \frac{13}{5} & 0 & \frac{1}{10} & 1 & 120 \end{bmatrix}$$

Row operations:

1. $\frac{1}{10} \cdot$ Row 2

2. $-5 \cdot$ Row 2 + Row 1 = Row 1

3. Row 2 + Row 3 = Row 3

$x = 120, \ y = 0, \ u = -500, \ v = 0, \ M = 120$

(d)

$$\begin{bmatrix} x & y & u & v & M & \\ -\frac{5}{3} & 0 & 1 & -\frac{2}{3} & 0 & -700 \\ \frac{5}{3} & 1 & 0 & \frac{1}{6} & 0 & 200 \\ -\frac{13}{3} & 0 & 0 & -\frac{1}{6} & 1 & -400 \end{bmatrix}$$

Row operations:

1. $\frac{1}{6} \cdot$ Row 2

2. $-4 \cdot$ Row 2 + Row 1

3. $-2 \cdot$ Row 2 + Row 3

$x = 0, \ y = 200, \ u = -700, \ v = 0, \ M = -400$

15. (d)   16.   (c)

4.2   The Simplex Method, I   Maximum Problems

1. (a)   3

(b)

$$\begin{array}{c}\ \\ u \\ \\ y \\ \\ M\end{array}\begin{bmatrix} x & y & u & v & M & \\ \frac{16}{3} & 0 & 1 & -\frac{2}{3} & 0 & 6 \\ \frac{1}{3} & 1 & 0 & \frac{1}{3} & 0 & 2 \\ \hline 0 & 0 & 0 & 4 & 1 & 24 \end{bmatrix}$$

(c) $x = 0, \ y = 2, \ u = 6, \ v = 0, \ M = 24$

109

2. (a) 1 - first row, first column

(b)

	x	y	u	v	M	
x	1	0	3	1	0	5
Y	0	1	2	0	0	12
M	0	0	23	6	1	40

(c) $x = 5$, $y = 12$, $u = 0$, $v = 0$, $M = 40$

3. (a) 10

(b)

	x	y	u	v	M	
u	-13	0	1	$-\frac{6}{5}$	0	6
Y	$\frac{3}{2}$	1	0	$\frac{1}{10}$	0	$\frac{1}{2}$
M	7	0	0	$\frac{1}{5}$	1	1

(c) $x = 0$, $y = \frac{1}{2}$, $u = 6$, $v = 0$, $M = 1$

4. (a) 3

(b)

	x	y	u	v	M	
u	0	2	1	$\frac{1}{3}$	0	$\frac{5}{3}$
x	1	-9	0	$-\frac{2}{3}$	0	$\frac{14}{3}$
M	0	40	0	$\frac{10}{3}$	1	$\frac{116}{3}$

(c) $x = \frac{14}{3}$, $y = 0$, $u = \frac{5}{3}$, $v = 0$, $M = \frac{116}{3}$

5.

	x	y	u	v	M	
u	1	1	1	0	0	7
v	1	(2)	0	1	0	10
M	-1	-3	0	0	1	0

$$\begin{array}{c}\quad\ \ \begin{matrix}x & y & u & v & M\end{matrix} \\ \begin{matrix}u\\[3ex]y\\[4ex]M\end{matrix}\left[\begin{array}{ccccc|c}\frac{1}{2} & 0 & 1 & -\frac{1}{2} & 0 & 7 \\[2ex] \frac{1}{2} & 1 & 0 & \frac{1}{2} & 0 & 5 \\[2ex]\hline \frac{1}{2} & 0 & 0 & \frac{3}{2} & 1 & 15\end{array}\right]\end{array}$$

$x = 0,\ y = 5,\ u = 7,\ v = 0,\ M = 15.$

6.

$$\begin{array}{c}\quad\ \ \begin{matrix}x & y & u & v & M\end{matrix} \\ \begin{matrix}u\\v\\[2ex]M\end{matrix}\left[\begin{array}{ccccc|c}-1 & (1) & 1 & 0 & 0 & 100 \\ 6 & 6 & 0 & 1 & 0 & 1200 \\\hline -1 & -2 & 0 & 0 & 1 & 0\end{array}\right]\end{array} \longrightarrow \begin{array}{c}\quad\ \ \begin{matrix}x & y & u & v & M\end{matrix} \\ \begin{matrix}y\\v\\[2ex]M\end{matrix}\left[\begin{array}{ccccc|c}-1 & 1 & 1 & 0 & 0 & 100 \\ (12) & 0 & -6 & 1 & 0 & 600 \\\hline -3 & 0 & 2 & 0 & 1 & 200\end{array}\right]\end{array}$$

$$\begin{array}{c}\quad\ \ \begin{matrix}x & y & u & v & M\end{matrix} \\ \begin{matrix}y\\[3ex]x\\[3ex]M\end{matrix}\left[\begin{array}{ccccc|c}0 & 1 & \frac{1}{2} & \frac{1}{2} & 0 & 150 \\[2ex] 1 & 0 & -\frac{1}{2} & \frac{1}{2} & 0 & 50 \\[2ex]\hline 0 & 0 & \frac{1}{2} & \frac{1}{4} & 1 & 350\end{array}\right]\end{array}$$

$x = 50,\ y = 150,\ u = 0,\ v = 0,\ M = 350.$

7.

$$\begin{array}{c}\quad\ \ \begin{matrix}x & y & u & v & M\end{matrix} \\ \begin{matrix}u\\[2ex]v\\[2ex]M\end{matrix}\left[\begin{array}{ccccc|c}(5) & 1 & 1 & 0 & 0 & 80 \\[1ex] 3 & 2 & 0 & 1 & 0 & 76 \\[1ex]\hline -4 & -2 & 0 & 0 & 1 & 0\end{array}\right]\end{array}$$

$$\begin{array}{c}\begin{matrix}x\\[3ex]v\\[3ex]M\end{matrix}\left[\begin{array}{ccccc|c}1 & \frac{1}{5} & \frac{1}{5} & 0 & 0 & 16 \\[2ex] 0 & (\frac{7}{5}) & -\frac{3}{5} & 1 & 0 & 28 \\[2ex]\hline 0 & -\frac{6}{5} & \frac{4}{5} & 0 & 1 & 64\end{array}\right]\end{array}$$

$$\begin{array}{c}\begin{matrix}x\\[3ex]y\\[3ex]M\end{matrix}\left[\begin{array}{ccccc|c}1 & 0 & \frac{2}{7} & -\frac{1}{7} & 0 & 12 \\[2ex] 0 & 1 & -\frac{3}{7} & \frac{5}{7} & 0 & 20 \\[2ex]\hline 0 & 0 & \frac{2}{7} & \frac{6}{7} & 1 & 88\end{array}\right]\end{array}$$

$x = 12,\ y = 20,\ u = 0,\ v = 0;\quad M = 88$

8.

	x	y	u	v	M	
u	-1	(8)	1	0	0	160
v	3	-1	0	1	0	3
M	-2	-6	0	0	1	0

	x	y	u	v	M	
y	$-\frac{1}{8}$	1	$\frac{1}{8}$	0	0	20
v	$(\frac{23}{8})$	0	$\frac{1}{8}$	1	0	23
M	$-\frac{11}{4}$	0	$\frac{6}{8}$	0	1	120

	x	y	u	v	M	
y	0	1	$\frac{3}{23}$	$\frac{1}{23}$	0	21
x	1	0	$\frac{1}{23}$	$\frac{8}{23}$	0	8
M	0	0	$\frac{20}{23}$	$\frac{22}{23}$	1	142

$x = 8$ $y = 21$, $u = 0$,

$v = 0$ $M = 142$.

9.

	x	y	z	u	v	M	
u	1	0	(2)	1	0	0	10
v	0	3	1	0	1	0	24
M	-1	-3	-5	0	0	1	0

	x	y	z	u	v	M	
z	$\frac{1}{2}$	0	1	$\frac{1}{2}$	0	0	5
v	$-\frac{1}{2}$	(3)	0	$-\frac{1}{2}$	1	0	19
M	$\frac{3}{2}$	-3	0	$\frac{5}{2}$	0	1	25

	x	y	z	u	v	M	
z	$\frac{1}{2}$	0	1	$\frac{1}{2}$	0	0	5
y	$-\frac{1}{6}$	1	0	$-\frac{1}{6}$	$\frac{1}{3}$	0	$\frac{19}{3}$
M	1	0	0	2	1	1	44

$x = 0$, $y = \frac{19}{3}$, $z = 5$, $u = 0$, $v = 0$, $M = 44$

10.

	x	y	z	u	v		
u	1	-2	9	1	0	0	10
v	0	(1)	4	0	1	0	12
M	1	-8	-1	0	0	1	0

$\longrightarrow$

	x	y	z	u	v	M	
u	1	0	17	1	2	0	34
y	0	1	4	0	1	0	12
M	1	0	31	0	8	1	96

$x = 0$, $y = 12$, $z = 0$, $u = 34$, $v = 0$, $M = 96$.

11.

$$
\begin{array}{c}
u \\
v \\
w \\
\\
M
\end{array}
\left[
\begin{array}{cccccc|c}
x & y & u & v & w & M & \\
5 & (1) & 1 & 0 & 0 & 0 & 30 \\
3 & 2 & 0 & 1 & 0 & 0 & 60 \\
1 & 1 & 0 & 0 & 1 & 0 & 50 \\
\hline
-2 & -3 & 0 & 0 & 0 & 1 & 0
\end{array}
\right]
\longrightarrow
\begin{array}{c}
y \\
v \\
w \\
\\
M
\end{array}
\left[
\begin{array}{cccccc|c}
x & y & u & v & w & M & \\
5 & 1 & 1 & 0 & 0 & 0 & 30 \\
-7 & 0 & -2 & 1 & 0 & 0 & 0 \\
-4 & 0 & -1 & 0 & 1 & 0 & 20 \\
\hline
13 & 0 & 3 & 0 & 0 & 1 & 90
\end{array}
\right]
$$

$x = 0, \quad y = 30,$
$u = 0, \quad v = 0,$
$w = 20, \quad M = 90.$

12.

$$
\begin{array}{c}
u \\
v \\
w \\
\\
M
\end{array}
\left[
\begin{array}{ccccccc|c}
x & y & z & u & v & w & M & \\
1 & -2 & 0 & 1 & 0 & 0 & 0 & 6 \\
3 & 0 & 1 & 0 & 1 & 0 & 0 & 9 \\
0 & (1) & 3 & 0 & 0 & 1 & 0 & 12 \\
\hline
-10 & -12 & -10 & 0 & 0 & 0 & 1 & 0
\end{array}
\right]
$$

$$
\begin{array}{c}
u \\
v \\
y \\
\\
M
\end{array}
\left[
\begin{array}{ccccccc|c}
1 & 0 & 6 & 1 & 0 & 2 & 0 & 30 \\
(3) & 0 & 1 & 0 & 1 & 0 & 0 & 9 \\
0 & 1 & 3 & 0 & 0 & 1 & 0 & 12 \\
\hline
-10 & 0 & 26 & 0 & 0 & 12 & 1 & 144
\end{array}
\right]
$$

$$
\begin{array}{c}
u \\
x \\
y \\
\\
M
\end{array}
\left[
\begin{array}{ccccccc|c}
0 & 0 & \frac{17}{3} & 1 & -\frac{1}{3} & 2 & 0 & 27 \\
1 & 0 & \frac{1}{3} & 0 & \frac{1}{3} & 0 & 0 & 3 \\
0 & 1 & 3 & 0 & 0 & 1 & 0 & 12 \\
\hline
0 & 0 & \frac{88}{3} & 0 & \frac{10}{3} & 12 & 1 & 174
\end{array}
\right]
$$

$x = 3, \; y = 12, \; z = 0, \; u = 27, \; v = 0, \; w = 0; \; M = 174$

13.

$$
\begin{array}{c}
u \\
v \\
\\
M
\end{array}
\left[
\begin{array}{ccccc|c}
x & y & u & v & M & \\
2 & (3) & 1 & 0 & 0 & 400 \\
1 & 1 & 0 & 1 & 0 & 150 \\
\hline
-6 & -7 & 0 & 0 & 1 & 300
\end{array}
\right]
$$

$$
\begin{array}{c}
y \\
v \\
\\
M
\end{array}
\left[
\begin{array}{ccccc|c}
x & y & u & v & M & \\
\frac{2}{3} & 1 & \frac{1}{3} & 0 & 0 & \frac{400}{3} \\
(\frac{1}{3}) & 0 & -\frac{1}{3} & 1 & 0 & \frac{50}{3} \\
\hline
-\frac{4}{3} & 0 & \frac{7}{3} & 0 & 1 & \frac{3700}{3}
\end{array}
\right]
$$

113

$$\begin{array}{c}\quad\\ y\\ x\\ M\end{array}\begin{array}{c}x\quad y\quad u\quad v\quad M\\\left[\begin{array}{ccccc|c}0 & 1 & 1 & -2 & 0 & 100\\1 & 0 & -1 & 3 & 0 & 50\\\hline 0 & 0 & 1 & 4 & 1 & 1300\end{array}\right]\end{array}$$

x = 50, y = 100, u = 0, v = 0, M = 1300.

14.
$$\begin{array}{c}\quad\\ u\\ v\\ M\end{array}\begin{array}{c}x\quad y\quad u\quad v\quad M\\\left[\begin{array}{ccccc|c}1 & (1) & 1 & 0 & 0 & 10\\5 & 2 & 0 & 1 & 0 & 20\\\hline -10 & -20 & 0 & 0 & 1 & 50\end{array}\right]\end{array}\longrightarrow\begin{array}{c}\quad\\ y\\ v\\ M\end{array}\begin{array}{c}x\quad y\quad u\quad v\quad M\\\left[\begin{array}{ccccc|c}1 & 1 & 1 & 0 & 0 & 10\\3 & 0 & -2 & 1 & 0 & 0\\\hline 10 & 0 & 20 & 0 & 1 & 250\end{array}\right]\end{array}$$

x = 0, y = 10; M = 250

15.
$$\begin{array}{c}\quad\\ u\\ v\\ w\\ M\end{array}\begin{array}{c}x\quad y\quad z\quad u\,v\,w\,M\\\left[\begin{array}{ccccccc|c}6 & 3 & 8 & 1 & 0 & 0 & 0 & 768\\1 & 1 & (2) & 0 & 1 & 0 & 0 & 144\\2 & 5 & 0 & 0 & 0 & 1 & 0 & 216\\\hline -80 & -70 & -120 & 0 & 0 & 0 & 1 & 0\end{array}\right]\end{array}\longrightarrow$$

$$\begin{array}{c}x\quad y\quad z\,u\quad v\,w\,M\\\left[\begin{array}{ccccccc|c}(2) & -1 & 0 & 1 & -4 & 0 & 0 & 192\\\frac{1}{2} & \frac{1}{2} & 1 & 0 & \frac{1}{2} & 0 & 0 & 72\\2 & 5 & 0 & 0 & 0 & 1 & 0 & 216\\\hline -20 & -10 & 0 & 0 & 60 & 0 & 1 & 8640\end{array}\right]\end{array}$$

$$\begin{array}{c}\quad\\ x\\ z\\ v\\ M\end{array}\begin{array}{c}x\quad y\quad z\quad u\quad v\,w\,M\\\left[\begin{array}{ccccccc|c}1 & -\frac{1}{2} & 0 & \frac{1}{2} & -2 & 0 & 0 & 96\\0 & \frac{3}{4} & 1 & -\frac{1}{4} & \frac{3}{2} & 0 & 0 & 24\\0 & (6) & 0 & -1 & 4 & 1 & 0 & 24\\\hline 0 & -20 & 0 & 10 & 20 & 0 & 1 & 10560\end{array}\right]\end{array}\longrightarrow$$

$$\begin{array}{c}\quad\\ x\\ z\\ y\\ M\end{array}\begin{array}{c}x\;y\;z\quad u\quad\;v\quad\;w\;M\\\left[\begin{array}{ccccccc|c}1 & 0 & 0 & \frac{5}{12} & -\frac{5}{3} & \frac{1}{12} & 0 & 98\\0 & 0 & 1 & -\frac{1}{8} & 1 & -\frac{1}{8} & 0 & 21\\0 & 1 & 0 & -\frac{1}{6} & \frac{2}{3} & \frac{1}{6} & 0 & 4\\\hline 0 & 0 & 0 & \frac{20}{3} & \frac{100}{3} & \frac{10}{3} & 1 & 10640\end{array}\right]\end{array}$$

x = 98, y = 4, z = 21, M = 10640.

16.
$$\begin{array}{c}\quad\\ u\\ v\\ w\\ M\end{array}\begin{array}{c}x\quad\; y\quad\quad z\,u\,v\,w\,M\\\left[\begin{array}{ccccccc|c}1 & (1) & 1 & 1 & 0 & 0 & 0 & 100\\5 & 4 & 4 & 0 & 1 & 0 & 0 & 480\\40 & 20 & 30 & 0 & 0 & 1 & 0 & 3200\\\hline -70 & -210 & -140 & 0 & 0 & 0 & 1 & 0\end{array}\right]\end{array}\longrightarrow$$

$$\begin{array}{c}\quad\\ y\\ v\\ w\\ M\end{array}\begin{array}{c}x\;y\;\;z\quad\; u\,v\,w\,M\\\left[\begin{array}{ccccccc|c}1 & 1 & 1 & 1 & 0 & 0 & 0 & 100\\1 & 0 & 0 & -4 & 1 & 0 & 0 & 80\\20 & 0 & 10 & -20 & 0 & 1 & 0 & 1200\\\hline 140 & 0 & 70 & 210 & 0 & 0 & 1 & 2100\end{array}\right]\end{array}$$

100 of brand B, none of others, for a $2100 maxumum profit.

17.

$$
\begin{array}{c}
\begin{array}{c} \\ u \\ v \\ w \\ \\ M \end{array}
\left[
\begin{array}{ccccccc|c}
x & y & z & u & v & w & M & \\
1 & 1 & 1 & 1 & 0 & 0 & 0 & 30 \\
0 & 0 & 1 & 0 & 1 & 0 & 0 & 4 \\
-1 & (1) & -1 & 0 & 0 & 1 & 0 & 0 \\
\hline
-200 & -475 & -275 & 0 & 0 & 0 & 1 & 0
\end{array}
\right]
\end{array}
\rightarrow
\begin{array}{c}
\begin{array}{c} \\ u \\ v \\ y \\ \\ M \end{array}
\left[
\begin{array}{ccccccc|c}
x & y & z & u & v & w & M & \\
2 & 0 & 2 & 1 & 0 & -1 & 0 & 30 \\
0 & 0 & (1) & 0 & 1 & 0 & 0 & 4 \\
-1 & 1 & -1 & 0 & 0 & 1 & 0 & 0 \\
\hline
-675 & 0 & -750 & 0 & 0 & 475 & 1 & 0
\end{array}
\right]
\end{array}
$$

$$
\begin{array}{c}
\begin{array}{c} \\ u \\ z \\ y \\ \\ M \end{array}
\left[
\begin{array}{ccccccc|c}
x & y & z & u & v & w & M & \\
(2) & 0 & 0 & 1 & -2 & -1 & 0 & 22 \\
0 & 0 & 1 & 0 & 1 & 0 & 0 & 4 \\
-1 & 1 & 0 & 0 & 1 & 1 & 0 & 4 \\
\hline
-675 & 0 & 0 & 0 & 750 & 475 & 1 & 3000
\end{array}
\right]
\end{array}
\rightarrow
\begin{array}{c}
\begin{array}{c} \\ x \\ z \\ y \\ \\ M \end{array}
\left[
\begin{array}{ccccccc|c}
x & y & z & u & v & w & M & \\
1 & 0 & 0 & \frac{1}{2} & -1 & -\frac{1}{2} & 0 & 11 \\
0 & 0 & 1 & 0 & 1 & 0 & 0 & 4 \\
0 & 1 & 0 & \frac{1}{2} & 0 & \frac{1}{2} & 0 & 15 \\
\hline
0 & 0 & 0 & \frac{675}{2} & 75 & \frac{275}{2} & 1 & 0425
\end{array}
\right]
\end{array}
$$

To burn the maximum of 10425 calories and lose $\frac{10425}{3500} \cong$ 2.98lb, he must bicycle 11 hrs, jog 15 hrs and swim 4 hrs.

18.

$$
\begin{array}{c}
\begin{array}{c} \\ u \\ v \\ w \\ \\ \end{array}
\left[
\begin{array}{ccccccc|c}
x & y & z & u & v & w & M & \\
10 & 10 & 10 & 1 & 0 & 0 & 0 & 1200 \\
30 & 30 & 10 & 0 & 1 & 0 & 0 & 3000 \\
(20) & 0 & 10 & 0 & 0 & 1 & 0 & 1800 \\
\hline
-60 & -60 & -50 & 0 & 0 & 0 & 1 & 0
\end{array}
\right]
\end{array}
$$

$$
\begin{array}{c}
\begin{array}{c} \\ u \\ v \\ x \\ \\ \end{array}
\left[
\begin{array}{cccccc|c}
0 & 10 & 5 & 1 & 0 & 0 & 300 \\
0 & (30) & -5 & 0 & 1 & 0 & 300 \\
1 & 0 & \frac{1}{2} & 0 & 0 & 0 & 90 \\
\hline
0 & -60 & -20 & 0 & 0 & 0 & 5400
\end{array}
\right]
\end{array}
$$

$$
\begin{array}{c}
\begin{array}{c} \\ u \\ y \\ x \\ \\ \end{array}
\left[
\begin{array}{ccccccc|c}
0 & 0 & (\frac{20}{3}) & 1 & -\frac{1}{3} & 0 & 0 & 200 \\
0 & 1 & -\frac{1}{6} & 0 & \frac{1}{30} & -\frac{1}{20} & 0 & 10 \\
1 & 0 & \frac{1}{2} & 0 & 0 & \frac{1}{20} & 0 & 90 \\
\hline
0 & 0 & -3 & 0 & 2 & 0 & 0 & 6000
\end{array}
\right]
\end{array}
$$

$$\begin{array}{c}z\\y\\x\\{}\end{array}\left[\begin{array}{ccccccc|c} 0 & 0 & 1 & \frac{3}{20} & -\frac{1}{20} & 0 & 0 & 30 \\ 0 & 1 & 0 & \frac{1}{40} & \frac{1}{40} & -\frac{1}{20} & 0 & 15 \\ 1 & 0 & 0 & -\frac{3}{40} & \frac{1}{40} & \frac{1}{20} & 0 & 75 \\ \hline 0 & 0 & 0 & \frac{9}{2} & \frac{1}{2} & 0 & 1 & 6900 \end{array}\right]$$

Small sofas: 75
Large sofas: 15
Chairs: 30

19.

$$\begin{array}{c}\\u\\v\\w\\{}\\M\end{array} \begin{array}{ccccccc} x & y & z & u & v & w & M \end{array}$$

$$\begin{array}{c}u\\v\\w\\{}\\M\end{array}\left[\begin{array}{ccccccc|c} 1 & 1 & 1 & 1 & 0 & 0 & 0 & 70 \\ 600 & 400 & 300 & 0 & 1 & 0 & 0 & 48000 \\ 15 & 9 & 5 & 0 & 0 & 1 & 0 & 1000 \\ \hline -40 & -30 & -25 & 0 & 0 & 0 & 1 & 0 \end{array}\right] \longrightarrow$$

$$\begin{array}{c}\\u\\v\\x\\{}\\M\end{array} \begin{array}{ccccccc} x & y & z & u & v & w & M \end{array}$$

$$\begin{array}{c}u\\v\\x\\{}\\M\end{array}\left[\begin{array}{ccccccc|c} 0 & \frac{2}{5} & (\frac{2}{3}) & 1 & 0 & -\frac{1}{15} & 0 & \frac{10}{3} \\ 0 & 40 & 100 & 0 & 1 & -40 & 0 & 8000 \\ 1 & \frac{3}{5} & \frac{1}{3} & 0 & 0 & \frac{1}{15} & 0 & \frac{200}{3} \\ \hline 0 & -6 & -\frac{35}{3} & 0 & 0 & \frac{8}{3} & 1 & \frac{8000}{3} \end{array}\right]$$

$$\begin{array}{ccccccc} x & y & z & u & v & w & M \end{array}$$

$$\left[\begin{array}{ccccccc|c} 0 & \frac{3}{5} & 1 & \frac{3}{2} & 0 & -\frac{1}{10} & 0 & 5 \\ 0 & -20 & 0 & -150 & 1 & -30 & 0 & 7500 \\ 1 & \frac{2}{5} & 0 & -\frac{1}{2} & 0 & \frac{1}{10} & 0 & 65 \\ \hline 0 & 1 & 0 & \frac{35}{2} & 0 & \frac{3}{2} & 1 & 2725 \end{array}\right]$$

To maximize profit at
$2725 thousand, they must
open 65 type A, 0 type B
and 5 type C restaurants
($2,725,000 is max. profit).

20.

$$\begin{array}{c}\\u\\v\\w\\{}\\M\end{array} \begin{array}{ccccccc} x & y & z & u & v & w & M \end{array}$$

$$\begin{array}{c}u\\v\\w\\{}\\M\end{array}\left[\begin{array}{ccccccc|c} 1 & 1 & (1) & 1 & 0 & 0 & 0 & 600 \\ 1 & 3 & 0 & 0 & 1 & 0 & 0 & 600 \\ 2 & 0 & 1 & 0 & 0 & 1 & 0 & 900 \\ \hline -60 & -90 & -300 & 0 & 0 & 0 & 1 & 0 \end{array}\right] \longrightarrow$$

$$\begin{array}{c}\\z\\v\\w\\{}\\M\end{array} \begin{array}{ccccccc} x & y & z & u & v & w & M \end{array}$$

$$\begin{array}{c}z\\v\\w\\{}\\M\end{array}\left[\begin{array}{ccccccc|c} 1 & 1 & 1 & 1 & 0 & 0 & 0 & 600 \\ 1 & 3 & 0 & 0 & 1 & 0 & 0 & 600 \\ 1 & -1 & 0 & -1 & 0 & 1 & 0 & 300 \\ \hline 240 & 210 & 0 & 300 & 0 & 0 & 1 & 180000 \end{array}\right]$$

$x = 0$, $y = 0$, $z = 600$, $u = 0$, $v = 600$, $w = 300$, $M = 180{,}000$

21.

$$
\begin{array}{c@{}c}
 & \begin{array}{ccccc} x & y & u & v & M \end{array} \\
\begin{array}{c} u \\ v \\ \\ M \end{array} &
\left[\begin{array}{ccccc|c}
1 & (4) & 1 & 0 & 0 & 300 \\
1 & 2 & 0 & 1 & 0 & 200 \\ \hline
-200 & -500 & 0 & 0 & 1 & 0
\end{array}\right]
\end{array}
\longrightarrow
\begin{array}{c@{}c}
 & \begin{array}{ccccc} x & y & u & v & M \end{array} \\
\begin{array}{c} y \\ \\ v \\ \\ M \end{array} &
\left[\begin{array}{ccccc|c}
\frac{1}{4} & 1 & \frac{1}{4} & 0 & 0 & 75 \\
(\frac{1}{2}) & 0 & \frac{1}{2} & 1 & 0 & 50 \\ \hline
-75 & 0 & 125 & 0 & 1 & 37500
\end{array}\right]
\end{array}
$$

$$
\begin{array}{c@{}c}
 & \begin{array}{ccccc} x & y & u & v & M \end{array} \\
\begin{array}{c} y \\ \\ x \\ \\ M \end{array} &
\left[\begin{array}{ccccc|c}
0 & 1 & \frac{1}{2} & -\frac{1}{2} & 0 & 50 \\
1 & 0 & -1 & 2 & 0 & 100 \\ \hline
0 & 0 & 50 & 150 & 1 & 45000
\end{array}\right]
\end{array}
\quad
\begin{array}{l}
x = 100,\ y = 50,\ u = 0,\ v = 0, \\
\qquad\quad M = 45000.
\end{array}
$$

22. $x = 0$, $y = 5$, $M = 20$ 23. $x = 1.6$, $y = .6$, $M = 10$

24. $x = 0$, $y = 4$, $z = 0$, $M = 8$ 24. $x = 5$, $y = 0$, $z = 0$, $M = 80$

4.3 The Simplex Method, II Minimum Problems

1.

$$
\begin{array}{c@{}c}
 & \begin{array}{ccccc} x & y & u & v & M \end{array} \\
\begin{array}{c} u \\ v \\ \\ M \end{array} &
\left[\begin{array}{ccccc|c}
1 & 1 & 1 & 0 & 0 & 5 \\
2 & -3 & 0 & 1 & 0 & -12 \\ \hline
-40 & -30 & 0 & 0 & 1 & 0
\end{array}\right]
\end{array}
\longrightarrow
\begin{array}{c@{}c}
 & \begin{array}{ccccc} x & y & u & v & M \end{array} \\
\begin{array}{c} u \\ \\ y \\ \\ M \end{array} &
\left[\begin{array}{ccccc|c}
\frac{5}{3} & 0 & 1 & \frac{1}{3} & 0 & 1 \\
-\frac{2}{3} & 1 & 0 & -\frac{1}{3} & 0 & 24 \\ \hline
-60 & 0 & 0 & -10 & 1 & 120
\end{array}\right]
\end{array}
$$

$$
\begin{array}{c@{}c}
 & \begin{array}{ccccc} x & y & u & v & M \end{array} \\
\begin{array}{c} x \\ \\ y \\ \\ M \end{array} &
\left[\begin{array}{ccccc|c}
1 & 0 & \frac{3}{5} & \frac{1}{5} & 0 & \frac{3}{5} \\
0 & 1 & \frac{2}{5} & -\frac{1}{5} & 0 & \frac{22}{5} \\ \hline
0 & 0 & 36 & 2 & 1 & 156
\end{array}\right]
\end{array}
\quad
x = \frac{3}{5},\ y = \frac{22}{5},\ u = 0,\ v = 0,\ M = 156.
$$

117

2.

$$\begin{array}{c} \\ u \\ v \\ \hline M \end{array}\begin{array}{ccccc} x & y & u & v & M \\ 2 & 5 & 1 & 0 & 0 \\ (-1) & 0 & 0 & 1 & 0 \\ \hline -3 & 1 & 0 & 0 & 1 \end{array}\left|\begin{array}{c} 100 \\ -10 \\ \hline 0 \end{array}\right. \longrightarrow \begin{array}{c} \\ u \\ x \\ \hline M \end{array}\begin{array}{ccccc} x & y & u & v & M \\ 0 & 5 & 1 & (2) & 0 \\ 1 & 0 & 0 & -1 & 0 \\ \hline 0 & 1 & 0 & -3 & 1 \end{array}\left|\begin{array}{c} 80 \\ 10 \\ \hline 30 \end{array}\right.$$

$$\begin{array}{c} \\ v \\ x \\ \hline M \end{array}\begin{array}{ccccc} x & y & u & v & M \\ 0 & \frac{5}{2} & \frac{1}{2} & 1 & 0 \\ 1 & \frac{5}{2} & \frac{1}{2} & 0 & 0 \\ \hline 0 & \frac{17}{2} & \frac{3}{2} & 0 & 1 \end{array}\left|\begin{array}{c} 40 \\ 50 \\ \hline 150 \end{array}\right. \qquad x = 50,\ y = 0,\ u = 0,\ v = 40,\ M = 150.$$

3.

$$\begin{array}{c} \\ u \\ v \\ \hline M \end{array}\begin{array}{ccccc} x & y & u & v & M \\ -1 & -1 & 1 & 0 & 0 \\ (-2) & 0 & 0 & 1 & 0 \\ \hline 3 & 1 & 0 & 0 & 1 \end{array}\left|\begin{array}{c} -3 \\ -5 \\ \hline 0 \end{array}\right. \longrightarrow \begin{array}{c} \\ u \\ x \\ \hline M \end{array}\begin{array}{ccccc} x & y & u & v & M \\ 0 & -1 & 1 & -\frac{1}{2} & 0 \\ 1 & 0 & 0 & -\frac{1}{2} & 0 \\ \hline 0 & 1 & 0 & \frac{3}{2} & 1 \end{array}\left|\begin{array}{c} -\frac{1}{2} \\ \dagger\frac{5}{2} \\ \hline -\frac{15}{2} \end{array}\right.$$

$$\begin{array}{c} \\ y \\ x \\ \hline M \end{array}\begin{array}{ccccc} x & y & u & v & M \\ 0 & 1 & -1 & \frac{1}{2} & 0 \\ 1 & 0 & 0 & -\frac{1}{2} & 0 \\ \hline 0 & 0 & 1 & 1 & 1 \end{array}\left|\begin{array}{c} \frac{1}{2} \\ \frac{5}{2} \\ \hline -8 \end{array}\right. \qquad x = \frac{5}{2},\ y = \frac{1}{2},\ u = 0,\ v = 0,\ M = 8.$$

4.

$$\begin{array}{c} \\ u \\ v \\ \hline M \end{array}\begin{array}{cccccc} x & y & z & u & v & M \\ (-1) & -1 & -1 & 1 & 0 & 0 \\ 0 & -1 & -2 & 0 & 1 & 0 \\ \hline 3 & 5 & 1 & 0 & 0 & 1 \end{array}\left|\begin{array}{c} -20 \\ -10 \\ \hline 0 \end{array}\right. \longrightarrow \begin{array}{c} \\ x \\ v \\ \hline M \end{array}\begin{array}{cccccc} x & y & z & u & v & M \\ 1 & 1 & 1 & -1 & 0 & 0 \\ 0 & (-1) & -2 & 0 & 1 & 0 \\ \hline 0 & 2 & -2 & 3 & 0 & 1 \end{array}\left|\begin{array}{c} 20 \\ -10 \\ \hline -60 \end{array}\right.$$

$$
\begin{array}{c}
\begin{array}{cccccc} x\ y\ \ z\ \ \ u\ \ v\ M \end{array}\\
\begin{array}{c} x\\ y\\ \\ M \end{array}
\left[\begin{array}{cccccc|c}
1 & 0 & -1 & -1 & 1 & 0 & 10\\
0 & 1 & (2) & 0 & -1 & 0 & 10\\
\hline
0 & 0 & -6 & 3 & 2 & 1 & -60
\end{array}\right]
\end{array}
\longrightarrow
\begin{array}{c}
\begin{array}{cccccc} x\ \ y\ \ z\ \ u\ \ \ v\ \ \ M \end{array}\\
\begin{array}{c} x\\ \\ z\\ \\ M \end{array}
\left[\begin{array}{cccccc|c}
1 & \frac{1}{2} & 0 & -1 & \left(\frac{1}{2}\right) & 0 & 15\\
0 & \frac{1}{2} & 1 & 0 & -\frac{1}{2} & 0 & 5\\
\hline
0 & 3 & 0 & 3 & -1 & 1 & -50
\end{array}\right]
\end{array}
$$

$$
\begin{array}{c}
\begin{array}{cccccc} x\ y\ z\ \ u\ v\ M \end{array}\\
\begin{array}{c} v\\ z\\ \\ M \end{array}
\left[\begin{array}{cccccc|c}
2 & 1 & 0 & -2 & 1 & 0 & 30\\
1 & 1 & 1 & -1 & 0 & 0 & 20\\
\hline
2 & 4 & 0 & 1 & 0 & 1 & -20
\end{array}\right]
\end{array}
\qquad
\begin{array}{l}
x = 0,\ y = 0,\ z = 20,\\
u = 0,\ v = 30,\ M = 20
\end{array}
$$

5.

$$
\begin{array}{c}
\begin{array}{ccccccc} x\ \ \ y\,u\,v\,s\,t\,M \end{array}\\
\begin{array}{c} u\\ v\\ s\\ \\ t\\ \\ M \end{array}
\left[\begin{array}{ccccccc|c}
(-2) & -1 & 1 & 0 & 0 & 0 & 0 & -11\\
1 & 1 & 0 & 1 & 0 & 0 & 0 & 10\\
\frac{1}{3} & 1 & 0 & 0 & 1 & 0 & 0 & 6\\
-\frac{1}{4} & -1 & 0 & 0 & 0 & 1 & 0 & -4\\
\hline
13 & 4 & 0 & 0 & 0 & 0 & 1 & 0
\end{array}\right]
\end{array}
\longrightarrow
\begin{array}{c}
\begin{array}{ccccccc} x\ \ \ \ y\ \ \ \ u\,v\,s\,t\,M \end{array}\\
\begin{array}{c} x\\ \\ v\\ \\ s\\ \\ t\\ \\ M \end{array}
\left[\begin{array}{ccccccc|c}
1 & \frac{1}{2} & -\frac{1}{2} & 0 & 0 & 0 & 0 & \frac{1}{2}\\
0 & \frac{1}{2} & \frac{1}{2} & 1 & 0 & 0 & 0 & \frac{9}{2}\\
0 & \frac{5}{6} & \frac{1}{6} & 0 & 1 & 0 & 0 & \frac{25}{6}\\
0 & \left(-\frac{7}{8}\right) & -\frac{1}{8} & 0 & 0 & 1 & 0 & -\frac{21}{8}\\
\hline
0 & -\frac{5}{2} & \frac{13}{2} & 0 & 0 & 0 & 1 & -\frac{143}{2}
\end{array}\right]
\end{array}
$$

$$
\begin{array}{c}
\begin{array}{ccccccc} x\ y\ \ \ u\ v\ s\ \ \ \ t\ \ M \end{array}\\
\begin{array}{c} x\\ \\ v\\ \\ s\\ \\ y\\ \\ M \end{array}
\left[\begin{array}{ccccccc|c}
1 & 0 & -\frac{4}{7} & 0 & 0 & \frac{4}{7} & 0 & 4\\
0 & 0 & \frac{3}{7} & 1 & 0 & \frac{4}{7} & 0 & 3\\
0 & 0 & \frac{1}{21} & 0 & 1 & \left(-\frac{20}{21}\right) & 0 & \frac{5}{3}\\
0 & 1 & \frac{1}{7} & 0 & 0 & -\frac{8}{7} & 0 & 3\\
\hline
0 & 0 & \frac{48}{7} & 0 & 0 & -\frac{20}{7} & 1 & -64
\end{array}\right]
\end{array}
\longrightarrow
\begin{array}{c}
\begin{array}{ccccccc} x\ y\ \ u\ \ v\ \ \ s\ t\ M \end{array}\\
\begin{array}{c} x\\ \\ v\\ \\ t\\ \\ y\\ \\ M \end{array}
\left[\begin{array}{ccccccc|c}
1 & 0 & -\frac{3}{5} & 0 & -\frac{3}{5} & 0 & 0 & 3\\
0 & 0 & \frac{2}{5} & 1 & -\frac{3}{5} & 0 & 0 & 2\\
0 & 0 & \frac{1}{20} & 0 & \frac{21}{20} & 1 & 0 & \frac{7}{4}\\
0 & 1 & \frac{1}{5} & 0 & \frac{6}{5} & 0 & 0 & 5\\
\hline
0 & 0 & 7 & 0 & 3 & 0 & 1 & -59
\end{array}\right]
\end{array}
$$

$$
\begin{array}{l}
x = 3\\
y = 5\\
u = 0\\
v = 2\\
s = 0\\
t = 7/4\\
M = 59
\end{array}
$$

6.

$$
\begin{array}{c}
\quad\ \ x\ \ \ \ \ y\ u\ v\ M \\
\begin{array}{c}u\\v\\M\end{array}
\left[\begin{array}{ccccc|c}
1 & 1 & 1 & 0 & 0 & 20 \\
(-3) & -2 & 0 & 1 & 0 & -50 \\
\hline
-10 & -3 & 0 & 0 & 1 & -500
\end{array}\right]
\end{array}
\longrightarrow
\begin{array}{c}
\quad\ \ x\ \ \ y\ \ \ u\ \ \ \ v\ \ M \\
\begin{array}{c}u\\ \\x\\ \\ \\M\end{array}
\left[\begin{array}{ccccc|c}
0 & \frac{1}{3} & 1 & (\frac{1}{3}) & 0 & \frac{10}{3} \\
1 & \frac{2}{3} & 0 & -\frac{1}{3} & 0 & \frac{50}{3} \\
\hline
0 & \frac{11}{3} & 0 & -\frac{10}{3} & 1 & -\frac{1000}{3}
\end{array}\right]
\end{array}
$$

$$
\begin{array}{c}
\ x\ y\ \ \ u\ v\ M \\
\begin{array}{c}v\\x\\M\end{array}
\left[\begin{array}{ccccc|c}
0 & 1 & 3 & 1 & 0 & 10 \\
1 & 1 & 1 & 0 & 0 & 20 \\
\hline
0 & 7 & 10 & 0 & 1 & -300
\end{array}\right]
\end{array}
\quad x = 20,\ y = 0,\ u = 0,\ v = 10,\ M = 300.
$$

7. x = servings of food
    y = servings of food
    Minimize 3x + 1.5y subject to the constraints
    30x + 10y ≥ 60
    10x + 10y ≥ 40
    20x + 60y ≥ 120

$$
\begin{array}{c}
\quad\ \ x\ \ \ \ \ \ y\ u\ v\ w\ M \\
\begin{array}{c}u\\v\\w\\M\end{array}
\left[\begin{array}{cccccc|c}
(-30) & -10 & 1 & 0 & 0 & 0 & -60 \\
-10 & -10 & 0 & 1 & 0 & 0 & -40 \\
-20 & -60 & 0 & 0 & 1 & 0 & -120 \\
\hline
3 & 1.5 & 0 & 0 & 0 & 1 & 0
\end{array}\right]
\end{array}
\longrightarrow
\begin{array}{c}
\quad\ \ x\ \ \ \ \ \ y\ \ \ \ \ \ u\ \ v\ w\ M \\
\begin{array}{c}x\\ \\v\\ \\w\\ \\ \\M\end{array}
\left[\begin{array}{cccccc|c}
1 & \frac{1}{3} & -\frac{1}{30} & 0 & 0 & 0 & 2 \\
0 & -\frac{20}{3} & -\frac{1}{3} & 1 & 0 & 0 & -20 \\
0 & (-\frac{160}{3}) & -\frac{1}{3} & 0 & 1 & 0 & -80 \\
\hline
0 & \frac{1}{2} & \frac{1}{10} & 0 & 0 & 1 & -6
\end{array}\right]
\end{array}
$$

$$
\begin{array}{c}
\ x\ y\ \ \ \ u\ \ \ v\ \ \ \ w\ \ \ M \\
\begin{array}{c}x\\v\\y\\M\end{array}
\left[\begin{array}{cccccc|c}
1 & 0 & -\frac{3}{80} & 0 & \frac{1}{160} & 0 & \frac{3}{2} \\
0 & 0 & (-\frac{1}{4}) & 1 & -\frac{1}{8} & 0 & -10 \\
0 & 1 & \frac{1}{80} & 0 & -\frac{3}{160} & 0 & \frac{3}{2} \\
\hline
0 & 0 & \frac{3}{32} & 0 & \frac{3}{320} & 1 & -\frac{27}{4}
\end{array}\right]
\end{array}
\longrightarrow
\begin{array}{c}
\ x\ y\ u\ \ \ \ v\ \ \ \ w\ \ \ M \\
\begin{array}{c}x\\u\\y\\M\end{array}
\left[\begin{array}{cccccc|c}
1 & 0 & 0 & -\frac{3}{20} & \frac{1}{40} & 0 & 3 \\
0 & 0 & 1 & -4 & (\frac{1}{2}) & 0 & 40 \\
0 & 1 & 0 & \frac{1}{20} & -\frac{1}{40} & 0 & 1 \\
\hline
0 & 0 & 0 & \frac{3}{8} & -\frac{3}{80} & 1 & -\frac{21}{2}
\end{array}\right]
\end{array}
$$

	x	y	u	v	w	M	
x	1	0	$-\frac{1}{20}$	$\frac{1}{20}$	0	0	1
w	0	0	2	-8	1	0	80
y	0	1	$\frac{1}{20}$	$-\frac{3}{20}$	0	0	3
M	0	0	$\frac{3}{40}$	$\frac{3}{40}$	0	1	$-\frac{15}{2}$

x = 1 so 1 serving of food A
y = 3 so 3 servings of food B
M = 15/2, Cost is $\frac{15}{2}$ or $7.50.

8. x = days Plant I operates
y = days Plant II operates
Minimize 1500x + 1200y subject to the constraints
10x + 20y + u ≥ 1000
30x + 20y + v ≥ 1800
20x + 10y + w ≥ 1000

	x	y	u	v	w	M	
u	-10	-20	1	0	0	0	-1000
v	-30	-20	0	1	0	0	-1800
w	(-20)	-10	0	0	1	0	-1000
M	1500	1200	0	0	0	1	0

$\longrightarrow$

	x	y	u	v	w	M	
u	0	(-15)	1	0	$-\frac{1}{2}$	0	-500
v	0	-5	0	1	$-\frac{3}{2}$	0	-300
x	1	$\frac{1}{2}$	0	0	$-\frac{1}{20}$	0	50
M	0	450	0	0	75	1	-75000

	x	y	u	v	w	M	
y	0	1	$-\frac{1}{15}$	0	$\frac{1}{3}$	0	$\frac{100}{3}$
v	0	0	$(-\frac{1}{3})$	1	$-\frac{4}{3}$	0	$-\frac{400}{3}$
x	1	0	$\frac{1}{3}$	0	$-\frac{1}{15}$	0	$\frac{100}{3}$
M	0	0	30	0	60	1	-90000

$\longrightarrow$

	x	y	u	v	w	M	
y	0	1	0	$-\frac{1}{5}$	$\frac{3}{10}$	0	60
u	0	0	1	-3	(4)	0	400
x	1	0	0	$\frac{1}{10}$	$-\frac{1}{5}$	0	20
M	0	0	0	90	-60	1	-102000

$$
\begin{array}{c}
\quad\;\; x \;\; y \quad\;\; u \quad\;\; v \;\; w \;\; M \\
\begin{array}{c} y \\[1.2em] w \\[1.2em] x \\[1.2em] \hline M \end{array}
\left[
\begin{array}{cccccc|c}
0 & 1 & -\dfrac{3}{40} & \dfrac{1}{40} & 0 & 0 & 30 \\[1em]
0 & 0 & \dfrac{1}{4} & -\dfrac{3}{4} & 1 & 0 & 100 \\[1em]
1 & 0 & \dfrac{1}{20} & -\dfrac{1}{20} & 0 & 0 & 40 \\[1em]
0 & 0 & 15 & 45 & 0 & 1 & -96000
\end{array}
\right]
\end{array}
$$

x = 40 so Plant I: 40 days
y = 30 sp Plant II: 30 days
Cost is $96,000 since M = -96000

9. x = # of Brand A sold
    y = # of Brand B sold
    z = # of Brand C sold
    Minimize   30x + 50y + 60z   subject to the constraints
    x + y + z ≤ 600   x ≥ 0
    x ≥ 100   y ≥ 0
    y ≥ 50   z ≥ 0
    y + z ≥ 200

	x	y	z	t	u	v	w	M	
t	1	1	1	1	0	0	0	0	600
u	(−1)	0	0	0	1	0	0	0	−100
v	0	−1	0	0	0	1	0	0	−50
w	0	−1	−1	0	0	0	1	0	−200
	−30	−50	−60	0	0	0	0	1	0

	x	y	z	t	u	v	w	M	
t	0	1	1	1	1	0	0	0	500
u	1	0	0	0	−1	0	0	0	100
v	0	(−1)	0	0	0	1	0	0	−50
z	0	−1	−1	0	0	0	1	0	−200
	0	−50	−60	0	−30	0	0	1	3,000

	x	y	z	t	u	v	w	M	
t	0	0	1	1	1	1	0	0	450
x	1	0	0	0	−1	0	0	0	100
v	0	1	0	0	0	1	0	0	50
z	0	0	−1	0	0	−1	1	0	−150
	0	0	−60	0	−30	−50	0	1	5,500

$$
\begin{array}{c}
\begin{array}{c} t \\ x \\ y \\ z \\ {} \end{array}
\left[
\begin{array}{cccccccc|c}
0 & 0 & 0 & 1 & 1 & 0 & (1) & 0 & 300 \\
1 & 0 & 0 & 0 & -1 & 0 & 0 & 0 & 100 \\
0 & 1 & 0 & 0 & 0 & -1 & 0 & 0 & 150 \\
0 & 0 & 1 & 0 & 0 & 1 & -1 & 0 & 150 \\ \hline
0 & 0 & 0 & 0 & -30 & 10 & -60 & 1 & 14{,}500
\end{array}
\right]
\end{array}
$$

$$
\begin{array}{c}
\begin{array}{c} w \\ x \\ y \\ z \\ {} \end{array}
\left[
\begin{array}{cccccccc|c}
0 & 0 & 0 & 1 & 1 & 0 & 1 & 0 & 300 \\
1 & 0 & 0 & 0 & -1 & 0 & 0 & 0 & 100 \\
0 & 1 & 0 & 0 & 0 & -1 & 0 & 0 & 50 \\
0 & 0 & 1 & 1 & 1 & 0 & 0 & 0 & 450 \\ \hline
0 & 0 & 0 & 60 & 30 & 10 & 0 & 1 & 32{,}500
\end{array}
\right]
\end{array}
$$

Brand A: 100; Brand B: 50; Brand C: 450

10. x = hours of door-to-door
y = hours of letter writing
z = hours of phone calls
Minimize   x + y + z,   subject to the constraints
$4x + 2y + 3z \ge 210$
$z \ge 7$
$x \le y + z$

$$
\begin{array}{c}
\begin{array}{cccccccc} & x & y & z & u & v & w & M \end{array} \\
\begin{array}{c} u \\ v \\ w \\ {} \\ M \end{array}
\left[
\begin{array}{ccccccc|c}
-4 & -2 & -3 & 1 & 0 & 0 & 0 & -210 \\
0 & 0 & (-1) & 0 & 1 & 0 & 0 & -7 \\
1 & -1 & -1 & 0 & 0 & 1 & 0 & 0 \\ \hline
1 & 1 & 1 & 0 & 0 & 0 & 1 & 0
\end{array}
\right]
\end{array}
\longrightarrow
\begin{array}{c}
\begin{array}{cccccccc} & x & y & z & u & v & w & M \end{array} \\
\begin{array}{c} u \\ z \\ w \\ {} \\ M \end{array}
\left[
\begin{array}{ccccccc|c}
-4 & -2 & 0 & 1 & (-3) & 0 & 0 & -189 \\
0 & 0 & 1 & 0 & -1 & 0 & 0 & 7 \\
1 & -1 & 0 & 0 & -1 & 1 & 0 & 7 \\ \hline
1 & 1 & 0 & 0 & 1 & 0 & 1 & -7
\end{array}
\right]
\end{array}
$$

$$
\begin{array}{c}
\begin{array}{ccccccc} x & y & z & u & v & w & M \end{array} \\
\begin{array}{c} v \\[6pt] z \\[6pt] w \\[6pt] {} \\ M \end{array}
\left[
\begin{array}{ccccccc|c}
\frac{4}{3} & \frac{2}{3} & 0 & -\frac{1}{3} & 1 & 0 & 0 & 63 \\[4pt]
\frac{4}{3} & \frac{2}{3} & 1 & -\frac{1}{3} & 0 & 0 & 0 & 70 \\[4pt]
(\frac{7}{3}) & -\frac{1}{3} & 0 & -\frac{1}{3} & 0 & 1 & 0 & 70 \\ \hline
-\frac{1}{3} & \frac{1}{3} & 0 & \frac{1}{3} & 0 & 0 & 1 & -70
\end{array}
\right]
\end{array}
\longrightarrow
\begin{array}{c}
\begin{array}{ccccccc} x & y & z & u & v & w & M \end{array} \\
\begin{array}{c} v \\[6pt] z \\[6pt] x \\[6pt] {} \\ M \end{array}
\left[
\begin{array}{ccccccc|c}
0 & \frac{6}{7} & 0 & -\frac{1}{7} & 1 & -\frac{4}{7} & 0 & 23 \\[4pt]
0 & \frac{6}{7} & 1 & -\frac{1}{7} & 0 & -\frac{4}{7} & 0 & 30 \\[4pt]
1 & -\frac{1}{7} & 0 & -\frac{1}{7} & 0 & \frac{3}{7} & 0 & 30 \\ \hline
0 & -\frac{1}{7} & 0 & \frac{2}{7} & 0 & \frac{1}{7} & 1 & -60
\end{array}
\right]
\end{array}
$$

Door-to-door canvassing: 30 hours
Letter writing: 0 hours
Phone calls: 30 hours

11. x = 1.25, y = 0, M = 1.25   12. x = 2/3, y = 0, M = 20

4.4 Marginal Analysis and Matrix Formulation of Linear Programming Problems

1. The final tableau of the orginal problem was:

	x	y	(Lbr) u	(Stl) v	(Wood) w	M	
y	0	1	$\frac{7}{27}$	$-\frac{1}{9}$	0	0	8
x	1	0	$-\frac{5}{27}$	$\frac{2}{9}$	0	0	14
w	0	0	$-\frac{1}{27}$	$-\frac{5}{9}$	1	0	40
M	0	0	$\frac{20}{27}$	$\frac{1}{9}$	0	1	82

Man-hours corresponds to the labor (column 3), so for the present situation we must add to the right-most column 54 times the 3rd column. The result of this is a right-most column of

$$\begin{pmatrix} 8 \\ 14 \\ 40 \\ 82 \end{pmatrix} + 54 \begin{pmatrix} \frac{7}{27} \\ -\frac{5}{27} \\ -\frac{1}{27} \\ \frac{20}{27} \end{pmatrix} = \begin{pmatrix} 22 \\ 4 \\ 38 \\ 122 \end{pmatrix}.$$

The optimal number of paring knives will decrease by 10 to 4, and the optimal number of pocket knives will increase by 14 to 22. The profit will increase by $40 to $122.

2. The final right column will be

$$\begin{pmatrix} 8 \\ 14 \\ 40 \\ 82 \end{pmatrix} + h \cdot \begin{pmatrix} \frac{7}{27} \\ -\frac{5}{27} \\ -\frac{1}{27} \\ \frac{20}{27} \end{pmatrix} = \begin{pmatrix} 8 + h \cdot \frac{7}{27} \\ 14 - h \cdot \frac{5}{27} \\ 40 - h \cdot \frac{1}{27} \\ 82 + h \cdot \frac{20}{27} \end{pmatrix},$$

so that
$$8 + h \cdot \frac{7}{27} \geq 0,$$

$$14 - h \cdot \frac{5}{27} \geq 0$$

$$40 - h \cdot \frac{1}{27} \geq 0,$$

which results in
$$-\frac{216}{7} \le h \le \frac{378}{5}.$$

3. The final tableau of the original problem was

	x	y	t	u	v	w	M	
v	0	0	0	0	1	1	0	30
t	0	0	1	1	0	-1	0	10
x	1	0	0	-1	0	1	0	20
y	0	1	0	1	0	0	0	25
M	0	0	0	1	0	2	1	-260

and the constraint of the number of sets stocked in College Park corresponds to the column w. For the present situation, we must add to the right-most column 5 times the w column, which gives a right-most column of

$$\begin{pmatrix}30\\10\\20\\25\\-260\end{pmatrix} + 5\begin{pmatrix}1\\-1\\1\\0\\2\end{pmatrix} = \begin{pmatrix}35\\5\\25\\25\\-250\end{pmatrix}.$$

College Park should send 25 sets to each of Rockville and Annapolis, and that Baltimore should send 5 sets to Rockville and 0 to Annapolis.

4. The final right column will be

$$\begin{pmatrix}30\\10\\20\\25\\-260\end{pmatrix} + h\begin{pmatrix}1\\-1\\1\\0\\2\end{pmatrix} = \begin{pmatrix}30+h\\10-h\\20+h\\25\\60+2h\end{pmatrix},$$

so that $30 + h \ge 0$, $10 - h \ge 0$ and $20 + h \ge 0$, Valid range for h is $-20 \le h \le 10$.

5. The final tableau of the original problem was

	x	y	u	v	w	M	
x	1	0	$\frac{1}{3}$	-1	0	0	14
y	0	1	$-\frac{1}{3}$	2	0	0	4
w	0	0	$\frac{4}{3}$	-10	1	0	20
M	0	0	$\frac{10}{3}$	60	0	1	1400

The column that corresponds to the carpentry constraint was the u column. With h more man-hours available for carpentry, the right-most column will be

$$\begin{bmatrix} 14 + \dfrac{h}{3} \\[2mm] 4 - \dfrac{h}{3} \\[2mm] 20 + \dfrac{4h}{3} \\[2mm] 1400 + \dfrac{10h}{3} \end{bmatrix}$$, so that $14 + \dfrac{h}{3} \geq 0$, $4 - \dfrac{h}{3} \geq 0$, and $20 + \dfrac{4h}{3} \geq 0$ which results in $-15 \leq h \leq 12$.

6. The original problem is to minimize $21x + 14y$ or maximize $-21x - 14y$ subject to $15x + 22.5y \geq 90$

$$810x + 270y \geq 1620$$
$$x + y \geq 1$$
$$x \geq 0, \quad y \geq 0.$$

I. Introduce slack variables, w, v, u, all ≥ 0, and M so that $15x + 22.5y - u = 90$

$$810x + 270y - v = 1620$$
$$x + y - w = 1$$
$$M = -21x - 14y.$$

The corresponding original tableau is

$$
\begin{array}{c}
\quad\quad x \quad\quad y \ u \ v \ w \ M \\
\begin{array}{c} u \\ v \\ w \\ \\ M \end{array}
\left[
\begin{array}{cccccc|c}
-15 & 22.5 & 1 & 0 & 0 & 0 & -90 \\
(-810) & -270 & 0 & 1 & 0 & 0 & -1620 \\
-\frac{1}{9} & -\frac{1}{3} & 0 & 0 & 1 & 0 & -1 \\
\hline
2 & 1 & 0 & 0 & 0 & 0 & 0
\end{array}
\right]
\end{array}
\longrightarrow
$$

$$
\begin{array}{c}
\quad x \quad\quad y \quad\quad u \quad\quad v \quad w \ M \\
\begin{array}{c} u \\ \\ x \\ \\ w \\ \\ M \end{array}
\left[
\begin{array}{cccccc|c}
0 & -\frac{35}{2} & 1 & -\frac{1}{54} & 0 & 0 & -60 \\
1 & \frac{1}{3} & 0 & -\frac{1}{810} & 0 & 0 & 2 \\
0 & (-\frac{8}{27}) & 0 & -\frac{1}{7290} & 1 & 0 & -\frac{7}{9} \\
\hline
0 & 7 & 0 & \frac{7}{270} & 0 & 1 & -42
\end{array}
\right]
\end{array}
$$

$$
\begin{array}{c}
\ x\ y\ u \quad\quad v \quad\quad\ w \ \ M \\
\begin{array}{c} u \\ \\ x \\ \\ y \\ \\ M \end{array}
\left[
\begin{array}{cccccc|c}
0 & 0 & 1 & (-\frac{1}{96}) & -\frac{945}{16} & 0 & -\frac{225}{16} \\
1 & 0 & 0 & -\frac{1}{720} & \frac{9}{8} & 0 & \frac{9}{8} \\
0 & 1 & 0 & \frac{1}{2160} & -\frac{27}{8} & 0 & \frac{21}{8} \\
\hline
0 & 0 & 0 & \frac{49}{2160} & \frac{189}{8} & 1 & -\frac{483}{8}
\end{array}
\right]
\end{array}
\longrightarrow
$$

$$
\begin{array}{c}
\ x\ y \quad\ u\ v \quad\quad\ w \ \ M \\
\begin{array}{c} v \\ \\ x \\ \\ y \\ \\ M \end{array}
\left[
\begin{array}{cccccc|c}
0 & 0 & -96 & 1 & (5670) & 0 & 1350 \\
1 & 0 & -\frac{2}{15} & 0 & 9 & 0 & 3 \\
0 & 1 & \frac{2}{45} & 0 & -6 & 0 & 2 \\
\hline
0 & 0 & \frac{98}{45} & 0 & -105 & 1 & -91
\end{array}
\right]
\end{array}
$$

$$
\begin{array}{c}
\begin{array}{cccccc} \ x\ \ y\ \ \ \ \ u\ \ \ \ \ \ \ \ v\ \ \ \ \ \ w\ \ M \end{array}\\
\begin{array}{c} w\\[18pt] x\\[18pt] y\\[24pt] M \end{array}
\left[
\begin{array}{cccccc|c}
0 & 0 & -\dfrac{16}{945} & \dfrac{1}{5670} & 1 & 0 & \dfrac{5}{21}\\[12pt]
1 & 0 & \dfrac{2}{105} & -\dfrac{1}{630} & 0 & 0 & \dfrac{6}{7}\\[12pt]
0 & 1 & -\dfrac{2}{35} & \dfrac{1}{945} & 0 & 0 & \dfrac{24}{7}\\[12pt]
\hline
0 & 0 & \dfrac{2}{5} & \dfrac{1}{54} & 0 & 1 & -66
\end{array}
\right]
\end{array}
$$

which finally represents a feasible vertex. As the bottom row is entirely positive except for the right-most column, this tableau also represents the optimum solution, for the original problem. The column that corresponds to the calorie constraint is the v column, and the present situation would require us to add -80 times this column to the right-most column. The resulting right-most column is then

$$
\begin{pmatrix} \dfrac{5}{21} \\[10pt] \dfrac{6}{7} \\[10pt] \dfrac{24}{7} \\[10pt] -66 \end{pmatrix}
+ \ -80 \begin{pmatrix} \dfrac{1}{5760} \\[10pt] -\dfrac{1}{630} \\[10pt] \dfrac{1}{945} \\[10pt] \dfrac{1}{54} \end{pmatrix}
= \begin{pmatrix} \dfrac{5}{21} - \dfrac{80}{5760} \\[10pt] \dfrac{6}{7} + \dfrac{80}{630} \\[10pt] \dfrac{24}{7} - \dfrac{80}{945} \\[10pt] -66 - \dfrac{80}{54} \end{pmatrix}
= \begin{pmatrix} \dfrac{113}{504} \\[10pt] \dfrac{62}{63} \\[10pt] \dfrac{632}{189} \\[10pt] -\dfrac{1822}{27} \end{pmatrix}
$$

It follows that the optimal quantities are:

$\dfrac{62}{63} \cong .98$ cups of rice and $\dfrac{632}{198} \cong 3.34$ cups of soybeans

The new optimal cost is $\dfrac{1822}{27} \cong 67.48¢$.

In general, for an increase of h calories, the right-most column becomes

$$
\begin{pmatrix} \dfrac{5}{21} - \dfrac{h}{5760} \\[10pt] \dfrac{6}{7} + \dfrac{h}{630} \\[10pt] \dfrac{24}{7} - \dfrac{h}{945} \\[10pt] -66 - \dfrac{h}{54} \end{pmatrix},
\qquad
\begin{array}{l}
\dfrac{5}{21} - \dfrac{h}{5760} \ge 0 \ \text{or}\ h \le 1371.43 \\[10pt]
\dfrac{6}{7} + \dfrac{h}{630} \ge 0 \ \text{or}\ h \ge -540 \\[10pt]
\dfrac{24}{7} - \dfrac{h}{945} \ge 0 \ \text{or}\ h \le 3240
\end{array}
$$

This results in $-540 \le h \le 1371.43$.

7. $\begin{bmatrix} 9 & 1 & 1 \\ 4 & 8 & -3 \end{bmatrix}$.   8. $[4 \quad 0 \quad 6]$.

9. $\begin{bmatrix} 7 \\ 6 \\ 5 \\ 1 \end{bmatrix}$.   10. $\begin{bmatrix} 5 & 3 \\ 2 & -1 \end{bmatrix}$.

11. Yes.   12. $\begin{bmatrix} 1 & 2 \\ 2 & 1 \end{bmatrix}$ It must be a square matrix with anything along the diagonal and simetrix across that diagonal.

13. Minimize $[7 \quad 5 \quad 4] \begin{bmatrix} x \\ y \\ z \end{bmatrix}$ subject to

$\begin{bmatrix} 3 & 8 & 9 \\ 1 & 2 & 5 \\ 4 & 1 & 7 \end{bmatrix} \begin{bmatrix} x \\ y \\ z \end{bmatrix} \geq \begin{bmatrix} 75 \\ 80 \\ 67 \end{bmatrix}$ and $\begin{bmatrix} x \\ y \\ z \end{bmatrix} \geq \begin{bmatrix} 0 \\ 0 \\ 0 \end{bmatrix}$.

14. Maximize $[20 \quad 30] \begin{bmatrix} x \\ y \end{bmatrix}$ subject to

$\begin{bmatrix} 7 & 8 \\ 1 & 2 \\ 1 & 0 \end{bmatrix} \begin{bmatrix} x \\ y \end{bmatrix} \leq \begin{bmatrix} 55 \\ 78 \\ 25 \end{bmatrix}$ and $\begin{bmatrix} x \\ y \end{bmatrix} \geq \begin{bmatrix} 0 \\ 0 \end{bmatrix}$.

15. Maximize $[3 \quad 5] \begin{bmatrix} x \\ y \end{bmatrix}$ subject to the constraints

$\begin{bmatrix} 3 & 6 \\ 7 & 5 \\ 4 & 3 \end{bmatrix} \begin{bmatrix} x \\ y \end{bmatrix} \leq \begin{bmatrix} 90 \\ 138 \\ 120 \end{bmatrix}$ and $\begin{bmatrix} x \\ y \end{bmatrix} \geq \begin{bmatrix} 0 \\ 0 \end{bmatrix}$.

16. The linear inequalities (other than $x \geq 0$, $y \geq 0$, etc.) must all have the same inequality sign.

17. Minimize the objective function $2x + 3y$ subject to the constraints

$\begin{cases} 7x + 4y \geq 33 \\ 5x + 8y \geq 44 \\ \ x + 3y \geq 55 \\ \ x \geq 0, \quad y \geq 0. \end{cases}$

18. Maximize $33u + 44v + 55w$ subject to the constraints

$\begin{cases} 7u + 5v + \ w \leq 2 \\ 4u + 8v + 3w \leq 3 \\ \ u \geq 0, \quad\ \ v \geq 0. \end{cases}$

4.5 Duality

1. Minimize $80u + 76v$ subject to the constraints
$$\begin{cases} 5u + 3v \geq 4 \\ u + 2v \geq 2 \\ u \geq 0, \quad v \geq 0. \end{cases}$$

2. Maximize $2u + 3v$ subject to the constraints
$$\begin{cases} 5u + v \leq 30 \\ 3u + 2v \leq 60 \\ u + v \leq 50 \\ u \geq 0, \quad v \geq 0. \end{cases}$$

3. Maximize $u + 2v + w$ subject to the constraints
$$\begin{cases} u - v + 2w \leq 10 \\ 2u + v + 3w \leq 12 \\ u \geq 0, \quad v \geq 0, \quad w \geq 0. \end{cases}$$

4. Minimize $768u + 144v + 216w$ subject to the constraints
$$\begin{cases} 6u + v + 2w \geq 80 \\ 3u + v + 5w \geq 70 \\ 8u + 2v \geq 120 \\ u \geq 0, \quad v \geq 0, \quad w \geq 0. \end{cases}$$

5. Maximize $-7u + 10v$ subject to the constraints
$$\begin{cases} -2u + 8v \leq 3 \\ 4u + v \leq 5 \\ 6u + 9v \leq 1 \\ u \geq 0, \quad v \geq 0. \end{cases}$$

6. Minimize $16u - 5v$ subject to the constraints
$$\begin{cases} u - 7v \geq 2 \\ u - 9v \geq -3 \\ u + 4v \geq 4 \\ u + 3v \geq -5 \\ u \geq 0, \quad v \geq 0. \end{cases}$$

7. $x = 12$, $y = 20$, $M = 88$;

   Dual solution: $u = \dfrac{2}{7}$, $v = \dfrac{6}{7}$, $M = 88$.

8. $x = 3$, $y = 0$, $z = 0$, $M = 90$;
   Dual solution: $u = 0$, $v = 30$, $M = 90$.

9. $x = 0$, $y = 2$, $M = 24$;
   Dual solution: $u = 0$, $v = 12$, $w = 0$, $M = 24$.

10. $x = 98$, $y = 4$, $z = 21$, $M = 10{,}640$;

    Dual solution: $u = \dfrac{20}{3}$, $v = \dfrac{100}{3}$, $w = \dfrac{10}{3}$, $M = 10{,}640$.

11. The dual is to maximize $3u + 5v$ subject to the constraints

$$\begin{cases} u + 2v \le 3 \\ u \le 1 \\ u \ge 0, \ v \ge 0. \end{cases}$$

Original:

	x	y	u	v	M	
u	(−1)	−1	1	0	0	−3
v	−2	0	0	1	0	−5
M	3	1	0	0	1	0

Dual:

	u	v	x	y	M	
x	1	(2)	1	0	0	3
y	1	0	0	1	0	1
M	−3	−5	0	0	1	0

	x	y	u	v	M	
u	0	(−1)	1	$-\frac{1}{2}$	0	$-\frac{1}{2}$
x	1	0	0	$-\frac{1}{2}$	0	$\frac{5}{2}$
M	0	1	0	$\frac{3}{2}$	1	$-\frac{15}{2}$

	u	v	x	y	M	
v	$\frac{1}{2}$	1	$\frac{1}{2}$	0	0	$\frac{3}{2}$
y	(1)	0	0	1	0	1
M	$-\frac{1}{2}$	0	$\frac{5}{2}$	0	1	$\frac{15}{2}$

	x	y	u	v	M	
y	0	1	−1	$\frac{1}{2}$	0	$\frac{1}{2}$
x	1	0	0	$-\frac{1}{2}$	0	$\frac{5}{2}$
M	0	0	1	1	1	−8

	u	v	x	y	M	
v	0	1	$\frac{1}{2}$	$-\frac{1}{2}$	0	1
u	1	0	0	1	0	1
M	0	0	$\frac{5}{2}$	$\frac{1}{2}$	1	8

Original solution:

$x = \frac{1}{2}$, $y = \frac{5}{2}$, $M = 8$;

Dual solution:

$u = 1$, $v = 1$, $M = 8$

12. The dual is to maximize $20u$ subject to the constraints

$$\begin{cases} u \qquad \le 3 \\ u + \ v \le 5 \\ u + 2v \le 1 \\ u \ge 0, \ v \ge 0. \end{cases}$$

Original:

	x	y	z	u	v	M	
u	(-1)	-1	-1	1	0	0	-20
v	0	-1	-2	0	1	0	0
M	3	5	1	0	0	1	0

	x	y	z	u	v	M	
x	1	1	(1)	-1	0	0	20
v	0	-1	-2	0	1	0	0
M	0	2	-2	3	0	1	-60

	x	y	z	u	v	M	
z	1	1	1	-1	0	0	20
v	2	1	0	-2	1	0	40
M	2	4	0	1	0	1	-20

Original solution:
x = 0, y = 0, z = 20, M = 20;

Dual:

	u	v	x	y	z	M	
x	1	0	1	0	0	0	3
y	1	1	0	1	0	0	5
z	(1)	2	0	0	1	0	1
M	-20	0	0	0	0	1	0

	u	v	x	y	z	M	
x	0	-2	1	0	-1	0	2
y	0	-1	0	1	-1	0	4
u	1	2	0	0	1	0	1
M	0	40	0	0	20	1	20

Dual solution:
u = 1, v = 0, M = 20

13. The dual is to minimize $6u + 9v + 12w$ subject to the constraints

$$\begin{cases} u + 3v & \geq 10 \\ -2u + & w \geq 12 \\ v + 3w \geq 10 \\ u \geq 0, \ v \geq 0, \ w \geq 0 \end{cases}$$

Original:

	x	y	z	u	v	w	M	
u	1	-2	0	1	0	0	0	6
v	3	0	1	0	1	0	0	9
w	0	(1)	3	0	0	1	0	12
M	-10	-12	-10	0	0	0	1	0

	x	y	z	u	v	w	M	
u	1	0	6	1	0	2	0	30
v	(3)	0	1	0	1	0	0	9
y	0	1	3	0	0	1	0	12
M	-10	0	26	0	0	12	1	144

Dual:

	u	v	w	x	y	z	M	
x	(-1)	-3	0	1	0	0	0	-10
y	2	0	-1	0	1	0	0	-12
z	0	-1	-3	0	0	1	0	-10
M	6	9	12	0	0	0	1	0

	u	v	w	x	y	z	M	
u	1	(3)	0	-1	0	0	0	10
y	0	-6	-1	2	1	0	0	-32
z	0	-1	-3	0	0	1	0	-10
M	0	-9	12	6	0	0	1	-60

$$
\begin{array}{c|ccccccc|c}
u & 0 & 0 & \frac{17}{3} & 1 & -\frac{1}{3} & 2 & 0 & 27 \\
x & 1 & 0 & \frac{1}{3} & 0 & \frac{1}{3} & 0 & 0 & 3 \\
y & 0 & 1 & 3 & 0 & 0 & 1 & 0 & 12 \\
\hline
M & 0 & 0 & \frac{88}{3} & 0 & \frac{10}{3} & 12 & 1 & 174
\end{array}
$$

$$
\begin{array}{c|ccccccc|c}
v & \frac{1}{3} & 1 & 0 & -\frac{1}{3} & 0 & 0 & 0 & \frac{10}{3} \\
y & 2 & 0 & -1 & 0 & 1 & 0 & 0 & -12 \\
z & \frac{1}{3} & 0 & (-3) & -\frac{1}{3} & 0 & 1 & 0 & -\frac{20}{3} \\
\hline
M & 3 & 0 & 12 & 3 & 0 & 0 & 1 & -30
\end{array}
$$

$$
\begin{array}{c|ccccccc|c}
 & u & v & w & x & y & z & M & \\
v & \frac{1}{3} & 1 & 0 & -\frac{1}{3} & 0 & 0 & 0 & \frac{10}{3} \\
y & \frac{17}{9} & 0 & 0 & \frac{1}{9} & 1 & (-\frac{1}{3}) & 0 & -\frac{88}{9} \\
w & -\frac{1}{9} & 0 & 1 & \frac{1}{9} & 0 & -\frac{1}{3} & 0 & \frac{20}{9} \\
\hline
M & \frac{13}{3} & 1 & 0 & \frac{5}{3} & 0 & 4 & 1 & -\frac{170}{3}
\end{array}
$$

$$
\begin{array}{c|ccccccc|c}
 & u & v & w & x & y & z & M & \\
v & \frac{1}{3} & 1 & 0 & -\frac{1}{3} & 0 & 0 & 0 & \frac{10}{3} \\
z & -\frac{17}{3} & 0 & 0 & -\frac{1}{3} & -3 & 1 & 0 & \frac{88}{3} \\
w & -2 & 0 & 1 & 0 & -1 & 0 & 0 & 12 \\
\hline
M & 27 & 0 & 0 & 3 & 12 & 0 & 1 & -174
\end{array}
$$

Original solution:
$x = 3$, $y = 12$, $z = 0$, $M = 174$
Dual solution:

$u = 0$, $v = \frac{10}{3}$, $w = 12$, $M = 174$.

14. The dual is to minimize $7u + 10v$ subject to
$$\begin{cases} u + v \geq 1 \\ u + 2v \geq 3 \\ u \geq 0, \ v \geq 0. \end{cases}$$

Original:

	x	y	u	v	M	
u	1	1	1	0	0	7
v	1	(2)	0	1	0	10
M	-1	-3	0	0	1	0

	x	y	u	v	M	
u	$\frac{1}{2}$	0	1	$-\frac{1}{2}$	0	2
y	$\frac{1}{2}$	1	0	$\frac{1}{2}$	0	5
M	$\frac{1}{2}$	0	0	$\frac{3}{2}$	1	15

Dual:

	u	v	x	y	M	
x	(-1)	-1	1	0	0	-1
y	-1	-2	0	1	0	-3
M	7	10	0	0	1	0

	u	v	x	y	M	
u	1	(1)	-1	0	0	1
y	0	-1	-1	1	0	-2
M	0	3	0	0	1	-7

	u	v	x	y	M	
v	1	1	-1	0	0	1
y	1	0	(-2)	1	0	-1
M	-3	0	10	0	1	-10

	u	v	x	y	M	
v	$\frac{1}{2}$	1	0	$-\frac{1}{2}$	0	$\frac{3}{2}$
x	$-\frac{1}{2}$	0	1	$-\frac{1}{2}$	0	$\frac{1}{2}$
M	2	0	0	5	1	-15

Original solution:

$x = 0$, $y = 5$, $M = 15$;

Dual solution:

$u = 0$, $v = \frac{3}{2}$, $M = 15$

15. Suppose we could hire out our workers at a profit of u dollars per hour, and sell our supply of steel and wood at a profit of v and w dollars per unit, respectively. Then the least acceptable profits are determined by minimizing the objective function $M = 90u + 138v + 120w$ subject to the constraints $3u + 7v + 4w \geq 3$, $6u + 5v + 3w \geq 5$, $u \geq 0$, $v \geq 0$, $w \geq 0$.

16. The manufacturer could buy radios, TV sets, and stereos to supply his customers. He should pay a maximum of $1000r + 1800t + 1000s$, where r, t, and s are the respective costs of each radio, TV, and stereo. Costs should not exceed the amount needed to run plants I and II. The maximum value of the daily operation is given by the maximum of the objective function of the dual.

133

17. Suppose we could buy coal from another miner at the costs of u, v, and w dollars per ton for ordinary coal, bituminous coal, and anthracite, respectively, and supply it to our customer. The other miner would want to maximize $M = 80u + 60v + 75w$ subject to the constraints $4u + 4v + 7w \leq 150$, $10u + 5v + 5w \leq 200$, $u \geq 0$, $v \geq 0$, $w \geq 0$.

18. The maximum value of the nutritionist's diet is the maximum of the objective function. The dual variables represent the optimal price per unit of protein, per calorie, and per unit of riboflavin in any comparable diet. The nutritionist would pay no more than 66¢ per day for such a diet.

19. Let z be the number of table knives manufactured. Then
$$3x + 6y + 4z \leq 90$$
$$7x + 5y + 6z \leq 138$$
$$4x + 3y + 2z \leq 120$$
$$z \geq 0, \ y \geq 0, \ z \geq 0$$
and we must maximize $3x + 5y + pz$, where p is the profit realized per table knife. The dual problem is to minimize $90u + 138v + 120w$ subject to:
$$3u + 7v + 4w \geq 3$$
$$6u + 5v + 3w \geq 5$$
$$4u + 6v + 2w \geq p$$
$$u \geq 0, \ v \geq 0, \ w \geq 0.$$
The tableau which provided the optimal solution for the original primal problem was

$$
\begin{bmatrix}
x & y & u & v & w & M & \\
0 & 1 & \frac{7}{27} & -\frac{1}{9} & 0 & 0 & 8 \\
1 & 0 & -\frac{5}{27} & \frac{2}{9} & 0 & 0 & 14 \\
0 & 0 & -\frac{1}{27} & -\frac{5}{9} & 1 & 0 & 40 \\
\hline
0 & 0 & \frac{20}{27} & \frac{1}{9} & 0 & 1 & 82
\end{bmatrix}
$$

and the maximum solution was \$82, which was therefore the minimum solution of the dual problem, which was produced by (see entries in the corresponding columns of the bottom of the row) $u = \frac{20}{27}$, $v = \frac{1}{9}$, $w = 0$. \$82 is the maximal solution of the new primal problem if, and only if, it is a feasible solution of the new dual problem, which is true if, and only if, the new constraint $4u + 6v + 2w \geq p$ is still satisfied by the point $u = \frac{20}{27}$, $v = \frac{1}{9}$, $w = 0$ which produced that solution; that is, if $4 \cdot \frac{20}{27} + 6 \cdot \frac{1}{9} + 2 \cdot 0 = \frac{98}{27} \cong 3.63 \geq p$, so

it is if, and only if, the profit per table knife exceeds \$3.63 that the existence of the table knives will increase the optimal solution. Note that this solution assumes that

in the original dual problem the point $u = \frac{20}{27}$, $v = \frac{1}{9}$, $w = 0$
was the only optimal solution, which can be justified by the fact that the entries in the right-most column are all > 0, except possibly for the bottom entry.

Supplementary Exercises

1.

$$
\begin{array}{c}
\quad\;\; x \;\; y \;\;\; u \; v \; M \\
\begin{array}{c} u \\ v \end{array}
\left[\begin{array}{ccccc|c}
2 & 1 & 1 & 0 & 0 & 7 \\
-1 & (1) & 0 & 1 & 0 & 1 \\
\hline
-3 & -4 & 0 & 0 & 1 & 0
\end{array}\right]
\begin{array}{c} \\ \\ M \end{array}
\end{array}
\longrightarrow
\begin{array}{c}
\quad\;\; x \;\;\; y \; u \;\; v \; M \\
\begin{array}{c} u \\ y \end{array}
\left[\begin{array}{ccccc|c}
(3) & 0 & 1 & -1 & 0 & 6 \\
-1 & 1 & 0 & 1 & 0 & 1 \\
\hline
-7 & 0 & 0 & 4 & 1 & 4
\end{array}\right]
\begin{array}{c} \\ \\ M \end{array}
\end{array}
$$

$$
\begin{array}{c}
\quad\;\;\; x \; y \;\;\; u \;\;\;\; v \;\; M \\
\begin{array}{c} x \\ \\ y \\ \\ M \end{array}
\left[\begin{array}{ccccc|c}
1 & 0 & \frac{1}{3} & -\frac{1}{3} & 0 & 2 \\[4pt]
0 & 1 & \frac{1}{3} & \frac{2}{3} & 0 & 3 \\[4pt]
\hline
0 & 0 & \frac{7}{3} & \frac{5}{3} & 1 & 18
\end{array}\right]
\end{array}
\qquad x = 2,\; y = 3,\; M = 18.
$$

2.

$$
\begin{array}{c}
\quad\;\; x \;\;\; y \; u \; v \; M \\
\begin{array}{c} u \\ v \end{array}
\left[\begin{array}{ccccc|c}
1 & (1) & 1 & 0 & 0 & 7 \\
4 & 3 & 0 & 1 & 0 & 24 \\
\hline
-2 & -5 & 0 & 0 & 1 & 0
\end{array}\right]
\begin{array}{c} \\ \\ M \end{array}
\end{array}
\longrightarrow
\begin{array}{c}
\quad\;\; x \; y \;\;\;\; u \; v \; M \\
\begin{array}{c} y \\ v \end{array}
\left[\begin{array}{ccccc|c}
1 & 1 & 1 & 0 & 0 & 7 \\
1 & 0 & -3 & 1 & 0 & 3 \\
\hline
3 & 0 & 5 & 0 & 1 & 35
\end{array}\right]
\begin{array}{c} \\ \\ M \end{array}
\end{array}
\qquad
\begin{array}{l}
x = 0,\; y = 7, \\
\quad M = 35.
\end{array}
$$

3.

$$
\begin{array}{c}
\quad\;\; x \;\; y \;\; u \; v \; w \; M \\
\begin{array}{c} u \\ v \\ w \end{array}
\left[\begin{array}{cccccc|c}
1 & (2) & 1 & 0 & 0 & 0 & 14 \\
1 & 1 & 0 & 1 & 0 & 0 & 9 \\
3 & 2 & 0 & 0 & 1 & 0 & 24 \\
\hline
-2 & -3 & 0 & 0 & 0 & 1 & 0
\end{array}\right]
\begin{array}{c} \\ \\ \\ M \end{array}
\end{array}
\longrightarrow
\begin{array}{c}
\quad\;\;\; x \;\; y \;\;\; u \;\; v \; w \; M \\
\begin{array}{c} y \\ \\ v \\ \\ w \\ \\ M \end{array}
\left[\begin{array}{cccccc|c}
\frac{1}{2} & 1 & \frac{1}{2} & 0 & 0 & 0 & 7 \\[4pt]
(\frac{1}{2}) & 0 & -\frac{1}{2} & 1 & 0 & 0 & 2 \\[4pt]
2 & 0 & -1 & 0 & 1 & 0 & 10 \\[4pt]
\hline
-\frac{1}{2} & 0 & \frac{3}{2} & 0 & 0 & 1 & 21
\end{array}\right]
\end{array}
$$

$$
\begin{array}{c}
\quad\ \ \text{x y}\quad \text{u}\quad \text{v w M}\\
\begin{array}{c}
y\\ x\\ w\\ \\ M
\end{array}
\left[
\begin{array}{cccccc|c}
0 & 1 & 1 & -1 & 0 & 0 & 5\\
1 & 0 & -1 & 2 & 0 & 0 & 4\\
0 & 0 & 1 & -4 & 1 & 0 & 2\\
\hline
0 & 0 & 1 & 1 & 0 & 1 & 23
\end{array}
\right]
\end{array}
\qquad x = 4,\ y = 5,\ M = 23
$$

4.

$$
\begin{array}{c}
\quad\ \text{x}\quad \text{y}\quad \text{u v w M}\\
\begin{array}{c}
u\\ v\\ w\\ \\ M
\end{array}
\left[
\begin{array}{cccccc|c}
1 & 2 & 1 & 0 & 0 & 0 & 10\\
4 & 3 & 0 & 1 & 0 & 0 & 30\\
-2 & (1) & 0 & 0 & 1 & 0 & 0\\
\hline
-3 & -7 & 0 & 0 & 0 & 1 & 0
\end{array}
\right]
\end{array}
\longrightarrow
\begin{array}{c}
\quad\ \text{x}\quad \text{y u v}\quad \text{w M}\\
\begin{array}{c}
u\\ v\\ y\\ \\ M
\end{array}
\left[
\begin{array}{cccccc|c}
(5) & 0 & 1 & 0 & -2 & 0 & 10\\
10 & 0 & 0 & 1 & -3 & 0 & 30\\
-2 & 1 & 0 & 0 & 1 & 0 & 0\\
\hline
-17 & 0 & 0 & 0 & 7 & 1 & 0
\end{array}
\right]
\end{array}
$$

$$
\begin{array}{c}
\quad\ \ \text{x y}\quad\ \text{u}\quad \text{v}\quad\ \text{w M}\\
\begin{array}{c}
x\\ \\ v\\ \\ y\\ \\ \\ M
\end{array}
\left[
\begin{array}{cccccc|c}
1 & 0 & \frac{1}{5} & 0 & -\frac{2}{5} & 0 & 2\\
0 & 0 & -2 & 1 & 1 & 0 & 10\\
0 & 1 & \frac{2}{5} & 0 & \frac{1}{5} & 0 & 4\\
\hline
0 & 0 & \frac{17}{5} & 0 & \frac{1}{5} & 1 & 34
\end{array}
\right]
\end{array}
\qquad x = 2,\ y = 4,\ z = 0,\ M = 34.
$$

5.

$$
\begin{array}{c}
\quad\ \ \text{x}\quad\quad \text{y u v M}\\
\begin{array}{c}
u\\ v\\ \\ M
\end{array}
\left[
\begin{array}{ccccc|c}
(-7) & -5 & 1 & 0 & 0 & -40\\
-1 & -4 & 0 & 1 & 0 & -9\\
\hline
1 & 1 & 0 & 0 & 1 & 0
\end{array}
\right]
\end{array}
\longrightarrow
\begin{array}{c}
\quad\ \ \text{x}\quad\ \ \text{y}\quad\quad \text{u v M}\\
\begin{array}{c}
x\\ \\ v\\ \\ \\ M
\end{array}
\left[
\begin{array}{ccccc|c}
1 & \frac{5}{7} & -\frac{1}{7} & 0 & 0 & \frac{40}{7}\\
0 & (-\frac{23}{7}) & -\frac{1}{7} & 1 & 0 & -\frac{23}{7}\\
\hline
0 & \frac{2}{7} & \frac{1}{7} & 0 & 1 & -\frac{40}{7}
\end{array}
\right]
\end{array}
$$

$$
\begin{array}{c}
\quad\ \text{x y}\quad\ \text{u}\quad\ \text{v M}\\
\begin{array}{c}
x\\ \\ y\\ \\ \\ M
\end{array}
\left[
\begin{array}{ccccc|c}
1 & 0 & -\frac{4}{23} & \frac{5}{23} & 0 & 5\\
0 & 1 & -\frac{1}{23} & -\frac{7}{23} & 0 & 1\\
\hline
0 & 0 & \frac{3}{23} & \frac{2}{23} & 1 & -6
\end{array}
\right]
\end{array}
\qquad x = 5,\ y = 1,\ M = 6.
$$

6.

	x	y	u	v	M	
u	(−1)	−1	1	0	0	−6
v	−1	−2	0	1	0	0
M	3	2	0	0	1	0

$\longrightarrow$

	x	y	u	v	M	
x	1	(1)	−1	0	0	6
v	0	−1	−1	1	0	6
M	0	−1	3	0	1	−18

	x	y	u	v	M	
y	1	1	−1	0	0	6
v	1	0	−1	1	0	12
M	1	0	2	0	1	−12

$x = 0, \; y = 6 \; M = 12.$

7.

	x	y	u	v	w	M	
u	−1	(−4)	1	0	0	0	−8
v	−1	−1	0	1	0	0	−5
w	−2	−1	0	0	1	0	−7
M	20	30	0	0	0	1	0

$\longrightarrow$

	x	y	u	v	w	M	
y	$\frac{1}{4}$	1	$-\frac{1}{4}$	0	0	0	2
v	$-\frac{3}{4}$	0	$-\frac{1}{4}$	1	0	0	−3
w	$-\frac{7}{4}$	0	$(-\frac{1}{4})$	0	1	0	−5
M	$\frac{25}{2}$	0	$\frac{15}{2}$	0	0	1	−60

	x	y	u	v	w	M	
y	2	1	0	0	−1	0	7
v	1	0	0	1	−1	0	2
u	7	0	1	0	−4	0	20
M	−40	0	0	0	30	1	−210

$\longrightarrow$

	x	y	u	v	w	M	
y	0	1	0	−2	1	0	3
x	1	0	0	1	−1	0	2
u	0	0	1	−7	(3)	0	6
M	0	0	0	40	−10	1	−130

	x	y	u	v	w	M	
y	0	1	$-\frac{1}{3}$	$\frac{1}{3}$	0	0	1
x	1	0	$\frac{1}{3}$	$-\frac{4}{3}$	0	0	4
w	0	0	$\frac{1}{3}$	$-\frac{7}{3}$	1	0	2
M	0	0	$\frac{10}{3}$	$\frac{50}{3}$	0	1	−110

$x = 4, \; y = 1, \; M = 110.$

8.

$$\begin{array}{c}\quad\quad x \quad y \;\; u \; v \; w \; M\\[4pt]\begin{array}{c}u\\v\\w\\[2pt]M\end{array}\left[\begin{array}{cccccc|c}(-2)&-1&1&0&0&0&-10\\-3&-2&0&1&0&0&-18\\-1&-2&0&0&1&0&-10\\[2pt]5&7&0&0&0&1&0\end{array}\right]\end{array}\longrightarrow\begin{array}{c}\quad\quad x \quad\; y \quad\; u \; v \; w \; M\\[4pt]\begin{array}{c}x\\[6pt]v\\[6pt]w\\[6pt]M\end{array}\left[\begin{array}{cccccc|c}1&\frac12&-\frac12&0&0&0&5\\[4pt]0&-\frac12&-\frac32&1&0&0&-3\\[4pt]0&(-\frac32)&-\frac12&0&1&0&-5\\[4pt]0&\frac92&\frac52&0&0&1&-25\end{array}\right]\end{array}$$

$$\begin{array}{c}\quad x \; y \quad\; u \quad v \quad w \; M\\[4pt]\begin{array}{c}x\\[6pt]v\\[6pt]y\\[6pt]M\end{array}\left[\begin{array}{cccccc|c}1&0&-\frac23&0&\frac13&0&\frac{10}{3}\\[4pt]0&0&(-\frac43)&1&-\frac13&0&\frac43\\[4pt]0&1&\frac13&0&-\frac23&0&\frac{10}{3}\\[4pt]0&0&1&0&3&1&-40\end{array}\right]\end{array}\longrightarrow\begin{array}{c}\quad x \; y \; u \quad\; v \quad w \; M\\[4pt]\begin{array}{c}x\\[6pt]u\\[6pt]y\\[6pt]M\end{array}\left[\begin{array}{cccccc|c}1&0&0&-\frac12&\frac12&0&4\\[4pt]0&0&1&-\frac34&\frac14&0&1\\[4pt]0&1&0&\frac14&-\frac34&0&3\\[4pt]0&0&0&\frac34&\frac{11}{4}&1&-41\end{array}\right]\end{array}$$

$x = 4$
$y = 3$
$M = 41.$

9.

$$\begin{array}{c}\quad\;\; x \quad y \quad z \;\; s \; t \; u \; v \; M\\[4pt]\begin{array}{c}s\\t\\u\\v\\[2pt]M\end{array}\left[\begin{array}{cccccccc|c}1&0&0&1&0&0&0&0&4\\0&1&0&0&1&0&0&0&6\\0&0&(1)&0&0&1&0&0&8\\(+4)&3&2&0&0&0&1&0&38\\[2pt]-36&-48&-70&0&0&0&0&1&0\end{array}\right]\end{array}\longrightarrow\begin{array}{c}\quad\; x \quad y \; z \;\; s \; t \;\; u \; v \; M\\[4pt]\begin{array}{c}s\\t\\z\\v\\[2pt]M\end{array}\left[\begin{array}{cccccccc|c}1&0&0&1&0&0&0&0&4\\0&(1)&0&0&1&0&0&0&6\\0&0&1&0&0&1&0&0&8\\4&3&0&0&0&-2&1&0&22\\[2pt]-36&-48&0&0&0&70&0&1&560\end{array}\right]\end{array}$$

$$\begin{array}{c}\quad\; x \; y \; z \; s \quad t \;\; u \;\; v \; M\\[4pt]\begin{array}{c}x\\y\\z\\v\\[2pt]M\end{array}\left[\begin{array}{cccccccc|c}1&0&0&1&0&0&0&0&4\\0&1&0&0&1&0&0&0&6\\0&0&1&0&0&1&0&0&8\\(4)&0&0&0&-3&-2&1&0&4\\[2pt]-36&0&0&0&48&70&0&1&848\end{array}\right]\end{array}\longrightarrow\begin{array}{c}\;\; x \; y \; z \; s \quad t \quad u \quad\; v \; M\\[4pt]\begin{array}{c}s\\[6pt]y\\[6pt]z\\[6pt]x\\[6pt]M\end{array}\left[\begin{array}{cccccccc|c}0&0&0&1&\frac34&\frac12&-\frac14&0&3\\[4pt]0&1&0&0&1&0&0&0&6\\[4pt]0&0&1&0&0&0&0&0&8\\[4pt]1&0&0&0&-\frac34&-\frac12&\frac14&0&1\\[4pt]0&0&0&0&21&52&9&1&884\end{array}\right]\end{array}$$

$x = 1,\; y = 6,\; z = 8,\; M = 884.$

10.

$$
\begin{array}{c}
\quad\quad x\ \ y\ \ z\ \ \ \ w\ t\ u\ v\ M \\
\begin{array}{c} t \\ u \\ v \\[4pt] M \end{array}
\left[
\begin{array}{cccccccc|c}
6 & 9 & 12 & 15 & 1 & 0 & 0 & 0 & 672 \\
1 & -1 & (2) & 2 & 0 & 1 & 0 & 0 & 92 \\
5 & 10 & -5 & 4 & 0 & 0 & 1 & 0 & 280 \\ \hline
-3 & -4 & -5 & -4 & 0 & 0 & 0 & 1 & 0
\end{array}
\right]
\end{array}
$$

$$
\longrightarrow
\begin{array}{c}
\quad\quad x\ \ \ y\ \ \ z\ w\ t\ \ u\ v\ M \\
\begin{array}{c} u \\ z \\ v \\[4pt] M \end{array}
\left[
\begin{array}{cccccccc|c}
0 & (15) & 0 & 3 & 1 & -6 & 0 & 0 & 120 \\
\tfrac12 & -\tfrac12 & 1 & 1 & 0 & \tfrac12 & 0 & 0 & 46 \\
\tfrac{15}{2} & \tfrac{15}{2} & 0 & 9 & 0 & \tfrac52 & 1 & 0 & 510 \\ \hline
-\tfrac12 & -\tfrac{13}{2} & 0 & 1 & 0 & \tfrac52 & 0 & 1 & 230
\end{array}
\right]
\end{array}
$$

$$
\begin{array}{c}
\quad\quad x\ \ y\ \ z\ \ \ w\ \ \ t\ \ \ \ u\ v\ M \\
\begin{array}{c} y \\[6pt] z \\[6pt] v \\[10pt] M \end{array}
\left[
\begin{array}{cccccccc|c}
0 & 1 & 0 & \tfrac15 & \tfrac{1}{15} & -\tfrac25 & 0 & 0 & 8 \\[4pt]
\tfrac12 & 0 & 1 & \tfrac{11}{5} & \tfrac{1}{30} & \tfrac{3}{10} & 0 & 0 & 50 \\[4pt]
(\tfrac{15}{2}) & 0 & 0 & \tfrac{15}{2} & -\tfrac12 & \tfrac{11}{2} & 1 & 0 & 450 \\[6pt] \hline
-\tfrac12 & 0 & 0 & \tfrac{23}{10} & \tfrac{13}{30} & -\tfrac{1}{10} & 0 & 1 & 282
\end{array}
\right]
\end{array}
$$

$$
\begin{array}{c}
\quad\quad x\ y\ z\ \ \ w\ \ \ \ t\ \ \ \ u\ \ \ \ v\ M \\
\begin{array}{c} y \\[6pt] z \\[6pt] x \\[10pt] M \end{array}
\left[
\begin{array}{cccccccc|c}
0 & 1 & 0 & \tfrac15 & \tfrac{1}{15} & -\tfrac25 & 0 & 0 & 8 \\[4pt]
0 & 0 & 1 & \tfrac35 & \tfrac{1}{15} & -\tfrac{1}{15} & -\tfrac{1}{15} & 0 & 20 \\[4pt]
1 & 0 & 0 & 1 & -\tfrac{1}{15} & \tfrac{11}{15} & \tfrac{2}{15} & 0 & 60 \\[6pt] \hline
0 & 0 & 0 & \tfrac{14}{5} & \tfrac25 & \tfrac{4}{15} & \tfrac{1}{15} & 1 & 312
\end{array}
\right]
\end{array}
$$

$x = 60$, $y = 8$, $z = 20$, $w = 0$, $M = 312$.

11. Minimize $14u + 9v + 24w$ subject to the

constraints $\begin{cases} u+v +3w \geq 2 \\ 2u+v +2w \geq 3 \\ u \geq 0,\ v \geq 0,\ w \geq 0. \end{cases}$

12. Maximize $8u + 5v + 7w$ subject to the

constraints $\begin{cases} u+v +2w \leq 20 \\ 4u+v + w \leq 30 \\ u \geq 0,\ v \geq 0,\ w \geq 0. \end{cases}$

13. $x = 4$, $y = 5$, $M = 23$; $u = 1$, $v = 1$, $w = 0$, $M = 23$.

14. $x = 4$, $y = 1$, $M = 110$; $u =$, $v =$, $M = 110$. 15. $A =$

$\begin{bmatrix} 1 & 2 \\ 1 & 1 \\ 3 & 2 \end{bmatrix}$, $B = \begin{bmatrix} 14 \\ 9 \\ 24 \end{bmatrix}$, $C = [2 \quad 3]$, $X = \begin{bmatrix} x \\ y \end{bmatrix}$. Maximize

CX to $AX \leq V$, $X \geq 0$. Dual: $U = [u \quad v \quad w]$. Minimize UB
subject to $UA \geq C$, $U \geq 0$.

15. $A = \begin{bmatrix} 1 & 2 \\ 1 & 1 \\ 3 & 2 \end{bmatrix}$, $B = \begin{bmatrix} 14 \\ 9 \\ 24 \end{bmatrix}$, $C = [2 \quad 3]$, $X = \begin{bmatrix} x \\ y \end{bmatrix}$, $U = \begin{bmatrix} u & v & w \end{bmatrix}$.

Problem: Maximize CX subject to the constraints $AX \leq B$, $X \geq 0$.
Dual: Minimize B^TU subject to the constraints $A^TU \geq C^T$, $U \geq 0$.

16. $A = \begin{bmatrix} 1 & 4 \\ 1 & 1 \\ 2 & 1 \end{bmatrix}$, $B = \begin{bmatrix} 8 \\ 5 \\ 7 \end{bmatrix}$, $C = [20 \quad 30]$, $X = \begin{bmatrix} x \\ y \end{bmatrix}$, $U = $

[u v w]. Problem: Minimize CX subject to the constraints

$AX \geq B$, $X \geq 0$. Dual: Maximize B^TU subject to the

constraints $A^TU \leq C^T$, $U \geq 0$.

17. (a) x and y were the number of sticks of types A
and B, respectively, and the system was: maximize 8x +
10y subject to

$$\begin{cases} 2x + y \leq 120 \\ x + 3y \leq 150 \\ 2x + 2y \leq 140 \\ x \geq 0, \ y \geq 0. \end{cases}$$

Let u, v, w and M be such that u, v, w $\geq$ 0 and 2x + y
+ u = 120, x + 3y + v = 150, 2x + 2y + w = 140 and M = 8x +
10y. Then the initial tableau is

$$\begin{bmatrix} x & y & u & v & w & M & \\ 2 & 1 & 1 & 0 & 0 & 0 & 120 \\ 1 & 3 & 0 & 1 & 0 & 0 & 150 \\ 2 & 2 & 0 & 0 & 1 & 0 & 140 \\ \hline -8 & -10 & 0 & 0 & 0 & 1 & 0 \end{bmatrix}$$

follow this by

$$\begin{bmatrix} & y & u & & w & M & \\ & 0 & 1 & - & 0 & 0 & 70 \\ & 1 & 0 & & 0 & 0 & 50 \\ & 0 & 0 & - & 1 & 0 & 40 \\ \hline -1 & 0 & 0 & 1 & 0 & 1 & 500 \end{bmatrix}$$

and follow this by

$$\begin{bmatrix} \begin{array}{ccccc} x & y & u & & M \\ 0 & 0 & 1 & - & 0 \\ 0 & 1 & 0 & - & 0 \\ 1 & 0 & 0 & - & 0 \\ \hline 0 & 0 & 0 & & 1 \end{array} & \left| \begin{array}{c} 20 \\ 40 \\ 30 \\ \hline 640 \end{array} \right. \end{bmatrix}.$$

Final tableau: optimal solution is 30 sticks of type A and 40 of type B, which produces a profit of $640.
(b)   Let z be the number of tennis racquets manufactured. Then we must maximize $8x + 10y + pz$, subject to

$$\begin{cases} 2x + y + z \le 120 \\ x + 3y + 4z \le 150 \\ 2x + 2y + 2z \le 140 \\ x \ge 0, \ y \ge 0, \ z \ge 0 \end{cases}$$

where p is the profit in dollars realized per tennis racquet. The dual problem is to minimize $120u + 150v + 140w$ subject to:

$$\begin{cases} 2u + v + 2w \ge 8 \\ u + 3v + 2w \ge 10 \\ u + 4v + 2w \ge p \\ u \ge 0, \ v \ge 0, \ w \ge 0. \end{cases}$$

From the final tableau of the original problem in the solution of 17(a), it follows that the minimum solution of the original dual was $640, which was produced by $u = 0$, $v = 1$ and $w = 7/2$. It also follows from the fact that every element of the right-most column was > 0 that $u = 0$, $v = 1$ and $w = 7/2$ was the only optimal solution. $640 is the maximal solution of the new primal system if, and only if, it is a feasible solution of the new dual problem, which is true if, and only if, the new constraint $u + 4v + 2w \ge p$ is still satisfied by the point $u = 0$, $v = 1$ and $w = 7/2$ which produced that solution; that is, if $0 + 4.1 + 2.7/2 = 11 \ge p$, so it is if, and only if, the profit per tennis racquet exceeds $11 and that the existence of the tennis racquet will increase maximum profit.

18.   x, y and z were the numbers sold of brands A, B, and C, respectively. Let t be the number sold of brand D.   Let $p be the profit realized for each sale of brand D. Following the same logic used in the solution of 17(b) above leads to that the new constraint of the dual problem is $u + 3v + 30w \ge p$ and that the dual problem is minimized when $u = 210$, $v = 0$, $w = 0$ (for this last assertion, check the final tableau in the solution of exercise 16 of Section 4.2. These were the numbers in the bottom row corresponding to the respective columns of u, v and w). The same logic

used in the solution of 17(b) also leads to the criterion that the use of brand D will increase the maximum profit if, and only if, $p \geq \$u + \$3v + \$30v = \$210 + \$3.0 + \$30.0 = \$210$. (Also notice that in the final tableau of the original primal problem that once again the elements of the right-most column are all > 0, the importance of which was pointed out in the solution of 17(b) above.)

5

SETS AND COUNTING

5.1. Sets

1. (a) S' consists of the elements in U but *not* in S. S' = {5,6,7}.

   (b) S ∪ T = elements in S *or* in T = {1,2,3,4,5,7}.

   (c) S ∩ T = elements in *both* S *and* T = {1,3}.

   (d) S' ∩ T = elements in S' *and* in T = {5,7}.

2. (a) S' consists of the elements in U but *not* in S. S' = {4,5}.

   (b) S ∪ T = elements in S *or* in T = {1,2,3,5}.

   (c) S ∩ T = elements in *both* S *and* T = ∅.

   (d) S' ∩ T = elements in S' *and* in T = {5}.

3. (a) R ∪ S = elements in R *or* in S = {a,b,c,d,e,f}.

   (b) R ∩ S = elements in R *and* in S = {c}.

   (c) S ∩ T = elements in S *and* in T = ∅.

4. (a) R ∪ S = elements in R *or* in S = {a,b}.

   (b) R ∩ S = elements in R *and* in S = {a}.

   (c) T' = elements in U but *not* in T = {a,c}.

   (d) T' ∪ S = elements *not* in T *or* in S = {a,b,c}.

5. All subsets of the set {1,2} are the sets {1,2}, {1}, {2}, ∅.

6. All subsets of the set {1} are the sets {1}, ∅.

7. (a) M ∩ F = {all male college students who like football}.

   (b) M' = {all female college students}.

   (c) M' ∩ F' = {all female college students who do *not* like football}.

   (d) M ∪ F = {all students who are either male *or* like football}.

8. (a) S' = {all corporations with headquarters *not* in New York City}.

   (b) T' = {all publicly owned corporations}.

(c) S ∩ T = {all privately owned corporations with headquarters in New York City}.

(d) S ∩ T' = {all corporations with headquarters in New York City that are publicly owned}.

9. (a) S = {1976,1975,1967,1963,1958,1951,1950}.

    (b) T = {1976,1975,1967,1963,1961,1958,1955,1954,1951,1950}.

    (c) S ∩ T = {1976,1975,1967,1963,1958,1951,1950}.

    (d) S' ∩ T = {1961,1955,1954}.

    (e) S ∩ T' = ø.

10. (a) A = {1977,1974,1969,1962,1960,1957,1956,1955,1953}

    (b) B = {1977,1974,1973,1970,1969,1968,1966,1962,1960, 1957,1953}.

    (c) A ∩ B = {1977,1974,1969,1962,1960,1957,1953}.

    (d) A' ∩ B = {1973,1970,1968,1966}.

    (e) A ∩ B' = {1956,1955}.

11. S ∩ T' = ø.
From 1950 to 1977, whenever the Standard and Poor's Index increased by 2 or more percent during the first five days of a year, it always increased by at least 16% for that year.

12. A ∩ B' = {1956,1955}
From 1950 to 1977, during only two years did the index decline for the first five days of the year and yet increase for the entire year.

13. (a) (R ∪ S)' = elements *not* in either R or S = {d,f}.

    (b) R ∪ S ∪ T = elements in R *or* in S or in T = {a,b,c,e,f}.

    (c) R ∩ S ∩ T = elements in all three sets = none = ø.

    (d) R ∩ S ∩ T' = elements in R *and* in S *and* not in T = {a,c}.

    (e) R' ∩ S ∩ T = elements *not* in R which are in S and in T = {e}.

    (f) S ∪ T = elements in either S *or* T = {a,c,e,f}.

    (g) (R ∪ S) ∩ (R ∪ T) = {a,b,c,e} ∩ {a,b,c,e,f} = {a,b,c,e}.

    (h) (R ∩ S) ∪ (R ∩ T) = {a,c} ∪ ø = {a,c}.

    (i) R' ∩ T' = elements in R' *and* in T' = {d,e,f} ∩ {a,b,c,d} = {d}.

14. (a) $R \cap S \cap T = \emptyset$.   (b) $R \cap S \cap T' = \{3,5\}$.

    (c) $R \cap S' \cap T = \emptyset$.   (d) $R' \cap T = \{2,4\}$.

    (e) $R \cup S = \{1,3,4,5\}$.   (f) $R' \cup R = U$.

    (g) $(S \cap T)' = \{1,2,3,5\}$.   (h) $S' \cup T' = \{1,2,3,5\}$.

15. $(S')'$ = elements *not* in (the set of elements *not* in S) = S.

16. $S \cap S'$ = elements in S *and* elements *not* in S = none = $\emptyset$.

17. $S \cup S'$ = elements in S *or* elements *not* in S = U.

18. $S \cap \emptyset$ = elements in S *and* in the empty set = $\emptyset$.

19. $T \cap S \cap T' = T \cap T' \cap S = \emptyset \cap S = \emptyset$. Results from problems 16 and 18.

20. $S \cup \emptyset$ = elements in S *or* in the empty set = S.

21. This is the set of divisions in L *or* T = $L \cup T$.

22. This is the set of divisions that are not in P = P'.

23. This is the set of divisions in *both* P and L = $P \cap L$.

24. This is the set of divisions in L *and* not in P *or* T = $L \cap (P' \cup T')$.

25. This is the set of divisions in P *and* L *and* T = $P \cap L \cap T$.

26. This is the set of divisions *not* in P *or* not in L *or* T = $P' \cup (L \cup T)'$.

27. This is the set of applicants *not* in S = S'.

28. This is the set of applicants in *both* A and D = $A \cap D$.

29. This is the set of applicants in S *or* D *or* A = $S \cup D \cup A$.

30. This is the set of applicants *not* in D *and* in S *or* A = $D' \cap (S \cup A)$.

31. This is the set of applicants *not* in *both* A and S *and* in D = $(A \cap S)' \cap D$.

32. This is the set of applicants *not* in A *or* *not* in D = $A' \cup D'$.

33. Students at Mount College who are male.

34. Teachers at Mount College who are female.

35. Students at Mount College who are also teachers.

36. People at Mount College who are teachers or female.

37. People at Mount College who are either students or male.

38. People at Mount College who are either not students or female.

39. Females at Mount College.   40. Males at Mount College.

41. S' 42. $V \cap C'$ 43. $(V \cup C) \cap S'$

44. $V' \cap C' \cap S'$ 45. $V' \cap C'$ 46. $S \cap V' \cap C'$

47. (a) $R = \{B,C,D,E\}$ (b) $S = \{C,D,E,F\}$ (c) $T = \{A,D,E,F\}$

(d) $R' \cup S$ = elements *not* in R *or* elements in S = $\{A,C,D,E,F\}$.

(e) $R' \cap T$ = elements *not* in R and *in* T = $\{A,F\}$.

(f) $R \cap S \cap T$ = elements in all three sets = $\{D,E\}$.

48. plain, {butter}, {cheese}, {chives}, {butter,cheese}, {cheese,chives}, {butter,chives}, {butter,cheese,chives}

49. $\{2\} \subset T$ and $2 \notin S$.   50. If T is a subset of S then $S \cap T = T$.

51. If S is a subset of T then $S \cup T = T$.

52. R, S, and T such that $R \cup (S \cap T) \neq (R \cup S) \cap T$.
$R = \{2\}$, $S = \{1,2\}$, $T = \{1,3\}$

5.2. A Fundamental Principle of Counting

1 - 4   Use $n(S \cup T) = n(S) + n(T) - n(S \cap T)$
1. $5 + 4 - 2 = 7$.   2. $17 + 13 - 9 = 21$.

3. $7 + 8 - 15 = 0$.   4. $4 + 12 - 15 = 1$.

5. Use $n(S) = n(S \cap T) - n(T) + n(S \cup T) = 5 - 7 + 13 = 11$.

6. Use $n(T) = n(S \cap T) - n(S) + n(S \cup T) = 6 - 14 + 14 = 6$.

7. If $n(S) = n(S \cap T)$ then $n(T) = n(S \cup T)$, and S is a subset of T.

8. If $n(T) = n(S \cup T)$ then $n(S) = n(S \cap T)$ and T is a subset of S.

9. If P = {adults fluent in Portuguese} and
S = {adults fluent in Spanish} then $n(P) = 99$, $n(S) = 95$,
and $n(P \cup S) = 180$ then $n(P \cap S) = n(P) + n(S) - n(P \cup S) = 99 + 95 - 180 = 14$. So 14 million are fluent in both languages.

10. If M = {freshmen enrolled in a math course} and
E = {freshmen enrolled in an English course}
$n(M \cup E) = 1000$, $n(M \cap E) = 400$, $n(E) = 600$
$n(M) = n(M \cup E) + n(M \cap E) - n(E) = 1000 + 400 - 600 = 800$
So 800 freshmen are enrolled in math courses.

11. If M = {members of the MAA} and A = {members of the AMS}
$n(M \cup A) = 43{,}000$, $n(A) = 23{,}000$, $n(M \cap A) = 7000$
$n(M) = n(M \cap A) + n(M \cup A) - n(A) = 43{,}000 + 7000 - 23{,}000$
$n(M) = 27{,}000$, So 27,000 people belong to the MAA.

12. If N = {people who subscribe to Newsweek} and T = {people who subscribe to Time}
$n(N) = 300$, $n(T) = 200$, $n(N \cap T) = 50$
$n(N \cup T) = n(N) + n(T) - n(N \cap T) = 300 + 200 - 50 = 450$.
So, 450 people subscribe to at least one of these magazines.

13. If A = {cars with automatic transmission} and
P = {cars with power steering}
$n(A) = 325$, $n(P) = 216$, $n(A \cap P) = 89$
$n(A \cup P) = n(A) + n(P) - n(A \cap P) = 325 + 216 - 89 = 452$.
So, 452 cars are manufactured with at least one of these two options.

14. If S = {investors who own stocks} and B = {investors who own bonds}
$n(S) = 80$, $n(B) = 70$, $n(S \cup B) = 100$
$n(S \cap B) = n(S) + n(B) - n(S \cup B) = 80 + 70 - 100 = 50$.
So, 50 investors own both stocks and bonds.

15.

16.

17.

18.

19.

20.

21.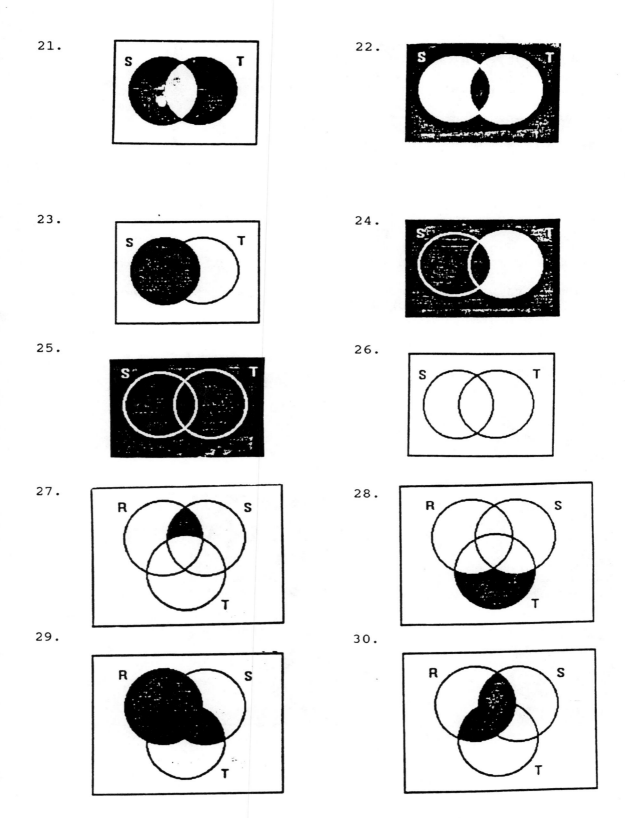

22.

23.

24.

25.

26.

27.

28.

29.

30.

148

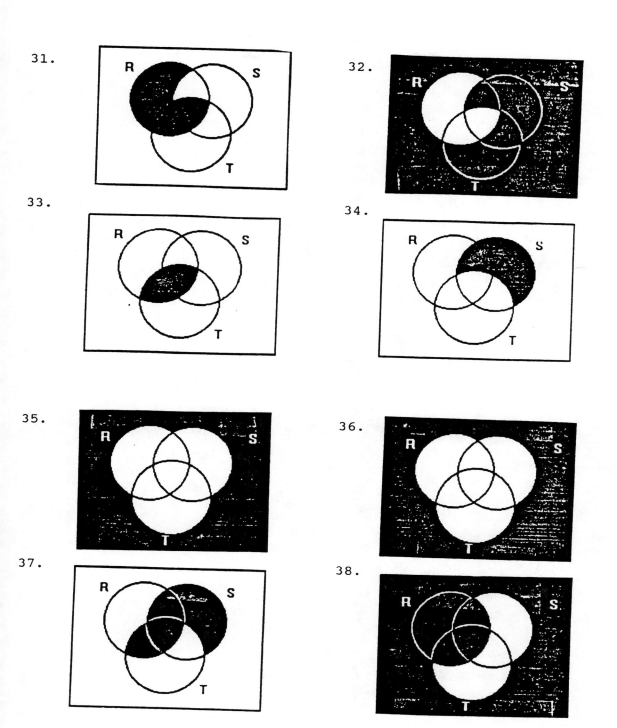

39. $S' \cup (S \cap T)' = S' \cup (S' \cup T') = (S' \cup S') \cup (S' \cup T') = S' \cup T'$.

40. $T \cap (S \cup T)' = T \cap (S' \cap T') = (T \cap S') \cap (T \cap T') = (T \cap S') \cap \varnothing = \varnothing$

41. $(S' \cup T)' = (S')' \cap T' = S \cap T'$

42. $(S' \cap T')' = (S')' \cup (T')' = S \cup T$

43. $T \cup (S \cap T)' = T \cup (S' \cup T') = (T \cup S') \cup (T \cup T') = (T \cup S') \cup U = U$

44. $(S' \cap T)' \cup S = ((S')' \cup T') \cup S = (S \cup T') \cup S = S \cup T'$

45. S' 46. $(S \cup T) \cap (S \cap T)' = (S \cap T') \cup (S' \cap T)$ 47. $R \cap T$

48. $S \cap (R \cup T)' = S \cap R' \cap T'$ 49. $S \cap T \cap R'$ 50. $R \cap (T \cup S')$

51. $(T \cap S) \cup (T \cap R) \cup (R \cap S') \cup (T \cap R' \cap S')$

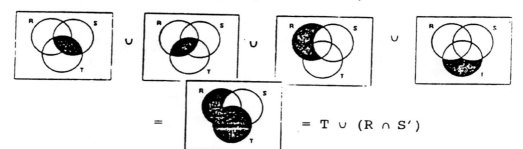

$= T \cup (R \cap S')$

52. $(R \cap S) \cup (S \cap T) \cup (R \cap S' \cap T')$

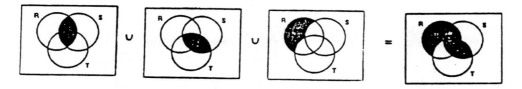

$= (R \cap T') \cup (S \cap T)$

53. $((R \cap S') \cup (S \cap T') \cup (T \cap R'))' =$

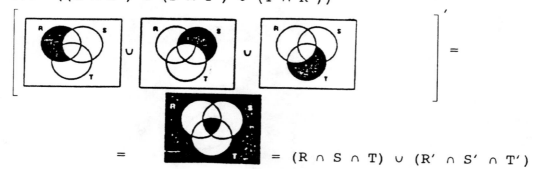

$= (R \cap S \cap T) \cup (R' \cap S' \cap T')$

150

5.3. Venn Diagrams and Counting

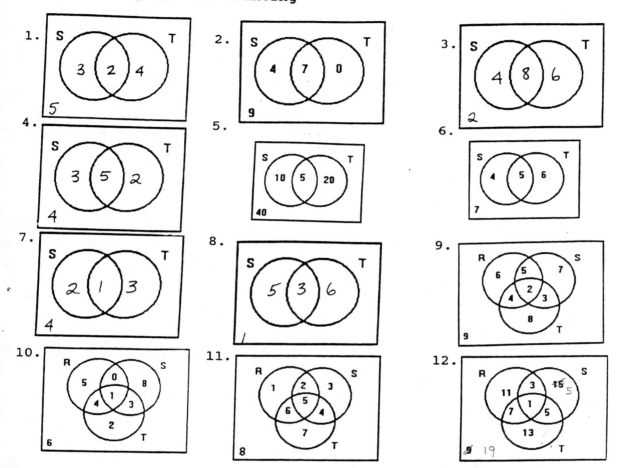

1. S ⬭ 3 (2) 4 ⬭ T   5
2. S ⬭ 4 (7) 0 ⬭ T   9
3. S ⬭ 4 8 6 ⬭ T   2
4. S ⬭ 3 (5) 2 ⬭ T   4
5. S ⬭ 10 (5) 20 ⬭ T   40
6. S ⬭ 4 (5) 6 ⬭ T   7
7. S ⬭ 2 (1) 3 ⬭ T   4
8. S ⬭ 5 (3) 6 ⬭ T   1
9. R/S/T diagram: 6 5 7 / 4 2 3 / 8   9
10. R/S/T diagram: 5 0 8 / 4 1 3 / 2   6
11. R/S/T diagram: 1 2 3 / 6 5 4 / 7   8
12. R/S/T diagram: 11 3 15 5 / 7 1 5 / 13   19

13. If U = {high school students}, F = {high school students who like folk music}
    C = {high school students who like classical music}
    $n(U) = 70$, $n(F) = 35$, $n(C) = 15$, $n(F \cap C) = 5$,
    $n(F \cup C) = 35 + 15 - 5 = 45$, $n(F \cup C)' = 70 - 45 = 25$
    25 students do not like either folk or classical music.

14. If N = {Nobel prizes awarded by 1993}
    L = {Nobel prizes in literature}
    S = {Scandinavians who received an award}
    $n(N) = 633$, $n(L) = 91$, $n(S) = 44$, $n(S \cap L) = 14$
    $n(L \cup S) = 91 + 44 - 14 = 121$, $n(L \cup S)' = 633 - 121 = 512$
    512 Nobel prizes outside of literature have been awarded to non-Scandinavians.

15. If M = {males}, B = {business majors}, F = {freshmen}

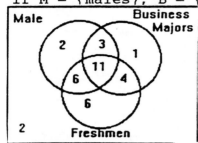

There are 2 upper class women nonbusiness majors in the class.

There are 5 women business majors in the class.

16. If J = {faculty who jog}, S = {faculty who swim}, C = {faculty who cycle}

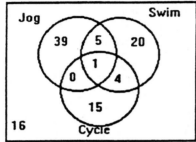

There are 16 faculty members who do not jog, swim, or cycle.

There are 39 faculty members who only jog.

17. Of 100 students 50 are freshmen. Of the 55 voting democratic, 25 **are** nonfreshmen. So, 30 are freshmen.

18. If G = {college graduates}, M = {union members}
$n(G)' = 60$, $n(G \cap M') = 20$, $n(M) = 30$
$n(G' \cap M') = n(G') + n(M') - n(G' \cup M') = 60 + 70 - 80 = 50$.
There are 50 workers that are neither college graduates nor union members.

19. If D = {students who passe the diagnostic test}
C = {students who passed te class}
$n(D' \cap C) = n(D') + n(C) - n(D' \cup C) = 9 + 23 - 28 = 4$

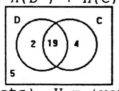

There are 4 students who passed the class even though they failed the diagnostic test

20. If P = {pilots}, V = {veterans}
$n(P \cup V \cup (P \cup V)') = 50 + 30 + 5 + 15 = 100$

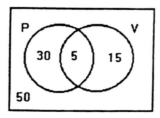

The group consisted of 100 people.

21. If V = {verbs}, A = {adjectives}
     $n(V \cap A') = n(V) + n(A') - n(V \cup A') = 11 + 5 - 12 = 4$
     4 lines have a verb but no adjective.

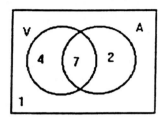

$n(A \cap V') = n(A) + n(V') - n(A \cup V')$
$= 9 + 3 - 10 = 2$
2 lines have an adjective and no verb.

$n(A' \cap V') = n(A') + n(V') - n(A' \cup V') = 5 + 3 - 7 = 1$
1 line had neither an adjective nor a verb.

22 - 26

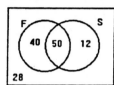

F = {first answer correct}
S = {second answer correct}
$n(F \cap S) = 50$, $n(F) = 90$, $n(S) = 62$

22. $n(F \cup S) = n(F) + n(S) - n(F \cap S) = 90 + 62 - 50 = 102$
     There were 102 students who correctly answered the first or second question.

23. $n(F' \cap S') = n(F \cup S)' = 130 - 102 = 28$
     There were 28 students who did not answer either of the two questions correctly.

24. $n((F \cup S) \cap (F \cap S)') = n(F \cup S) + n(F \cap S)' - n((F \cup S) \cup (F \cap S)')$
     $= 102 + 80 - 130 = 52$
     There were 52 students who answered either the first or second question correctly but not both.

25. $n(S \cap F') = n(S) + n(F') - n(S \cup F') = 62 + 40 - 90 = 12$
     There were 12 students who answered the second question correctly but not the first.

26. $n(S') = 130 - n(S) = 130 - 62 = 68$
     There were 68 students who missed the second question.

27 - 32

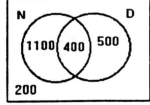

N = {players for the NFL}
D = {defensive players}
$n(N \cap D) = 400$, $n(N) = 1500$, $n(D) = 900$

27. $n(N \cup D) = n(N) + n(D) - n(N \cap D) = 1500 + 900 - 400 = 2000$
     2000 players were either in the NFL or played defense.

28. $n(D \cap N') = n(D) + n(N') - n(D \cup N') = 900 + 700 - 1100 = 500$

500 players played defense but were not in the NFL.

29. $n(D' \cap N') = n(D') + n(N') - n(D' \cup N') = 1300 + 700 - 1800 = 200$
   200 players played offense,but were not in the NFL.

30. $n(D' \cap N) = n(D') + n(N) - n(D' \cup N) = 1300 + 1500 - 1700 = 1100$
   1100 players played offense in the NFL.

31. $n((D \cup N) \cap (D \cap N)')$
   $= n(D \cup N) + n(D \cap N)' - n((D \cup N) \cup (D \cap N)')$
   $= 2000 + 1800 - 2200 = 1600$
   1600 players either played defense or were in the NFL, but not in both.

32. $n(D \cap N)' = n(D' \cup N') = n(D') + n(N') - n(D' \cap N')$
   $= 1300 + 700 - 200 = 1800$
   1800 players did not play defense for the NFL.

33 - 40

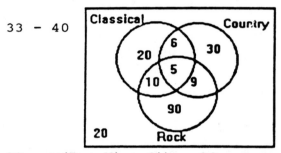

R = {students who like rock}
W = {students who like country}
C = {students who like classical}

33. $n(R \cap W' \cap C') = 90$
   There are 90 students who like only rock music.

34. $n(W \cap R') = 50 - 14 = 36$
   There are 36 students who like country,but do not like rock.

35. $n(C \cap W \cap R') = n(C \cap W) - n(C \cap W \cap R) = 11 - 5 = 6$
   There are 6 students who like country and classical,but not rock.

36. $n(C \cup W \cap R') = n(C \cup W) - n((R \cap C) \cup (R \cap W)) = 80 - 24 = 56$
   There are 56 students who like either country or classical,but do not like rock music.

37. $n((R \cup W \cup C) \cap ((R \cap W) \cup (R \cap C) \cup (W \cap C))) = 170 - 30 = 140$
   There are 140 students who like exactly one of the three types of music.

38. $n(R' \cap C' \cap W') = 190 - n(R \cup C \cup W) = 190 - 170 = 20$ There are 20 students who do not like any of the three types of music.

39. $n(R \cap C) + n(R \cap W) + n(C \cap W) - 2(n(R \cap W \cap C))$
   $= 15 + 14 + 11 - 2(5) = 30$
   There are 30 students who like at least two of the three types of music.

40. $n(R' \cap C') = 20 + 20 = 40$
There are 40 students who do not like either rock or country.

41 - 46

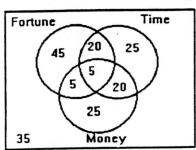

R = {radio}
T = {television}
N = {newspaper}

41. $n(N \cup R \cap (N \cap R)') = n(N) + n(R) - 2(n(N \cap R))$
$= 190 + 180 - 2(90) = 190$
There were 190 people who learned of the sale from newspapers or radio, but not from both.

42. $n(N \cap R' \cap T') = 80$
There were 80 people who learned about the sale from newspapers only.

43. $n(R \cup T \cap N') = n(R \cup T \cup N) - n(N) = 370 - 190 = 180$
There were 180 people who learned about the sale from radio or television but not from the newspaper.

44. $n((R \cap T) \cup (R \cap N) \cup (T \cap N)) = 80 + 50 + 90 - 2(30) = 160$
There were 160 people who learned about the sale from at least two of the three media.

45. $n(R \cup T \cup N) - n((R \cap T) \cup (R \cap N) \cup (T \cap N)) = 370 - 160 = 210$
There were 210 people who learned about the sale from exactly one of the three media.

46. $n(R \cap T \cap N') = 80 - 30 = 50$
There were 50 people who learned about the sale from radio and television but not from the newspaper.

47. F = {Fortune}, T = {Time}, M = {Money}

There are exactly 35 surveyed who who read none of these magazines.

48. M′ = {inexperienced management}, C′ = {under capitalized}
     L′ = {poor location}

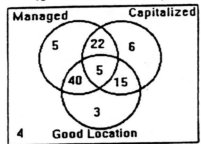

There were 37 small businesses
that had a poor location.

Under capitalization was most prevalent in the failed businesses.

5.4. The Multiplication Principle

1. $3 \cdot 5 = 15$ 2. $2 \cdot 3 = 6$ 3. $26 \cdot 26 = 676$

4. $26 \cdot 25 = 650$ 5. $20 \cdot 19 = 380$ 6. $10 \cdot 19 = 190$

7. $5 \cdot 4 = 20$ 8. $26 \cdot 26 \cdot 10 \cdot 10 \cdot 10 \cdot 10 = 6,760,000$

9. $5 \cdot 4 \cdot 3 \cdot 2 \cdot 1 = 120$ 10. $4 \cdot 3 \cdot 2 \cdot 1 = 24$

11. $2 \cdot 2 \cdot 2 \cdot 2 \cdot 2 \cdot 2 = 2^6 = 64$ 12. $2 \cdot 2 \cdot 2 \cdot 2 \cdot 2 = 2^5 = 32$

13. $20 \cdot 19 \cdot 18 = 6840$ 14. $8 \cdot 7 \cdot 6 \cdot 5 \cdot 4 \cdot 3 \cdot 2 \cdot 1 = 40,320$

15. $30 \cdot 29 = 870$ 16. $2 \cdot 3 \cdot 2 = 12$ 17. $4 \cdot 3 \cdot 2 \cdot 1 = 24$

18. $3 \cdot 2 = 6$ 19. $2 \cdot 2 \cdot 2 \cdot 2 \cdot 2 = 2^5 = 32$

20. The possible number of different pairs of initials is $26 \cdot 26 = 676$.
     Since there are 700 employees, at least two must have the same pair o
     initials.

21. $3 \cdot 12 \cdot 10 \cdot 10 \cdot 10 \cdot 10 = 360,000$ There are 360,000 possible serial numbers.

22. $(4 \cdot 3 \cdot 2 \cdot 1) \cdot 5 = 120$ Since the word 'statistics' has 5 different letters
     120 different 4-letter words can be made without using repeated
     letters.

23. (a) $7^4 = 2,401$ (b) $7 \cdot 6 \cdot 5 \cdot 4 = 840$
     (c) $7^3 = 343$ (d) $2 \cdot 6 \cdot 5 \cdot 4 = 240$

24. (a) $(8 \cdot 7 \cdot 6 \cdot 5 \cdot 4 \cdot 3 \cdot 2 \cdot 1) = 40,320$ (b) $(5 \cdot 4 \cdot 3 \cdot 2 \cdot 1) \cdot (3 \cdot 2 \cdot 1) = 720$

25 (a) $9 \cdot 8 \cdot 7 \cdot 6 \cdot 5 \cdot 4 \cdot 3 \cdot 2 \cdot 1 = 362,880$ (b) $8 \cdot 7 \cdot 6 \cdot 5 \cdot 4 \cdot 3 \cdot 2 \cdot 1 = 40,320$
   (c) $6 \cdot 5 \cdot 4 \cdot 3 \cdot 2 \cdot 1 = 720$

26. $2^4 = 16$ 27. $2^8 = 256$ 28. $23 \cdot 22 = 506$; 23 members

29. $3^6 = 729$ 30. $4 \cdot 3 \cdot 10 = 120$ 31. $6 \cdot 7 \cdot 4 = 168$

32. $8 \cdot 10 \cdot 10 = 800$ 33. $40^3 - 3^3 = 63,973$

34. $3 \cdot 20 = 60$ 35. $4 \cdot 3 \cdot 3 \cdot 3 \cdot 3 \cdot 3 = 962$ 36. $7 \cdot 7 \cdot 4 = 196$

37. 4^{10} 38. $10 \cdot 9 = 90$ 39. $4 \cdot 4 = 16$

40. $6 \cdot 10 \cdot 5 = 300$ 41. 5^{10} 42. $4 \cdot 2 \cdot 3 = 24$

5.5. Permutations and Combinations

1. $P(4,2) = 4 \cdot 3 = 12$ 2. $P(5,1) = 5$

3. $P(6,3) = 6 \cdot 5 \cdot 4 = 120$ 4. $P(5,4) = 5 \cdot 4 \cdot 3 \cdot 2 = 120$

5. $C(10,3) = \dfrac{(10 \cdot 9 \cdot 8)}{(3 \cdot 2 \cdot 1)} = \dfrac{720}{6} = 120$ 6. $C(10,3) = \dfrac{(12 \cdot 11)}{2} = 66$

7. $C(5,4) = \dfrac{(5 \cdot 4 \cdot 3 \cdot 2)}{(4 \cdot 3 \cdot 2 \cdot 1)} = \dfrac{120}{24} = 5$ 8. $C(6,3) = \dfrac{(6 \cdot 5 \cdot 4)}{6} = 20$

9. $P(5,1)$ 10. $P(5,5)$

11. $P(n,1)$ 12. $P(n,2)$ 13. $C(4,4)$

14. $C(n,2)$ 15. $C(n,n-2)$

16. $C(n,1)$ 17. $6! = 6 \cdot 5 \cdot 4 \cdot 3 \cdot 2 \cdot 1 = 720$

18. $\dfrac{10!}{4!} = 10 \cdot 9 \cdot 8 \cdot 7 \cdot 6 \cdot 5 = 151,200$ 19. $9!/7! = 9 \cdot 8 = 72$

20. $7!$ 21. $4! = 4 \cdot 3 \cdot 2 \cdot 1 = 24$

22. $6 \cdot 5 = 30$ 23. $C(9,2)$

24. $C(5,3) = 10$ 25. $15 \cdot 14 \cdot 13$

26. $6! = 720$ 27. $C(10,4)$

28. C(10,4)

29. C(10,4)

30. $\dfrac{10!}{4!6!}$

31. 5!=120

32. C(9,3) = $\dfrac{9!}{3!6!}$

33. C(8,2)

34. C(8,5)=56

35. $10\cdot9\cdot8\cdot7\cdot6$

36. C(10,5)

37. C(10,5)

38. $10\cdot9\cdot8\cdot7\cdot6$

39. $35\cdot34\cdot33\cdot32\cdot31$

40. C(20,4)

41. C(100,3)

42. C(7,5)

43. $26\cdot25\cdot24$

44. $40\cdot39\cdot38\cdot37\cdot36$

45. C(100,5)

46. (1000)(999)(998)

47. C(52,5)

48. C(8,5)=$\dfrac{(8\cdot7\cdot6\cdot5\cdot4)}{(5\cdot4\cdot3\cdot2\cdot1)}$ = 56

49. C(13,5)

50. C(26,5)

51. C(20,3)

52. C(n,5)> or = 700, find n

53. 5!

54. $6\cdot5\cdot4$

55. C(8,4)

56. 8!

57. Moe 36, Joe 35

58. C(752,40) vs. C(937,36) or 47.4×10^{65} vs. 1.3×10^{65}

59. (a) 50! = 3.04×10^{64} (b) $10!\times40!$ = 2.96×10^{64}

   (c) $40\cdot39\cdot\ldots\cdot31\cdot40!$ = 2.51×10^{63}

60. (a) C(45,5) = 1,221,759   (b)C(100,4) = 3,921,225

   (c)lottery (a)   (d)lottery (b)

5.6. Further Counting Problems

1. (a) 2^6 = 64 possible outcomes

   (b) C(6,3) = $\dfrac{(6\cdot5\cdot4)}{(3\cdot2)}$ = 20 possible outcomes

   (c) C(6,6) + C(6,5) + C(6,4) = 1 + 6 + 15 = 22

   (d) 2^6 - C(6,1) - C(6,6) = 64 - 6 - 1 = 57

2. $C(7,2) = \dfrac{(7 \cdot 6)}{2} = 21$

3. $C(9,4) = \dfrac{(9 \cdot 8 \cdot 7 \cdot 6)}{4!} = 126$

4. (a) $C(12,4) = \dfrac{(12 \cdot 11 \cdot 10 \cdot 9)}{4!} = 495$

   (b) $C(8,4) = \dfrac{(8 \cdot 7 \cdot 6 \cdot 5)}{4!} = 70$

   (c) $C(8,2) \cdot C(4,2) = 28 \cdot 6 = 168$

   (d) $C(8,4) + 4 \cdot C(8,3) = 70 + 224 = 294$

   (e) $C(12,4) - (C(8,2) \cdot C(4,2)) = 495 - 168 = 327$

5. (a) $C(10,3) = 120$ (b) $C(8,3) = 56$

   (c) $C(10,3) - C(8,3) = 120 - 56 = 64$

6. (a) $2^8 = 256$ possible outcomes   (b) $C(8,3) = 56$

   (c) $C(8,1) = 8$, $C(8,8) = 1$
       $2^8 - 8 - 1 = 256 - 8 - 1 = 247$

   (d) $C(8,4) + C(8,5) = 70 + 56 = 126$

7. $C(100,25) \cdot C(75,40) \cdot C(35,35) = C(100,25) \cdot C(75,40)$

8. $C(8,4) = 70$ 9. $C(5,2) \cdot C(4,2) = 10 \cdot 6 = 60$

10. (a) $C(100,5)$ (b) $C(10,2) \cdot C(90,3)$ (c) $C(100,5) - C(90,5)$

11. $C(50,5) \cdot 2^5$ 12. $2^5 - C(5,2) - C(5,1) - C(5,0) = 32 - 10 - 5 - 1 = 16$

13. $C(4,3) \cdot C(6,3)$ 14. $(2!6!4!)3!$ 15. $C(20,12) \cdot C(8,2)$

16. $C(4,2) \cdot C(5,2)$ 17. $C(9,5) \cdot C(8,6)$

18. $\dfrac{10!}{(5!)(4!)(1!)}$ 19. $\dfrac{15!}{(3!)(8!)(4!)}$

20. $\dfrac{10!}{7!3!}$ 21. $26 \cdot 25 \cdot 24 \cdot 23 \cdot 22 \cdot 21$

22. $\dfrac{15!}{5!4!6!}$ 23. $7 \cdot 6 \cdot 5$

24. $C(21,5) \cdot 7!$ 25. $26 \cdot 25 \cdot 24 \cdot 9 \cdot 8 \cdot 7$

26. $\dfrac{20!}{5!4!3!8!}$

27. $C(4,3)$=ways to choose freshmen

    $C(5,3)$=ways to choose sophomores

    $C(6,3)$=ways to choose juniors

    $C(7,3)$=ways to choose seniors

    $4!$=ways to arrange all four classes

    $=C(4,3)\cdot C(5,3)\cdot C(6,3)\cdot C(7,3)\cdot 4!$

28. $5!$

29. $(3!\cdot 2!)\cdot 2$

30. $\dfrac{14!}{3!4!5!2!}$ or $C(14,3)\cdot C(11,4)\cdot C(7,5)\cdot C(7,2)$

31. $C(4,3)\cdot C(4,2) = 4\cdot 6 = 24$

32. | $C(4,2)$ | $C(12,1)\cdot C(4,2)$ | $C(11,1)\cdot C(4,1)$ |
    | 2 aces | 2 cards of a | 1 card of another |
    | | different denomination | denomination |

    $6\cdot 12\cdot 6\cdot 11\cdot 4 = 19,008$

33. | $C(13,1)\cdot C(4,3)$ | $C(12,1)\cdot C(4,2)$ |
    | 3 cards of one | 2 cards of another |
    | denomination | denomination |

    $13\cdot 4\cdot 12\cdot 6 = 3744$

34. | $C(13,1)\cdot C(4,2)$ | $C(12,1)\cdot C(4,2)$ | $C(11,1)\cdot C(4,1)$ |
    | 2 cards of one | 2 cards of another | 1 card of a third |
    | denomination | denomination | denomination |

    $13\cdot 6\cdot 12\cdot 6\cdot 11\cdot 4 = 247,104$

35. There are 5 digits (0, 1, 6, 8, 9) that are also digits when
    turned upside down. Thus there are 5^5 possible ZIP CODES made of these
    digits. To obtain a "false" detour-prone code like 66899, one must
    have put one of three digits (0, 1, 8) in the middle; the first two
    digits may be any of the five, but once they are known there is no
    choice for the last two. Thus there are $3\cdot 5^2$ such cases. The answer
    is therefore
    $$5^5 - 3\cdot 5^2 = 5^2(5^3 - 3) = 3050$$

36. (a) $C(38,22) = 2.22\times 10^{10}$ (b) $C(20,12)\cdot C(18,10) = 5.5\times 10^9$;
    (a) is greater.

37. $C(48,9)/C(52,13) = .264\%$

38. Four aces occur .264% of the time and two kings and two queens occur
    $C(4,2)C(4,2)C(49,9)/C(52,13)$. Two queens and two kings occur

more often.
39. Four aces are more likely. See #37.

$$\text{Pr(2 Red K, 2 Red Q, no other K or Q)} = \binom{2}{2}\binom{2}{2}\binom{44}{9} / \binom{52}{13}.$$

5.7. The Binomial Theorem

1. $\binom{6}{2} = \dfrac{6!}{2! \cdot 4!} = 15$

2. $\binom{7}{3} = \dfrac{7!}{3!4!}$

3. $\binom{8}{1} = \dfrac{8!}{1!7!} = 8$

4. $\binom{9}{9} = \dfrac{9!}{0!9!}$

5. $\binom{18}{16} = \dfrac{18!}{16!2!}$

6. $\binom{25}{24} = \dfrac{25!}{24!1!} = 25$

7. $\binom{7}{0} = \dfrac{7!}{0!7!} = 1$

8. $\binom{6}{1} = \dfrac{6!}{1!5!} = 6$

9. $\binom{8}{8} = \dfrac{8!}{8!0!} = 1$

10. $\binom{9}{0} = \dfrac{9!}{0!9!} = 1$

11. $\binom{n}{n-1} = \dfrac{n!}{(n-1)!1!} = n$

12. $\binom{n}{n} = \dfrac{n!}{n!0!} = 1$

13. $0! = 1$

14. $1! = 1$

15. $n \cdot (n-1)! = n!$

16. $\dfrac{n!}{n} = (n-1)!$ (see #15)

17. $\binom{6}{0} + \binom{6}{1} + \binom{6}{2} + \cdots \binom{6}{6} = 2^6$

18. $\binom{7}{0} + \binom{7}{1} + \cdots \binom{7}{7} = 2^7$

19. $(x+y)^{10} = \binom{10}{0}x^{10} + \binom{10}{1}x^9 y + \binom{10}{2}x^8 y + \cdots$

The first three terms are: x^{10}, $10x^9 y$, $45x^8 y^2$

20. $(x+y)^{20} = \begin{pmatrix} 20 \\ 0 \end{pmatrix} x^{20} + \begin{pmatrix} 20 \\ 1 \end{pmatrix} x^{19}y + \begin{pmatrix} 20 \\ 2 \end{pmatrix} x^{18}y^2 = \ldots$

The first three terms are: x^{20}, $20x^{19}y$, $190x^{18}y^2$

21. $(x+y)^{15} = \ldots + \begin{pmatrix} 15 \\ 13 \end{pmatrix} x^2y^{13} + \begin{pmatrix} 15 \\ 14 \end{pmatrix} xy^{14} + \begin{pmatrix} 15 \\ 15 \end{pmatrix} y^{15}$

The last three terms are: $105x^2y^{13}$, $15xy^{14}$, y^{15}

22. $(x+y)^{12} = \ldots + \begin{pmatrix} 12 \\ 10 \end{pmatrix} x^2y^{10} + \begin{pmatrix} 12 \\ 11 \end{pmatrix} xy^{11} + \begin{pmatrix} 12 \\ 12 \end{pmatrix} y^{12}$

The last three terms are: $66x^2y^{10}$, $12xy^{11}$, y^{12}

23. $\begin{pmatrix} 20 \\ 10 \end{pmatrix} x^{10}y^{10}$ is the middle term in $(x+y)^{20}$

24. $\begin{pmatrix} 10 \\ 5 \end{pmatrix} x^5y^5$ is the middle term in $(x+y)^{10}$

25. $\begin{pmatrix} 11 \\ 7 \end{pmatrix}$ = coeficient of x^8y^5 in $(x+y)^{11}$

26. $\begin{pmatrix} 13 \\ 5 \end{pmatrix}$ = coeficient of x^8y^5 in $(x+y)^{13}$

27. $2^6 = 64$ different subsets can be chosen.

28. 2^{100} different subsets can be chosen.

29. $2^4 = 16$ different tips could be left on the table.

30. $2^4 = 16$ different pizzas can be made.

31. $2^6 = 64$ different channel selections are available

32. $4 \cdot 2^3 \cdot 2 = 64$

33. 2^8 = number of possible subsets of eight books, but this includes choosing the empty set (no books).

The number of ways to select at least one book is $2^8 - 1$

34. $2^6 - 1$ (excludes the choice of all six desserts)

35. $2 \cdot 3 \cdot (2^{15} - 1)$ since there are two choices of crust, three choices of pan size and $2^{15} - 1$ choices of toppings. This assumes that one would not order only crust.

36. Number of ways to select a subset of CD's with at least two elements=
Total number of subsets - n (subsets with 1 CD) -n(subsets with 0 CD's)
$$= 2^7 - \binom{7}{1} - \binom{7}{0} = 2^7 - 7 - 1.$$

37. 2^7 =Total number of ways to choose appetizers

    number of sets of 7 appetizers = 1

    number of sets of 6 apppetizers = $\binom{7}{6} = 7$

    therefore, at least five appetizers can be chosen in
    $2^7 - 1 - 7$ ways.

38. $4 \cdot (2^3)(2) = 64$ $4 = \#$ of options of ice cream

    $2^3 = \#$ of ways to choose toppings

    $2 = \#$ of ways to choose a glass

39. There are 2^4 subsets of $\{a, b, c, d, e\}$. None contain e.
These are the only subsets of $\{a, b, c, d, e\}$ without e.

40. There are two even digits in the set $\{1, 2, 3, 4, 5\}$.
Hence there are 2^3 subsets of $\{1, 3, 5\}$; none contain even digits.

41. There are 8 lab projects. Hence 2^8 subsets; but 1 set has no
elements, and $\binom{8}{1} = 8$ have only one element. Hence, students

    may satisfy the requirement in $2^8 - 1 - 8$ ways.

42. A set has an odd number of elements, say n. Half of the subsets
will have an odd number of elements because there are
$\binom{n}{0} + \binom{n}{2} + \binom{n}{4} + \ldots + \binom{n}{n-1}$ subsets with an even number of elements

    and $\binom{n}{1} + \binom{n}{3} + \binom{n}{5} + \ldots + \binom{n}{n}$ subsets with an odd number of elements.

    But, $\binom{n}{1} + \binom{n}{3} + \binom{n}{5} + \ldots + \binom{n}{n} = \binom{n}{n-1} + \binom{n}{n-3} = \binom{n}{n-5} + \ldots + \binom{n}{0}$

since $\begin{bmatrix} n \\ k \end{bmatrix} = \begin{bmatrix} n \\ n-k \end{bmatrix}$

43. $\begin{bmatrix} n \\ 0 \end{bmatrix} + \begin{bmatrix} n \\ 1 \end{bmatrix} + \ldots + \begin{bmatrix} n \\ n \end{bmatrix} = 2^n$ because of the binomial theorem

applied to $(1+1)^n$.

44. $(x+y)^n = \begin{bmatrix} n \\ 0 \end{bmatrix} x^n + \begin{bmatrix} n \\ 1 \end{bmatrix} x^{n-1} y + \ldots + \begin{bmatrix} n \\ n \end{bmatrix} y^n$

Let $x=1$, $y=-1$

Then $(1+(-1))^n = \begin{bmatrix} n \\ 0 \end{bmatrix} 1^n + \begin{bmatrix} n \\ 1 \end{bmatrix} 1^{n-1}(-1) + \begin{bmatrix} n \\ 2 \end{bmatrix} 1^{n-2}(-1)^2$

$+ \ldots + \begin{bmatrix} n \\ n \end{bmatrix} (1)^0 (-1)^n$

Depending on whether n is even or odd, the last term is $+1$ or -1.

45. $\begin{bmatrix} n \\ k-1 \end{bmatrix} + \begin{bmatrix} m \\ k \end{bmatrix} = \dfrac{n!}{(k-1)!(n-k)!} \cdot \left[\dfrac{1}{n-k+1} + 1/k \right]$

$= \dfrac{n!}{(k-1)!(n-k)!} \cdot \left[\dfrac{k+(n-k+1)}{k(n-k+1)} \right]$

$= \dfrac{n!}{(k-1)!(n-k)!} \cdot \dfrac{n+1}{k(n-k+1)}$

$= \dfrac{(n+1)!}{k(k-1)! \cdot (n+k+1)(n-k)}$

$= \dfrac{(n+1)!}{(k)!(n-k+1)!} = \begin{bmatrix} n+1 \\ k \end{bmatrix}$

since $(n+1)-k = n-k+1$

46.
```
1    1
1    2    1
1    3    3    1
1    4    6    4    1
1    5    10   10   5    1
1    6    15   20   15   6    1
1    7    21   35   35   21   7    1
1    8    28   56   70   56   28   8    1
```

To calculate each row by using the row above simply apply the theorem from problem 25, $\begin{bmatrix} n+1 \\ k \end{bmatrix} = \begin{bmatrix} n \\ k-1 \end{bmatrix} + \begin{bmatrix} n \\ k \end{bmatrix}$.

For example: $\begin{bmatrix} 6 \\ 2 \end{bmatrix} = \begin{bmatrix} 5 \\ 1 \end{bmatrix} + \begin{bmatrix} 5 \\ 2 \end{bmatrix} = 5 + 10 = 15$

47. There are 2^5 possible feasible sets.

48. To have (3,6) as the vertex, we must have $x+3y \le 2$ and $x \ge -3$ therefore, we can choose from among inequalities: $2^3 = 8$.

5.8. Multinomial Coefficients and Partitions

1. $\dfrac{5!}{3! \cdot 1 \cdot 1} = 5 \cdot 4 = 20$

2. $\dfrac{5!}{2 \cdot 1 \cdot 2} = 5 \cdot 3 \cdot 2 \cdot 1 = 30$

3. $\dfrac{6!}{2 \cdot 1 \cdot 2 \cdot 1} = 6 \cdot 30 = 180$

4. $\dfrac{6!}{3!3!} = 5 \cdot 3 \cdot 2 \cdot 1 = 30$

5. $\dfrac{7!}{3! \cdot 2 \cdot 2} = 7 \cdot 5 \cdot 3 \cdot 2 = 210$

6. $\dfrac{7!}{3! \cdot 3!} = 7 \cdot 5 \cdot 3 = 105$

7. $\dfrac{12!}{4! \cdot 4! \cdot 4!} = 11 \cdot 10 \cdot 9 \cdot 7 \cdot 5 = 34,650$

8. $\dfrac{8!}{3! \cdot 3! \cdot 2} = 8 \cdot 7 \cdot 5 \cdot 2 = 560$

9. $\dfrac{12!}{5! \cdot 3! \cdot 2 \cdot 2} = 12 \cdot 11 \cdot 10 \cdot 9 \cdot 7 \cdot 2 = 166,320$

10. $\dfrac{8!}{2 \cdot 2 \cdot 2 \cdot 2} = 7 \cdot 6 \cdot 5 \cdot 4 \cdot 3 = 2,520$

11. $\dfrac{15!}{5! \cdot (3!)^5} = 1,401,400$

12. $\dfrac{10!}{2! \cdot (5!)^2} = 126$

13. $\dfrac{18!}{3! \cdot (6!)^3} = 2,858,856$

14. $\dfrac{12!}{3! \cdot (4!)^3} = 5,775$

15. $\dfrac{20!}{7! \cdot 5! \cdot 8!} = 99,768,240$

16. $\dfrac{15!}{(5!)^3} = 756,756$

17. $\dfrac{30!}{10! \cdot 2! \cdot 8!} = 9.06^{20}$

18. $\dfrac{20!}{5! \cdot (4!)^5}$

unordered partitions

19. $\dfrac{20!}{4! \cdot (5!)^4} = 488{,}864{,}376$

unordered partitions

20. $\dfrac{9!}{(3!)^3} = 1{,}680$

21. $\dfrac{4!}{1 \cdot 1 \cdot 2} = 12$

22. $\dfrac{10!}{4! \cdot 4! \cdot 2} = 3{,}150$

23. $\dfrac{14!}{7! \cdot (2!)^7} = 135{,}135$

unordered partitions

24. $\dfrac{6!}{2! \cdot 2! \cdot 2!} \left[\dfrac{10!}{6!4!} - 7 \right] = 18{,}270$

25. $\begin{pmatrix} n \\ n_1, n_2, \ldots, n_m \end{pmatrix} = \begin{pmatrix} n \\ n_1 \end{pmatrix} \cdot \begin{pmatrix} n-n_1 \\ n_2 \end{pmatrix} \cdots \begin{pmatrix} n-n-n_2 \ldots -n_{m-1} \\ n_m \end{pmatrix}$

$= \left[\dfrac{n!}{n!\,(n-n_1)!} \right] \left[\dfrac{(n-n_1)!}{n_2!\,(n-n_1-n_2)!} \right] \cdots \left[\dfrac{(n-n_1-n_2-\ldots n_{m-1})!}{n_m!\,(n-n_1-n_2-\ldots-n_m)!} \right]$

$= \dfrac{n!}{n_1!\,n_2!\ldots n_m!\,0!} = \dfrac{n!}{n_1 n_2!\ldots n_m!}$

5. Supplementary Exercises

1. $\emptyset, \{a\}, \{b\}, \{a,b\}$

2. $(S \cup T')'$

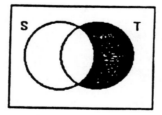

3. $C(16, 2) = 120$

4. $2(5!) = 240$

5. $R' \cap (S \cap T)$

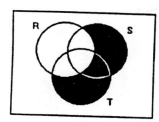

$R' \cap (S \cap T)$

6. $(x + y)^{12} = \begin{pmatrix} 12 \\ 0 \end{pmatrix} x^{12} + \begin{pmatrix} 12 \\ 1 \end{pmatrix} x^{11}y + \begin{pmatrix} 12 \\ 2 \end{pmatrix} x^{10}y^2 \ldots$

The first three terms are x^{12}, $12x^{11}y$, $66x^{10}y^2$.

7. $C(8,3) \cdot C(6,2) = 56 \cdot 15 = 840$

8. $60 - 15 = 45$ people received the actual drug, 30 of those 45 people showed improvement and 15 did not.

9. $7 \cdot 5 = 35$ different combinations of washers and dryers.

10. $\dfrac{12!}{6! \cdot 4! \cdot 2!} = 13,860$

11. $(F \cup G \cup S)' = 115 - [(70 + 65 + 65) - (40 + 45 + 35) + 35]$
$= 115 - 115 = 0$

12. $\begin{pmatrix} 17 \\ 15 \end{pmatrix} = \dfrac{17!}{15! \cdot 2!} = 136$

#'s 13 - 20

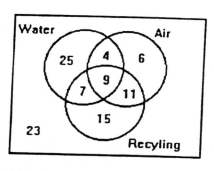

100 members of the Earth Club
W = {members for clean water}
A = {members for clean air}
R = {members for recycling}

13. 6 members thought the priority should be clean air only.

14. $17 + 32 = 49$ members thought the priority should be clean water or clean air, but not both.

15. $77 - 30 = 47$ members thought the priority should be clean water or recycling, but not clean air.

16. 11 members thought the priority should be clean air and recycling, but not clean water.

17. $25 + 6 + 15 = 46$ members thought the priority should be exactly one of the three issues.

18. 100 − 42 = 58 members thought the priority should be anything but recycling.

19. 15 + 7 = 22 members thought the priority should be recycling, but not clean air.

20. 23 members thought the priority should be anything but one of these three issues.

21. $\dfrac{9!}{5! \cdot 4!} = 126$ 22. 2^{40} different possibilities

23. 400 + 300 − 150 = 550 students participated in at least one of these sports.

24. $4 \cdot C(13,5)$

25. There are 9 choices for the hundreds column, 10 choices for the tens column and 10 choices for the ones column. So there are $9 \cdot 9 \cdot 8 = 648$ three-digit numbers in which no two digits are alike.

26. There are $9 \cdot 10 \cdot 10 = 900$ possible numbers and there are 9 numbers in which all three digits are the same. So, there are $900 - 648 - 9 = 243$ numbers in which only two digits are the same.

27. $\dbinom{4}{3} \cdot \dbinom{48}{2} = 4{,}512$

28. $24 \cdot 23 + 24 \cdot 23 \cdot 22 = 552 + 12{,}144 = 12{,}696$

29. $C(3,1) + C(2,1) + C(1,1) = 6$ 30. $3! \cdot 3! \cdot 2 = 72$

31. $2 \cdot 3! = 12$

32. There are $1 + 2 + 3 + 4 + 5 + 6 + 7 + 8 + 9 = 45$ points of intersection. $45 - 10 = 35$ points occur outside the feasible set.

33. The first teacher only has $\dfrac{1}{4!}\left(\dfrac{(24!)}{(6!)^4}\right) = 9.62 \times 10^{10}$ options

with his students, and the second teacher has $\dfrac{1}{6!}\left(\dfrac{(24!)}{(4!)^6}\right)$

$\cong 4.51 \times 10^{12}$ options with her students, so clearly the second teacher has more options.

34. She can schedule her consultations in $4200 = \dfrac{10!}{3! \cdot 4! \cdot 3!}$ different ways.

35. $x! = 120$, $120 = 2 \cdot 3 \cdot 4 \cdot 5 = 5!$ There are 5 books in the set.

36. $7! = 5040$

37. (a) $\begin{pmatrix} 12 \\ 2 \end{pmatrix} \begin{pmatrix} 12 \\ 3 \end{pmatrix} = 14{,}520$ (b) $\dfrac{24 \cdot 22 \cdot 20 \cdot 18 \cdot 16}{5!} = 25{,}344$

38. $\begin{pmatrix} 7 \\ 2 \end{pmatrix} + \begin{pmatrix} 7 \\ 1 \end{pmatrix} + \begin{pmatrix} 7 \\ 0 \end{pmatrix} = 29$

39. $2 \cdot 26 \cdot 26 \cdot 26 = 35{,}152$.

40. $12! = 479{,}001{,}600$

41. $\dfrac{25!}{10! 9! 6!} = 5.94 \times 10^{16}$

42. (a) 351,520,000 (b) The less restrictive rule allows 20 times as many combinations.

6

PROBABILITY

6.2. Experiments, Outcomes, Events

1. The sample space is all the possible pairs
   (a) S = {RS,RT,RU,RV,ST,SU,SV,TU,TV,UV}

   (b) All the pairs of which R is a member: {RS,RT,RU,RV}

   (c) All the pairs which contain T, U, V: {TU,TV, UV}

2. The sample space is all the different letters in 'MISSISSIPPI'
   (a) S = {M, I, S, P}

   (b) I is the only vowel, therefore the subset chosen is {I}

3. The sample space is all the possibilities of H and T for two tosses.
   (a) S = {HH, HT, TH, TT}

   (b) All pairs in which the first letter is H

4. Let F = Freshmen, So = Sophomore, J = Junior, Sr = Senior, L = Liberal, C = Conservative:
   (a) The sample space corresponding to the poll: {(F,L), (F,C), (So,L) (So,C), (J,L), (J,C), (Sr,L), (Sr,C)}

   (b) All pairs of which C is a member: {(F,C), (So,C), (J,C), (Sr,C)}

   (c) All pairs of which J and L are members: {(J,L)}

   (d) All pairs of which F and C are *not* members: {(So,L), (J,L), (Sr,L)}

5. The sample space is: {(Urn I, red), (Urn I, white), (Urn II, red), (Urn II, white)}

   (b) All pairs with Urn I as a member: {(Urn I, red), (Urn I, white)}

6. (a) The sample space is all the possibilities for 4 tosses:
   {HHHH, HHHT, HHTH, HHTT, HTHH, HTHT, HTTH, HTTT, THHH, THHT, THTH, THTT,TTHH, TTHT, TTTH, TTTT}

   (b) All members with 3 or 4 H's: {HHHH, HHHT, HHTH, HTHH, THHH}

   (c) All members with H for the first toss: {HHHH, HHHT, HHTH, HTHH, HHTT, HTHT, HTTH, HTTT}

   (d) All members with H for the first toss and 3 or 4 H's: {HHHH, HHHT, HHTH, HTHH}

7. (a) S = all the positive Real Numbers.

   (b) Where "t" is time,
   $E \cap F$ is *more* than 5 and *less* than 8: $5 < t < 8$.
   $E \cap G$ is *more* than 5 and *less* than 4. NOT possible, so
   $E \cap G = \emptyset$.
   E' means *not* more than 5: $t \le 5$
   F' means *not* less than 8: $t \ge 8$
   $E' \cap F$ is *not* more than 5 *and* less than 8: $t \le 5$
   $E' \cap F \cap G$ is the answer above *and* less than 4
   $t < 4$ satisfies all three.
   $E \cup F$ is *more* than 5 or *less* than 8: this includes all of the
   sample space.

8. $E \cap F$ = "more than nine months and less than 2 years"
   $E \cup F = S$ (the whole space) E' = "9 months or less"
   F' = "2 years or more" $(E \cup F)' = S' = \emptyset$

9. (a) The sample space is all the possible pairs of 1,2,3, and 4:
   {(1,1), (1,2), (1,3), (1,4), (2,1), (2,2), (2,3), (2,4), (3,1),
   (3,2), (3,3), (3,4), (4,1), (4,2), (4,3), (4,4)}

   (b) (i) pairs of 2 and 4: {(2,2), (2,4), (4,2), (4,4)}
   (ii) pairs in which at least one member is a 2 or a 4:
   {(1,2), (1,4), (2,1), (2,2), (2,3), (2,4), (3,2), (3,4), (4,1),
   (4,2), (4,3), (4,4)}
   (iii) pairs of 3 and 4: {(3,3), (3,4), (4,3), (4,4)}
   (iv) the sum of the members is 6: {(2,4), (3,3), (4,2)}
   (v) the sum of the members is greater than 4 and less than 9:
   {(1,4), (2,3), (2,4), (3,2), (3,3), (3,4), (4,1), (4,2), (4,3),
   (4,4)}
   (vi) both members of the pair are the same: {(1,1), (2,2), (3,3),
   (4,4)}
   (vii) one member is a 2 or a 3 but not both:
   {(1,2), (1,3), (2,1), (2,4), (3,1), (3,4), (4,2), (4,3)}
   (viii) pairs of 1,2 and 3: {(1,1), (1,2), (1,3), (2,1), (2,2),
   (2,3), (3,1), (3,2), (3,3)}

10. (a) The following pairs are mutually exclusive:
    (ii) $E \cap G = \emptyset$, (iii) $F \cap G = \emptyset$, (vi) $G \cap H = \emptyset$

    (b) cars that are: (i) red Chevrolets (ii) red or Chevrolets (iii)
    not red (iv) not Chevrolets (v) either not green or not Fords
    (vi) neither black nor Chryslers (vii) red or are green Fords
    (viii) no cars in event (ix) red Chryslers (x) red, black, or
    Chryslers (xi) no cars in event (xii) not red and are not
    Chevrolets (xiii) any type car

11. (a) $E \cap F = \{2\}$, so E and F are not mutually exclusive.

    (b) $F \cap G = \emptyset$, so F and G are mutually exclusive.

171

12. $E \cap E' = \emptyset$, so E and E' are mutually exclusive.

13. S, {a,b}, {a,c}, {b,c}, {a}, {b}, {c}, $\emptyset$

14. 2^n events are associated with S.

15. For the events $E \cup F$ and $E' \cap F'$ to be mutually exclusive they must have no end points in common.
$E \cup F = \{1,2,3\}$ $\qquad\qquad$ $E' \cap F' = \{2,3,4\} \cap \{1,4\} = \{4\}$
They do not have any common points, so they are mutually exclusive.

16. $E' \cap F' = (E \cup F)'$, $(E \cup F) \cap (E \cup F)' = \emptyset$, as a result of problem 12.

17. (a) The sample space is the possible number of heads tossed:
$\{0, 1, 2, 3, 4, 5, 6, 7, 8, 9, 10\}$

(b) The set of numbers greater than 5: $\{6, 7, 8, 9, 10\}$

18. (a) The sample space is the possible pairs of dimes and nickels showing heads or tails: $\{(0,0), (0,1), ..., (5,5)\}$

(b) The number of the first member is greater than the second for the pair: $\{(1,0), (2,0), (2,1), ..., (5,4)\}$

19. (a) $E \cap F$ = "all blue-eyed males", E and F are *not* mutually exclusive.

(b) $E \cap G = \emptyset$, E and G are mutually exclusive.

(c) $F \cap G = \emptyset$, F and G are mutually exclusive.

20. (a) $E \cup F$ = {students with blue eyes or who are male}

(b) $E \cap G = \emptyset$

(c) E' = {students who do not have blue eyes}

(d) F' = {female students}

(e) $(G \cup F) \cap E$ = {male students with blue eyes}

(f) $G' \cap E$ = {students with blue eyes}

21. Considering this "line" to be the number of people in it, we could describe it as all the non-negative integers.

22. The set of positive numbers

23. The set of nonnegative numbers

24. {(a,b)}, where *a* is a nonnegative integer and *b* is a positive number.

6.3. Assignment of Probabilities

1. (a) $\dfrac{46,277}{774,746} = \dfrac{\text{(number of "and"s)}}{\text{(Total number of words)}}$

   (b) $\dfrac{46,277 + 1855}{774,746} = \dfrac{48,132}{774,746}$

   (c) $\dfrac{774,746 - 48,132}{774,746} = \dfrac{726,614}{774,746}$

2. (a) $\dfrac{1}{4}$ (b) $\dfrac{3}{4}$ 3. (a) $\dfrac{5}{36}$ (b) $\dfrac{6}{36} = \dfrac{1}{6}$

4. $\dfrac{6}{50} = \dfrac{3}{25}$ 5. $\dfrac{2}{38} = \dfrac{1}{19}$

6. (a) $\dfrac{3}{9} = \dfrac{1}{3}$ (b) $\dfrac{5}{9}$ (c) $\dfrac{6}{9} = \dfrac{2}{3}$ 7. $1 - \left(\dfrac{1}{3} + \dfrac{1}{2}\right) = \dfrac{1}{6}$

8. Since, $\dfrac{1}{4} + \dfrac{1}{2} + \dfrac{1}{4} = 1$, then for the sample space $\{s_1,\ s_2,\ s_3\}$ the following probabilities are feasible

   (d) $\Pr(s_1) = \dfrac{1}{4}$, $\Pr(s_2) = \dfrac{1}{2}$, $\Pr(s_3) = \dfrac{1}{4}$

9. (a) $\Pr(\{s_1, s_2\}) = .1 + .6 = .7$

   (b) $\Pr(\{s_2, s_4\}) = .6 + .1 = .7$

10. (a) $\Pr(E) = .30$, $\Pr(F) = .69$ (b) $\Pr(E') = 1 - .30 = .70$

    (c) $\Pr(E \cap F) = 0$ (d) $\Pr(E \cup F) = .30 + .69 = .99$

11. (a) $\dfrac{10}{10 + 1} = \dfrac{10}{11}$ (b) $\dfrac{1}{1 + 2} = \dfrac{1}{3}$ (c) $\dfrac{4}{4 + 5} = \dfrac{4}{9}$

12. 1 to 5   13. 9 to 91   14. $\dfrac{16}{25} = .64$

15. wins $\dfrac{11}{18} = .61$, losses $\dfrac{7}{18} = .39$

16. (a) $1 - .18 - .23 - .31 = .28$ (b) $.18 + .31 = .49$

    (c) $1 - .31 = .69$ (d) $1 - .23 = .77$, 77:23

    (e) $.28 + .23 = .51$, 51:49   (f) 18:82 = 9:41

173

17. (a) $\Pr(E \cup F) = .6 + .5 - .4 = .7$ (b) $\Pr(E \cap F') = .6 - .4 = .2$

18. (a) $\Pr(E \cap F) = .4 - .3 = .1$ (b) $\Pr(E \cup F) = .5 + .4 - .1 = .8$

19. (a) $.2 + .25 + .25 = .7$ (b) $.7 \cdot 10,000 = 7000$

20. 1

21.

Failures in:	Prob.
Month 1	.05
Month 2	.05
Month 3	.10
Month 4	.05
Month 5	.05
Month 6	.02
No failures in months 1 - 6	.68

22. $.05 + .05 + .02 + .68 = .8, .68$

23. (a) $\Pr(20-34) = .15$, $\Pr(35-49) = .70 - .15 = .55$, $\Pr(50-64)$
     $= .90 - .70 = .20$, $\Pr(65-79) = 1 - .90 = .10$
     (b) $\Pr(\geq 50) = .20 + .10 = .30$

6.4. Calculating Probabilities

1. (a) $\Pr(\text{all choose A}) = \dfrac{[\text{number of outcomes}]}{N} = \dfrac{1}{3^3} = \dfrac{1}{3}\cdot\dfrac{1}{3}\cdot\dfrac{1}{3}$

    $= \Pr(\text{all choose B}) = \Pr(\text{all choose C})$

    $\Pr(\text{all choose the same section}) = 3 \cdot \dfrac{1}{27} = \dfrac{1}{9}$

    (b) $\Pr(\text{choose different sections}) = \dfrac{6}{27} = \dfrac{2}{9}$.

2. (a) There are $\begin{pmatrix} 12 \\ 6 \end{pmatrix} = 924$ ways to choose the 6 disks.

    (b) $\Pr(\text{two of the 6 boxes have gold disk}) = \dfrac{\begin{pmatrix} 2 \\ 2 \end{pmatrix}\begin{pmatrix} 10 \\ 4 \end{pmatrix}}{924} = \dfrac{210}{924} = .227$

    (c) $\Pr(\text{none of the 6 boxes has gold disk}) = \dfrac{\begin{pmatrix} 2 \\ 0 \end{pmatrix}\begin{pmatrix} 10 \\ 6 \end{pmatrix}}{\begin{pmatrix} 12 \\ 6 \end{pmatrix}} = \dfrac{210}{924} = .227$

3. (a) $\Pr(\text{number is odd}) = \dfrac{7}{13}$.   (b) $\Pr(\text{number is even}) = \dfrac{6}{13}$.

(c) Pr(number is multiple of 3) = Pr(3,6,9,12) = $\frac{4}{13}$.

(d) Pr(number is odd or multiple of 3) = $\frac{7}{13} + \frac{4}{13} - \frac{2}{13} = \frac{9}{13}$

since 3 and 9 satify both criteria.

4. Sampling is with replacement.

(a) Pr(all numbers are even) = $(\frac{6}{13})^5$ = .0209

(b) Pr(all numbers are odd) = $(\frac{7}{13})^5$ = .0453

(c) Pr(at least one number is odd) = 1 - Pr(all numbers are even)
= 1 - .0209 = .9791.

5. Sampling is without replacement.

—(a) Pr(all numbers are even) = $\frac{6}{13}\frac{5}{12}\frac{4}{11}\frac{3}{10}\frac{2}{9}$ = .0047

(b) Pr(all numbers are odd) = $\frac{7}{13}\frac{6}{12}\frac{5}{11}\frac{4}{10}\frac{3}{9}$ = .0163

(c) Pr(at least one number is odd) = 1 - .0047 = .9953.

6. (a) Pr(no one is in track A) = $(\frac{4}{5})^{10}$.

(b) There are 5 possible tracks. Pr(all are in A) = $(\frac{1}{5})^{10}$

Pr(all are in the same track) = $5 \cdot (\frac{1}{5})^{10}$

7. C(6,2) = 15, C(5,2) = 10, C(11,4) = 330
Pr(urn contains two white and two red balls)

= $\frac{(6,2) \cdot C(5,2)}{C(11,4)} = \frac{150}{330} = \frac{5}{11}$

8. N = $\binom{10}{3}$ = 120, outcomes = $\binom{5}{1} \cdot \binom{5}{2} + \binom{5}{2} \cdot \binom{5}{1} + \binom{5}{3}$
= 5·10 + 10·5 + 10 = 110
The probability that a box containing five defective fuses will be rejected is: $\frac{110}{120} = \frac{11}{12}$.

9. N = $\binom{9}{3}$ = 84, outcomes = $\binom{5}{2} \cdot \binom{4}{1} + \binom{5}{3}$ = 40 + 10 = 50,

Pr(at least two will agree with him) = $\frac{50}{84} = \frac{25}{42}$

10. $N = \binom{9}{2} = 36$, outcomes $= \binom{5}{1} \cdot \binom{4}{1} + \binom{5}{2} = 20 + 10 = 30$

Pr(atleast one of them is red) $= \frac{30}{36} = \frac{5}{6}$

11. $1 - \frac{(30)(29)(28)(27)}{30^4} = .188$ 12. $\frac{(26)(25)(24)(23)(22)}{26^5}$

13. Pr(3 Correct) $= \frac{C(5,3)}{2^5} = \frac{10}{32}$, Pr(4 Correct) $= \frac{C(5,4)}{2^5} = \frac{5}{32}$,

Pr(5 Correct) $= \frac{C(5,5)}{2^5} = \frac{1}{32}$, Adding these gives $\frac{16}{32} = \frac{1}{2}$

14. $1 - \frac{(6)(5)(4)(3)}{6^4} = 1 - \frac{5}{18} = \frac{13}{18}$

15. (a) $Pr(D \cup C) = .2 + .15 - .1 = .25$

(b) $Pr(D' \cap C') = P((D \cup C)') = 1 - .25 = .75$

(c) $Pr(D') = 1 - .2 = .8$

16.

$\binom{7}{4} = 35$, $2^7 = 128$

The probability of obtaining 4 heads and 3 tails is $\frac{35}{128}$

17. $Pr(E \cap F) = Pr(E) + Pr(F) - Pr(E \cup F) = .3 + (1-.6) - .7 = 0$

18. $Pr(I' \cap II') = Pr(I') + Pr(II') - Pr(I \cap II)'$
$= .88 + .78 - (1 - .02) = .68$

19. He has 12 socks and chooses 1. Out of the 11 left he has $\frac{1}{11}$ probability that he will select a matching sock.

20. $N = \binom{15}{6} = 5005$, outcomes $= \binom{10}{4} \cdot \binom{5}{2} = 2100$,

Pr(four of the six senators questioned plan to vote "yes")
$= \frac{2100}{5005} = \frac{60}{143}$

21. $N = \binom{5}{2} = 10$, since there are four positions in which the parents can stand side-by-side, outcomes $= \binom{4}{1} = 4$ and
Pr(that the parents will be standing next to each other) $= \frac{4}{10} = \frac{2}{5}$.

22. $.0019654 + .0039246 - .0000154 = .0058746$

23. (a) $\dfrac{\binom{3}{1}\cdot\binom{5}{2}}{\binom{8}{3}} = \dfrac{3\cdot 10}{56} = \dfrac{15}{28}$ This is the probability that he passes through point C.

(b) $\dfrac{\binom{3}{1}\cdot\binom{5}{4}}{\binom{8}{5}} = \dfrac{3\cdot 5}{56} = \dfrac{15}{56}$ This is the probability that he passes through point D.

(c) $\dfrac{\binom{3}{2}\cdot\binom{2}{0}}{\binom{5}{2}} = \dfrac{3\cdot 1}{10} = \dfrac{3}{10}$ This is the probability that he passes through D given that he already passed through C.

Pr(he passes through points C and D)

$= $ Pr(he passes through point C)$\cdot \dfrac{3}{10} = \dfrac{15}{28}\cdot\dfrac{3}{10} = \dfrac{9}{56}$

(d) $\dfrac{30}{56} + \dfrac{15}{56} - \dfrac{9}{56} = \dfrac{36}{56} = \dfrac{9}{14}$ This is the probability that he passes through point C or D.

24. $\dfrac{\binom{4}{3}+\binom{4}{4}}{2^4} = \dfrac{5}{16} = $ Pr(they will have more girls than boys)

25. $N = \binom{10}{3} = 120$, outcomes $= \binom{4}{1}\cdot\binom{6}{2} + \binom{4}{2}\cdot\binom{6}{1} + \binom{4}{3} = 60 + 36 + 4 = 100$. The probability that at least one of the junior partners is on the committee is $\dfrac{100}{120} = \dfrac{5}{6}$.

26. 2^6 possible outcomes, $\dfrac{\binom{6}{3}}{2^6} = \dfrac{5\cdot 4}{2^6} = \dfrac{5}{16}$

27. $\dfrac{\binom{1}{1}\cdot\binom{8}{2}}{\binom{9}{3}} = \dfrac{28}{84} = \dfrac{1}{3}$ 28. $\dfrac{\binom{4}{2}}{\binom{8}{2}} = \dfrac{6}{28} = \dfrac{3}{14}$ 29. $\dfrac{2}{\binom{40}{6}}$

30. Many people think that multiples of 7 are lucky numbers. The best strategy is to select numbers that are not considered lucky. Since many people bet their birthdays, perhaps numbers less than 32 also should be avoided.

31. (a) There are 3 bounded regions and 8 unbounded regions.

31. (a) There are 3 bounded regions and 8 unbounded regions.

The probability is therefore: $\dfrac{\binom{3}{2}}{\binom{11}{2}} = \dfrac{3}{55}$

(b) There are 3 regions with 2 edges and 6 regions with 3 edges. Thus the probability is: $\dfrac{\binom{3}{1}\binom{6}{1}}{\binom{11}{2}} = \dfrac{3 \cdot 6}{55} = \dfrac{18}{55}$

(c) There are 16 pairs of regions that have a common edge.

The probability is: $\dfrac{\binom{16}{1}}{\binom{11}{2}} = \dfrac{16}{55}$

(d) There are 5 on the left and 6 on the right. Thus there are 30 possible pairs that satisfy the requirement.

The probability is: $\dfrac{30}{\binom{11}{2}} = \dfrac{30}{55} = \dfrac{6}{11}$

32. 6 to 3 against her. If she chooses a subcommittee of 9 or 7 than she will lose the vote. If she chooses

$\qquad$ 5 $\qquad\qquad$ or $\qquad\qquad$ 3 $\qquad\qquad$ or $\qquad$ 1

$\dfrac{\binom{3}{3} \cdot \binom{6}{2}}{\binom{9}{5}} = \dfrac{15}{126}$ $\qquad$ $\dfrac{\binom{3}{3} + \binom{3}{2} \cdot \binom{6}{1}}{\binom{9}{3}} = \dfrac{19}{84}$ $\qquad$ $\dfrac{\binom{3}{1}}{\binom{9}{1}} = \dfrac{1}{3}$

$\qquad$ 11.9% $\qquad\qquad\qquad$ 22.6% $\qquad\qquad$ 33.3%
are her chances of winning.

33. (a) $\dfrac{\binom{10}{8} + \binom{10}{9} + \binom{10}{10}}{2^{10}} = \dfrac{45 + 10 + 1}{2^{10}} = \dfrac{7}{128} = .0547$

(b) $1 - (1 - \dfrac{7}{128})^{10} = 1 - \left(\dfrac{121}{128}\right)^{10}$ $\qquad$ (c) $1 - \dfrac{7}{128} = \dfrac{121}{128}$

34. (a) $1 - (.7)^4 = .7599$ $\qquad$ (b) $(.7599)^{10} = .0642$

(c) $1 - (1 - .0642)^{20} = .7348$

35. $1 - \dfrac{C(12,3)}{C(15,3)} = .5165$ $\qquad$ 36. $1 - \left(\dfrac{6}{7}\right) \cdot \left(\dfrac{6}{7}\right) \cdot \left(\dfrac{5}{6}\right) \cdot \left(\dfrac{5}{6}\right) = .49$

37. The probability that the writer chooses all 4 incorrectly is: $\left(\frac{5}{6}\right)\left(\frac{5}{6}\right)\left(\frac{4}{5}\right)\left(\frac{4}{5}\right) = .444$

So, Pr(atleast one is correct) = 1 - .444 = .556 ‾or 55.6%

38.
$$\frac{\binom{4}{1}\cdot\binom{22}{3} + \binom{4}{2}\cdot\binom{22}{2} + \binom{4}{3}\cdot\binom{22}{1} + \binom{4}{4}\cdot\binom{22}{0}}{\binom{26}{4}} = \frac{7635}{14,950} = .51$$

Increases to 51%

40. Find $1 - $ Pr(no two choose the same card) $= \dfrac{52\cdot51\cdot50\cdot49\cdot48}{52^5} = .1797.$

The probability of such a match first exceeds .50 when the group size, n = 10.

41. (a) $24\cdot(1/6) = 4$ (b) Pr(four 3's) $= \binom{24}{4}\dfrac{1^4}{6}\dfrac{5^{20}}{6} = .2139$

42. Pr(at least 2 are the same) = 1 - Pr(none match) = .5001

43. Determine the smallest n so that $\dfrac{n(n-1)\ldots(n-19)}{n^{20}}$ exceeds .5000.

6.5. Conditional Probability and Independence

1. (a) Pr(E|F) $= \dfrac{\text{Pr}(E \cap F)}{\text{Pr}(F)} = \dfrac{.1}{.3} = \dfrac{1}{3}$ (b) Pr(F|E) $= \dfrac{.1}{.5} = \dfrac{1}{5}$

2. Pr(E|F) ≠ Pr(E)   No, E and F are not independent events.

3. Pr(F') = 1 - .3 = .7, Pr(E ∩ F') = .5 - .1 = .4   E - E∩F

Pr(E|F') $= \dfrac{.4}{.7} = \dfrac{4}{7}$

4. Pr(F') = 1 - .3 = .7, Pr(E' ∩ F') = 1 - .5 - .3 + .1 = .3

Pr(E'|F') $= \dfrac{.3}{.7} = \dfrac{3}{7}$ $(E \cup F)' = 1 - (.5 + .3 - .1)$

5. Pr(resident has cancer) = .001, 30% of the residents work for Ajax,
Pr(worker for Ajax has cancer) = .003
Pr(resident works for Ajax and has cancer) = .003
Pr(resident works for Ajax)·Pr(resident has cancer)
         = (.30)·(.001) = .0003 ≠ .003

6. Pr(that he is a college graduate) $= \dfrac{.10}{.25} = \dfrac{2}{5}$

7. (a) Pr(I ∩ II ∩ III) = Pr(I)·Pr(II)·Pr(III) = .8 ·.75 ·.6 = .36

   (b) Pr(I ∩ II) · (1 - Pr(III)) = (.6)·(.4) = .24

$Pr(II \cap III) \cdot (1 - Pr(I)) = (.45) \cdot (.2) = .09$
$Pr(I \cap III) \cdot (1 - Pr(II)) = (.48) \cdot (.25) = .12$
$Pr(\text{of passing at least two tests}) = .24 + .12 + .09 + .36 = .81$

8. $(1 - .0005)^{50} = (.9995)^{50} = .975$

9. $(1 - .01)^5 \cdot (1 - .02)^5 \cdot (1 - .025)^3 = (.99)^5 \cdot (.98)^5 \cdot (.975)^3$

10. $1 - (.01)^n \geq .99999$

  $(.01)^n \leq 1 - .99999 = .00001$

  $(.01)^3 = .000001 < .00001$ 3 bulbs are needed

11. $Pr(E|F) = \dfrac{\frac{1}{4}}{\frac{1}{3}} = \dfrac{3}{4}$ $Pr(F|E) = \dfrac{\frac{1}{4}}{\frac{1}{2}} = \dfrac{1}{2}$

12. (a) $Pr(E \cap F) = .3 + .6 - .7 = .2$ (b) $Pr(E|F) = \dfrac{.2}{.6} = \dfrac{1}{3}$

  (c) $Pr(F|E) = \dfrac{.2}{.3} = \dfrac{2}{3}$ (d) $Pr(E' \cap F) = .6 - .2 = .4$

  (e) $Pr(E'|F) = \dfrac{.4}{.6} = \dfrac{2}{3}$

13. (a) $Pr(D' \cap L') = Pr(D \cup L)' = 1 - (.4 + .5 - .3) = .4$

  (b) $Pr(L|D) = \dfrac{.3}{.5} = \dfrac{3}{5}$ (c) $Pr(D|L) = \dfrac{.3}{.4} = \dfrac{3}{4}$

14. (a) $Pr(F \cap R) = .5 + .3 - (1 - .4) = .2$ (b) $Pr(R|F) = \dfrac{.2}{.3} = \dfrac{2}{3}$

  (c) $Pr(F|R) = \dfrac{.2}{.5} = \dfrac{2}{5}$

15. $Pr(HHH| \text{ 2 heads}) = \dfrac{\frac{1}{8}}{\frac{1}{2}} = \dfrac{1}{4}$

16. $Pr(\text{2 white}|\text{1 white}) = \dfrac{\binom{2}{2} \cdot \binom{3}{0}}{\binom{2}{1} \cdot \binom{3}{1} + \binom{2}{2} \cdot \binom{3}{0}} = \dfrac{1}{7}$

17. $Pr(A \cap B) = .8 \cdot .7 = .56$
    $Pr(A \cup B) = .8 + .7 - .56 = .94$

18. E = "the sample contains at least one white ball"
    F = "the sample contains balls of both colors"
    $Pr(E) = \frac{7}{10}$, $Pr(F) = \frac{6}{10}$, $Pr(E \cap F) = \frac{6}{10} \neq \frac{6 \cdot 7}{100}$

19. $Pr(\text{each friend will not tell Jane}) = .40.$

    $Pr(\text{neither tells Jane}) = .4 \cdot .4 = .16.$

20. $Pr(\text{she gets all questions right}) = (\frac{1}{2})^{10}$

21. $Pr(\text{none owns a CD}) = (.70)^4$

22. $Pr(B|A) = .25 = \frac{Pr(A \cap B)}{Pr(A)}.$ $Pr(A) = .40.$ So $Pr(A \cap B) = (.25)(.40) = .1$

    $Pr(B) = .30.$ Hence $Pr(A \cup B) = .40 + .30 - .10 = .60$

    $Pr(A' \cap B) = Pr(B) - Pr(A \cap B) = .30 - .10 = .20$

    $Pr(A|B) = \frac{.10}{.30}.$

23. If E and F are independent then $Pr(E \cap F) = Pr(E) \cdot Pr(F),$
    and $Pr(E \cup F) = Pr(E) + Pr(F) - Pr(E \cap F)$
    $Pr(E' \cap F') = Pr(E \cup F)'$
    $$= 1 - [Pr(E) + Pr(F) - Pr(E \cap F)]$$
    $$= Pr(E') - Pr(F) + Pr(E \cap F)$$
    $$= Pr(E') - Pr(F) + Pr(E) \cdot Pr(F)$$
    $$= Pr(E') - Pr(F) \cdot [1 - Pr(E)]$$
    $$= Pr(E') - Pr(F) \cdot Pr(E')$$
    $$= Pr(E') \cdot [1 - Pr(F)] = Pr(E') \cdot Pr(F')$$

24. $Pr(E \cup F) = Pr(E' \cap F')'$
    $$= 1 - Pr(E' \cap F')$$
    $$= 1 - Pr(E') \cdot Pr(F')$$

25. F = First, S = Second
    $Pr(F') = 1 - .6 = .4 = Pr(\text{player scores 0 points})$
    $Pr(F \cap S') = Pr(F) \cdot Pr(S') = .24 = Pr(\text{player scores 1 point})$
    $Pr(F \cap S) = Pr(F) \cdot Pr(S) = .36 = Pr(\text{player scores 2 points})$

26. (a) $Pr(E'|F) = Pr(E') = 1 - Pr(E) = 1 - Pr(E|F)$
    (b) $Pr(E) = \frac{1}{4}$, $Pr(F) = \frac{1}{4}$, $Pr(E|F') \neq 1 - Pr(E|F)$

27. $Pr(E \cup F|G) = \dfrac{Pr((E \cup F) \cap G)}{Pr(G)}$
    $$= \frac{Pr(E \cap G) + Pr(F \cap G) - Pr((E \cap F) \cap G)}{Pr(G)}$$
    $$= Pr(E|G) + Pr(F|G) - Pr(E \cap F|G)$$

28. % ever married among 25-29 year olds = Pr(ever married|25-29 yrs old)

29. (a) $Pr(death|A) = \frac{12,000}{120,000} = \frac{1}{10}$.

    (b) Death rate is 100 for every 1000.

    (c) $Pr(death|B) = \frac{4500}{90,000} = \frac{1}{20}$.

30. (a) $.3 + .5 - .6 = .2$ (b) $Pr(II|I) = \frac{.2}{.3} = \frac{2}{3}$

    (c) $Pr(I|II) = \frac{.2}{.5} = \frac{2}{5}$

    (d) $Pr(I) \cdot Pr(II) = .15 \neq .2 = Pr(I \cap II)$

31. (a) $Pr(B) = .8 \cdot .35 = .28$
    (b) $Pr(C) = 1 - (.65 + .28) = .07$
    (c) $Pr(H) = (.65 \cdot .75) + (.4 \cdot .28) + (.1 \cdot .07)$
    $= .4875 + .1120 + .007 = .6065$

32. M = "students taking a math course"
    C = "students taking a computer science course"
    (a) $Pr(C \cap M') = \frac{40}{250} = .16$

    (b) $Pr(M \cup C) - Pr(M \cap C) = \frac{200 - 70}{250} = .52$

    (c) $Pr(C) = \frac{110}{250} = .44$ (d) $Pr(M') = \frac{90}{250} = .36$

    (e) $Pr(M|C) = \frac{70}{110} = .64$ (f) $Pr(C|M) = \frac{70}{160} = .44$

    (g) $Pr(M|C \cup M) = \frac{160}{200} = .80$ (h) $Pr(C|M') = \frac{40}{90} = .44$

    (i) $Pr(M'|C') = \frac{50}{140} = .36$

33. (a) We are looking for Pr(over 65|lives alone) see (b).
    (b) Total percent living alone = $(.021)(.23) + (.114)(.25) +$
    $(.113)(.196) + (.326)(.113) = 9.23\%$ and percent
    over age 65 living alone = $(.326)(.113) = 3.68\%$ and the
    probability in (a) is $\frac{.0368}{.0923} = .399$.

34. B = "3rd grade boys that played baseball"
    S = "3rd grade boys that played soccer"
    (a) $Pr(S' \cap B') = \frac{40}{250}$ (b) $Pr(B \cup S) - Pr(B \cap S)$
    $= \frac{210 - 50}{250} = \frac{160}{250}$

    (c) $Pr(S \cap B') = \frac{90}{250}$ (d) $Pr(S|B) = \frac{50}{120}$

(e) $Pr(B|S') = \frac{70}{110}$

(f) $Pr(S'|B') = \frac{40}{130}$

35. (a) $\frac{550}{2700} = .20$

(b) $\frac{510}{2700} = .19$

(c) $\frac{460}{800} = .58$

(d) $\frac{210}{510} = .41$

(e) $\frac{150}{510} = .29$

(f) $\frac{1100}{1350} = .81$

36. (a) $\frac{1000}{2500} = .40$

(b) $\frac{1400}{2500} = .56$

(c) $\frac{200}{1100} = .18$

(d) $\frac{700}{1000} = .7$

(e) $\frac{900}{2000} = .45$

(f) $\frac{1000}{1500} = .67$

38. If the best player is given a number from 1 - 8, then for the best and second best to meet in the final round the second best player would need to be assigned a number from 9 - 16. There are 8 choices of 15 assignments left after choosing one for the best player. So, the probability of the best and second best players meeting in the final round is $\frac{8}{15}$.

39. $Pr(W) = \frac{53,010}{117,378}$, $Pr(U) = \frac{5725}{117,378}$, $Pr(W \cap U) = \frac{2555}{117,378}$.
$Pr(W) \cdot Pr(U) \neq Pr(W \cap U)$, so the events are not independent.

40. (a) $Pr(pos\ test|no\ disease) = \frac{53}{8288} = .00064056$

(b) $Pr(disease|pos\ test) = \frac{260}{313} = .83067$

(c) $Pr(disease) = \frac{274}{8562} = .032054$

41. (a) $\frac{24}{52 \cdot 51 \cdot 50 \cdot 49} = 3.6938 \times 10^{-6}$

(b) $\frac{4}{52 \cdot 51 \cdot 50 \cdot 49} = 6.156 \times 10^{-7}$

(c) Event (a) is more likely.

6.6 Tree Diagrams

1.

2.

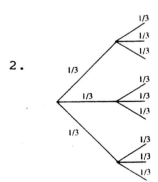

183

3.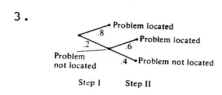

        Step I   Step II

4.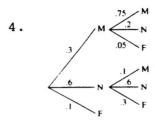

5. The probability that the procedure will fail to locate the problem is $(.2) \cdot (.4) = .08$.

6. The probability that a randomly chosen hiree will be assigned to a management position at the end of the training period is $(.3) \cdot (.75) + (.6) \cdot (.1) = .285$

7. $.1 + (.6) \cdot (.3) + (.3) \cdot (.05) = .295$

8. $(.3) \cdot (.05) + (.3) \cdot (.2) = .075$

9. W = White
   R = Red

$$\Pr(\text{second ball is red})$$
$$= \left(\tfrac{2}{3}\right) \cdot \left(\tfrac{1}{2}\right) + \left(\tfrac{1}{3}\right) \cdot \left(\tfrac{3}{4}\right) = \frac{7}{12}$$

10. $\Pr(\text{end with a '6' on the die}) = \dfrac{40}{52} \cdot \dfrac{1}{6} = \dfrac{5}{39}$.

    $\Pr(\text{end with a 'head' on the coin}) = \dfrac{12}{52} \cdot \dfrac{1}{2} = \dfrac{3}{26}$.

11. From the tree we see that the required probability is $\dfrac{1201}{5525}$.

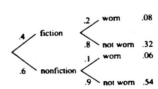

12. $(.40)(.20) + (.60)(.10) = .14 = \Pr(\text{book needs repair})$.

13. $Pr(\text{no final exam}) = (\frac{1}{6})(.8)(.8) + \frac{1}{6}(.8)(.87) + \frac{1}{6}(.9)(.8) + \frac{1}{6}(.9)(.87) + \frac{1}{6}(.95)(.8) + \frac{1}{6}(.95)(.87) = .7376$

Therefore, $Pr(\text{at least one final exam}) = 1 - .738 = .262$.

14. $Pr(\text{a child is bussed to school}) = \frac{87}{200}$. Since the total number of students is 2000, there are 870 students bussed.

15. $Pr(\text{the person is male}) = \frac{5\%}{(5 + .4)\%} = \frac{25}{27}$

16. R = Right
    L = Left

$Pr(\text{mouse will turn left on second trial})$
$= (.5) \cdot (.9) + (.5) \cdot (.7) =$

17. $Pr(\text{that the mouse will turn left on the third trial})$
$= (.5) \cdot (.9) \cdot (.9) + (.5) \cdot (.1) \cdot (.7) + (.5) \cdot (.7) \cdot (.9) + (.5) \cdot (.3) \cdot (.7) = .86$

18. G = Good, D = Defective

I .03 → D → .018

.6 .97 → G → .582

.4 .02 → D → .008

II .98 → G → .392

(a)
Pr(bolt selected will be def
= .018 + .008 = .026

(b)
Pr(machine I | defective)

$$= \frac{.018}{.026} = \frac{9}{13}$$

19. O = Ordinary
F = Fake
H = Heads
T = Tails

O $\frac{3}{4}$

H $\frac{1}{2}$

$\frac{1}{2}$ $\frac{1}{2}$ → H

$\frac{1}{2}$ → T

T $\frac{1}{2}$ $\frac{1}{2}$ → H

$\frac{1}{2}$ → T

F $\frac{1}{4}$

H 1

0 → T

1 → H

O

1 → H

T 0 → T

Pr(fake quarter | HH)

$$= \frac{\frac{1}{4} \cdot 1 \cdot 1}{\left(\frac{3}{4}\right) \cdot \left(\frac{1}{2}\right) \cdot \left(\frac{1}{2}\right) + \left(\frac{1}{4}\right)}$$

$$= \frac{\frac{1}{4}}{\frac{7}{16}} = \frac{4}{7}$$

20. H = people who have hepatitis, N = people who do not have hepatitis
+ = tested positive for hepatitis, - = tested negative for hepatiti

H .05% 95% → +

5% → -

N 99.95% 10% → +

90% → -

Pr(actually has hepatitis)

$$= \frac{(.0005) \cdot (.95)}{(.0005) \cdot (.95) + (.9995) \cdot (.1}$$

$$= .00473$$

21. Pr(that the crate is from grove I) $= \frac{1000}{2000} = \frac{1}{2}$

22. Pr(that there will be an accidental nuclear war

during the next 3 years) $= 1-(.9999)^3$

23. Pr(that there will be an accidental nuclear war

during the next n years) $= 1-(.9999)^n$

24.

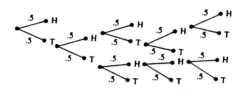

25.

Pr(winning the card game)

$$= \frac{1}{2} + \left(\frac{1}{2}\right)\left(\frac{3}{5}\right)\left(\frac{1}{2}\right) + \left(\frac{1}{2}\right)\left(\frac{3}{5}\right)\left(\frac{1}{2}\right)\left(\frac{2}{3}\right)\left(\frac{1}{2}\right) + \left(\frac{1}{2}\right)\left(\frac{2}{5}\right)\left(\frac{3}{4}\right)\left(\frac{2}{3}\right)\left(\frac{1}{2}\right) = .75$$

Yes, the probability of winning the card game is greater.

26. There are four choices left for the two cards: that both cards are red or black, or that the 51st card is red and the 52nd card is black, or that the 51st card is black and the 52nd card is red. He would know what the card is if they were the same color. The other option is that the top card is one color and the bottom card is another, that is a 50:50 guess. So, Pr(guessing the color of the 51st card) $= \frac{3}{4}$

6.7. Bayes' Theorem

1. $(.05)\cdot(.06)$ $= .0030$
    $(.10)\cdot(.04)$ $= .0040$
    $(.25)\cdot(.02)$ $= .0050$
    $(.20)\cdot(.015)$ $= .0030$
    $(.30)\cdot(.025)$ $= .0075$
    $(.10)\cdot(.040)$ $= .0040$
    —————
    $.0265$

Pr(over 60 | Accident)

$$= \frac{.0040}{.0265}$$

$$= \frac{40}{265} \cong .15$$

2. $(.30) \cdot (.0002) = .00006$
    $(.25) \cdot (.0004) = .00010$
    $(.20) \cdot (.0005) = .00010$
    $(.10) \cdot (.001) = .00010$
    $(.05) \cdot (.002) = .00010$
    $(.10) \cdot (.004) = .00040$
    $\overline{}$
    $.00086$

Pr(type I | transistor fails)
$$= \frac{.00006}{.00086} = \frac{3}{43}$$

3. $(.10) \cdot (.2) = .02$
    $(.30) \cdot (.4) = .12$
    $(.40) \cdot (.3) = .12$
    $(.20) \cdot (.1) = .02$
    $\overline{}$
    $.28$

Pr(sophomore | receives an A)
$$= \frac{.12}{.28} = \frac{3}{7}$$

4. $(.2) \cdot (.01) = .002$
    $(.1) \cdot (.02) = .002$
    $(.4) \cdot (.05) = .020$
    $(.3) \cdot (.04) = .012$
    $\overline{}$
    $.036$

Pr(he's from precinct 3 | larceny victim)
$$= \frac{.02}{.036} = \frac{10}{18} = \frac{5}{9}$$

5. $(.10) \cdot (.2) = .020$
    $(.20) \cdot (.5) = .100$
    $(.35) \cdot (.6) = .210$
    $(.30) \cdot (.75) = .225$
    $(.05) \cdot (.9) = .045$
    $\overline{}$
    $.600$

Pr($\geq$ 25,000 | 2 or more cars)
$$= \frac{.045}{.600} = .075$$

6. $(.50) \cdot (.4) = .20$
    $(.20) \cdot (.5) = .10$
    $(.30) \cdot (.7) = .21$
    $\overline{}$
    $.51$

Pr(independent | questioned at the polls)
$$= \frac{.21}{.51} = \frac{7}{17}$$

7. Pr(Guilty) = .70, Pr(Not Guilty) = .30
Now, since the thief is known to be left-handed, the conditional probability Pr(Left Handed | Guilty) = 1. This is the 1 in the following tree diagram.

G = Guilty
I = Innocent
R = Right
L = Left

The investigator should now assign the following probability of guilt: $\dfrac{.7}{.7 + .06} = .92$

8. (a)

$$(.07) \cdot (.51) = .0357$$
$$(.25) \cdot (.51) = .1275$$
$$(.37) \cdot (.49) = .1813$$
$$(.20) \cdot (.41) = .0820$$
$$(.11) \cdot (.40) = .0440$$
$$\overline{.4705}$$

Pr(the person is male) = .4705

(b) $Pr(5\text{-}19 \text{ years old}|\text{male}) = \dfrac{.1275}{.4705} = .27$

9. (a)

$$20,000 \cdot (.2) = 4000$$
$$15,000 \cdot (.15) = 2250$$
$$25,000 \cdot (.12) = 3000$$
$$30,000 \cdot (.10) = 3000$$
$$10,000 \cdot (.10) = 1000$$
$$\overline{13,250}$$

Pr(Bilingual) = $\dfrac{13,250}{100,000} = .1325$

(b) $Pr(C|\text{Bilingual}) = \dfrac{3000}{13,250} = .2264$

10. Pr(4-spot die|2-spot shows once)

$$= \frac{6 \cdot \frac{1}{2} \cdot \frac{2}{3} \cdot \frac{1}{3}^5}{6 \cdot \frac{1}{2}^7 + 6 \cdot \frac{1}{2} \cdot \frac{2}{3} \cdot \frac{1}{3}^5} = .1494$$

11. The probability that Bob and Al both choose their age is $(.2) \cdot (.2)$. The probability that they do not choose their age is $(.8) \cdot (.8)$. Given that Bob won the probability that Al chooses the same number Bob did and also wins is

$$(.2) \cdot (.2) + (.8) \cdot (.8) \cdot \left(\frac{1}{99}\right) = \frac{1}{25} + \frac{16}{25} \cdot \left(\frac{1}{99}\right) = \frac{115}{2475} \cong .46$$

12. (a) $Pr(\text{User}|\text{test positive}) = \dfrac{(.1)(.98)}{(.1)(.98) + (.9)(.05)} = \dfrac{.098}{.143}$
$$= 68.5\%$$
(b) Pr(nondrug user tests positive twice in a row) = $(.05) \cdot (.05) = .25\%$
(c) Pr(not a drug user|tests positive twice)
$$= \frac{(.9)(.05)(.05)}{(.1)(.98)^2 + (.9)(.05)^2} = 2.29\%$$

13. (a) Thirteen cards constitute $\frac{1}{4}$ of the deck, so the probability is $\frac{1}{4}$.
(b) B_1: None of the 13 is the ace of spades.
B_2: One of the 13 is the ace of spades.

A : The card chosen is not the ace of spades.

$Pr(B_1) = \frac{3}{4}$ $\qquad\qquad$ $Pr(B_2) = \frac{1}{4}$ from part (a)

$Pr(A|B_1) = 1$: if none of the thirteen is the ace of spades, then with certainty it will not be chosen.

$Pr(A|B_2) = \frac{12}{13}$: if one of the 13 is the ace of spades,

then the probability of not choosing it is $\frac{12}{13}$

We want to find $Pr(B_1|A)$. By Bayes' Theorem:

$$Pr(B_1|A) = \frac{(3/4)\cdot 1}{(3/4)\cdot 1 + (1/4)\cdot(12/13)} = .76 \quad \text{or } 76\%$$

(c) Repeating the experiment 10 times, $Pr(A|B_2) = (12/13)^{10} = .449$
The other probabilities remain the same.

$$Pr(B_2|A) = \frac{(1/4)\cdot(.449)}{(3/4)\cdot 1 + (1/4)\cdot(.449)} = .13 \quad \text{or } 13\%$$

14. $Pr(\text{blue jar}|\text{choc chip}) = \dfrac{Pr(\text{choc chip}|\text{blue jar})\cdot Pr(\text{blue jar})}{Pr(\text{choc chip})}$

$Pr(\text{choc chip}) =$
$\qquad Pr(\text{choc chip}|\text{blue})\cdot Pr(\text{blue}) + Pr(\text{choc chip}|\text{red})\cdot Pr(\text{red})$

$Pr(\text{choc chip}) = \dfrac{20}{30}\cdot\dfrac{1}{2} + \dfrac{10}{25}\cdot\dfrac{1}{2} = \dfrac{8}{15}.$

$Pr(\text{blue}|\text{choc chip}) = \dfrac{\frac{1}{3}}{\frac{8}{15}} = \dfrac{15}{24} = \dfrac{5}{8}.$

15. (a) $Pr(L|\text{winner}) = \dfrac{Pr(\text{win}|L)\cdot Pr(L)}{Pr(\text{win}|L)Pr(L) + Pr(\text{win}|P)Pr(P) + Pr(\text{win}|M)Pr(M)}$

$\qquad = \dfrac{(.05)(.40)}{(.05)(.40) + (.02)(.20) + (.03)(.40)}$

$\qquad = .556 \text{ or } \dfrac{5}{9}.$

(b) $Pr(\text{winner is from Pylesville}) = Pr(P|\text{win}) =$
$\qquad\qquad \dfrac{(.02)(.20)}{.036} = .11 = \dfrac{1}{9}.$

16. $\Pr(I\,|\,\text{math}) =$

$$\frac{\Pr(\text{math}\,|\,I)\,\Pr(I)}{\Pr(\text{math}\,|\,I)\,\Pr(I)\ +\ \Pr(\text{math}\,|\,II)\,\Pr(II)\ +\ \Pr(\text{math}\,|\,III)\,\Pr(III)}$$

The denominator is $\dfrac{5}{25}\cdot\dfrac{25}{80} + \dfrac{6}{20}\cdot\dfrac{20}{80} + \dfrac{5}{35}\cdot\dfrac{35}{80} = \dfrac{16}{80}$.

The numerator is $\dfrac{5}{25}\cdot\dfrac{25}{80} = \dfrac{5}{80}$. So $\Pr(I\,|\,\text{math}) = \dfrac{5}{16}$.

17. (a) $\Pr(\text{false neg}) = \Pr(\text{neg test}\,|\,\text{pregnant}) = 1 - .99 = .01$.

(b) $\Pr(\text{pregnant}\,|\,\text{pos test}) = \dfrac{(.99)(.40)}{(.99)(.40) + (.02)(.60)} = .971$.

18. $\Pr(\text{condition}\,|\,\text{pos test}) = \dfrac{(.90)(.65)}{(.90)(.65) + (.20)(.35)} = .893$

$\Pr(\text{condition}\,|\,\text{pos test}) = \dfrac{(.90)(.30)}{(.90)(.30) + (.20)(.70)} = .659$.

6. Supplementary Exercises

1. $\Pr(\text{at least one head})$ is the complement of $\Pr(\text{no heads}) =$

$$1 - \frac{1}{32} = \frac{31}{32}$$

2. E = "first toss is heads"
F = "there are more heads than tails"

$\Pr(E) = 4\cdot(.5)^3 = .5$ $\qquad\qquad$ $\Pr(F) = 4\cdot(.5)^3 = .5$

$\Pr(E \cap F) = 3\cdot(.5)^3 = .375$

$\Pr(E)\cdot\Pr(F) = (.5)\cdot(.5) = .25 \neq \Pr(E \cap F)$ No, they are not independent.

3. $\Pr(\text{person will receive 1 airplane and 1 gun from two boxes})$
$$= \left(\tfrac{1}{3}\right)\left(\tfrac{2}{3}\right) + \left(\tfrac{2}{3}\right)\left(\tfrac{1}{3}\right) = \tfrac{4}{9}$$

4. Of three committee members chosen the probability that they will all be men is:

$$\frac{\binom{5}{3}}{\binom{10}{3}} = \frac{10}{120} = \frac{1}{12}$$

5. $\Pr(\text{Engineering}\,|\,\text{Public college}) = \dfrac{15 - 5}{25} = \dfrac{10}{25} = \dfrac{2}{5}$

6. $\Pr(\text{correct} | \text{rejected}) = \dfrac{(.8)(.05)}{(.8)(.05) + (.2)(.9)} = \dfrac{.04}{.22} = \dfrac{2}{11}$

7. (a) $\Pr(\text{they will both hit}) = \left(\dfrac{1}{4}\right)\left(\dfrac{1}{3}\right) = \dfrac{1}{12}$

   (b) $\Pr(\text{at least one will hit the target}) = \dfrac{1}{12} + \left(\dfrac{1}{4}\right)\left(\dfrac{2}{3}\right) + \left(\dfrac{1}{3}\right)\left(\dfrac{3}{4}\right) = \dfrac{1}{2}$

8. $\Pr(\text{the event will occur}) = \dfrac{7}{12}$

9. $\Pr(\text{the Americans are assigned to the first two lanes})$ is:

   $\dfrac{\binom{2}{1}}{\binom{7}{1}} \cdot \dfrac{\binom{1}{1}}{\binom{6}{1}} = \dfrac{2}{7} \cdot \dfrac{1}{6} = \dfrac{1}{21}$

10. $\Pr(\text{stopping after exactly two balls are drawn})$

    $= \left(\dfrac{1}{3}\right) \cdot \left(\dfrac{1}{2}\right) + \left(\dfrac{1}{3}\right) \cdot \left(\dfrac{1}{2}\right) + \left(\dfrac{1}{3}\right) \cdot \left(\dfrac{1}{2}\right) = \dfrac{2}{3}$

11. E = "the red die shows a 2"
    F = "the sum of the numbers is 8"
    $\Pr(E) = \dfrac{1}{6}$ $\qquad$ $\Pr(F) = \dfrac{5}{6}$ $\qquad$ $\Pr(E \cap F) = \dfrac{1}{6} \cdot \dfrac{1}{6} = \dfrac{1}{36}$

    $\Pr(E) \cdot \Pr(F) = \dfrac{1}{6} \cdot \dfrac{5}{6} = \dfrac{5}{36} \neq \Pr(E \cap F)$
    The events are not independent.

12. $\Pr(E \cap F) = .4 + .3 - .5 = .2$, $\Pr(E|F) = \dfrac{.2}{.3} = \dfrac{2}{3}$

13. $\Pr(\text{Employee C} | \text{incorrect}) = \dfrac{(.2)(.05)}{(.02)(.4) + (.4)(.03) + (.2)(.05)}$

    $= \dfrac{1}{3}$

14. $\Pr(\text{at least two of them were born on the same day})$

    $\dfrac{\binom{3}{2}\binom{3}{1} + \binom{3}{1}\binom{3}{2} + \binom{3}{3}}{(7) \cdot (7)} = \dfrac{19}{49}$

15. $\Pr(B \cup A) = \dfrac{1}{2}$ $\qquad$ $\Pr(B \cap A') = \dfrac{1}{3}$ $\qquad$ $\Pr(A) = \dfrac{1}{2} - \dfrac{1}{3} = \dfrac{1}{6}$

16. Of the ten balls choose 3 of the 5 odd-numbered balls, $\binom{5}{3}$, then order those, 3! ways. Of the 4 odd positions choose 3, $\binom{4}{3}$. Choose 4 even balls from the 5 available, $\binom{5}{4}$, and place them in the 4 remaining slots, 4! ways.

$$\frac{\binom{5}{3} \cdot 6 \cdot \binom{4}{3} \cdot \binom{5}{4} \cdot 4!}{P(10,7)} = \frac{(240) \cdot (120)}{604,800} = \frac{1}{21}$$

17. Pr(second bill is 5 | first bill is 5) $= \dfrac{\frac{1}{3}}{\frac{1}{3} + \frac{1}{3} \cdot \frac{1}{2}} = \frac{2}{3}$

18. Switch and you will win two out of three times. You will only lose if the cup originally selected contained the coin, an event with probability 1/3.

Note: You might recognize this problem as being essentially the same as the Monte Hall problem that has caused quite a stir. "A game show contestant is asked to select one of three doors. A car is behind one door and goats are behind the other doors. After the selection is made, the host opens a door to reveal a goat and gives the contestant the opportunity to switch. Should the contestant switch?" When the problem and its correct solution appeared in the "Ask Marilyn" column of *Parade Magazine*, several college math teachers wrote derogatory responses criticizing Marilyn Vos Savant. Several articles about the matter have appeared in MAA publications. The only tricky point - which has nothing to do with mathematics - is the motivation of the host. If he only shows you the door when he knows you've made the right choice, then all bets are off!

19. To find the probability, we must express 13:12 as a fraction:
13 + 12 = 25, so it is $\frac{13}{25}$ = .52   or   52%

20. 26% are less than 18 years of age, the ratio is 26 to 74 or 13 to 37.

21. Since there are 9 letters there are 9! different ways to arrange them.
Pr(the word will be 'education', 'auctioned' or 'cautioned') is
$\frac{3}{9!}$ = .0000083

22. $\dfrac{1}{1 + 2 + 3} = \dfrac{1}{6}$

23. 35 people are needed.

24. Based on the test results, 421 people are expected to have the disease so the pool is not large enough.

PROBABILITY AND STATISTICS

7.1. Frequency and Probability Distribution

1.

Grade	Number of Occurrences	Relative Frequency
0	2	2/25 = .08
1	3	3/25 = .12
2	10	10/25 = .40
3	6	6/25 = .24
4	4	4/25 = .16
Total	25	

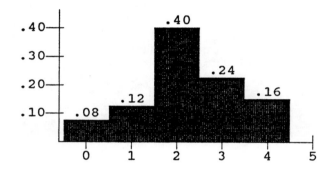

2.

Number of cars	Number of occurrences	Relative Frequency
0	0	0/60 = .00
1	9	9/60 = .15
2	21	21/60 = .35
3	15	15/60 = .25
4	12	12/60 = .20
5	3	3/60 = .05
Total	60	

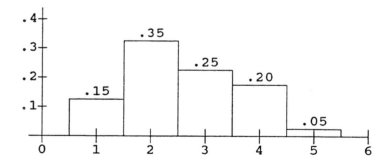

3.

No. of calls	No. of occur.	Rel. Freq.
20	3	3/60 = .05
21	3	3/60 = .05
22	0	0/60 = .00
23	6	6/60 = .10
24	18	18/60 = .30
25	12	12/60 = .20
26	0	0/60 = .00
27	9	9/60 = .15
28	6	6/60 = .10
29	3	3/60 = .05

4.

No. Produced	Rel. Freq.
50	2/40 = .05
51	0/40 = .00
52	4/40 = .10
53	6/40 = .15
54	14/40 = .35
55	8/40 = .20
56	4/40 = .10
57	0/40 = .00
58	0/40 = .00
59	2/40 = .05

5.

No. of heads	Rel. Freq.
0	$(.5)(.5)(.5) = 1/8$
1	$3 \cdot (.5)(.5)(.5) = 3/8$
2	$3 \cdot (.5)(.5)(.5) = 3/8$
3	$(.5)(.5)(.5) = 1/8$

6.

No. Red Balls	Prob.
0	$\dfrac{\binom{3}{0}\cdot\binom{4}{3}}{\binom{7}{3}} = \dfrac{4}{35}$
1	$\dfrac{\binom{3}{1}\cdot\binom{4}{2}}{\binom{7}{3}} = \dfrac{18}{35}$

No. Red Balls	Prob.
2	$\dfrac{\binom{3}{2}\cdot\binom{4}{1}}{\binom{7}{3}} = \dfrac{12}{35}$
3	$\dfrac{\binom{3}{3}\cdot\binom{4}{0}}{\binom{7}{3}} = \dfrac{1}{35}$

7.

No. of shots	Prob.
1	$\dfrac{1}{3}$
2	$\left(\dfrac{2}{3}\right)\left(\dfrac{1}{3}\right) = \dfrac{2}{9}$
3	$\left(\dfrac{2}{3}\right)\left(\dfrac{2}{3}\right)\left(\dfrac{1}{3}\right) = \dfrac{4}{27}$
4	$\left(\dfrac{2}{3}\right)\left(\dfrac{2}{3}\right)\left(\dfrac{2}{3}\right)\cdot 1 = \dfrac{8}{27}$

8.

Number	Probability
1	1/6
2	1/6
3	1/6
4	1/6
5	1/6
6	1/6

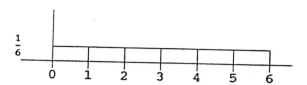

9.

Earnings	Prob.
$5	$\left(\frac{2}{6}\right)\left(\frac{1}{5}\right) = \frac{1}{15}$
$1	$\left(\frac{2}{6}\right)\left(\frac{4}{5}\right) + \left(\frac{4}{6}\right)\left(\frac{2}{5}\right) = \frac{8}{15}$

Earnings	Prob.
$-1	$\left(\frac{4}{6}\right)\left(\frac{3}{5}\right) = \frac{2}{5}$

10.

No. of tosses	Earnings	Probability
1	−50¢	$\frac{1}{2}$
2	0¢	$\left(\frac{1}{2}\right)\left(\frac{1}{2}\right) = \frac{1}{4}$
3	50¢	$\left(\frac{1}{2}\right)\left(\frac{1}{2}\right)\left(\frac{1}{2}\right) = \frac{1}{8}$
4	$1	$\left(\frac{1}{2}\right)\left(\frac{1}{2}\right)\left(\frac{1}{2}\right) \cdot 1 = \frac{1}{8}$

11.

Outcome	Prob.
5	.2
6	.1
7	.3

Probability that the outcome will be between 5 and 7 inclusive is .2 + .1 + .3 = .6

12. $\{8 \le x \le 12\}$

13.

k	$\Pr(X^2 = k)$
0	.1
1	.2
4	.3
9	.2
16	.2

14.

k	$\Pr(Y^2 = k)$
25	.3
100	.4
225	.1
400	.1
625	.1

15.

k	$\Pr(X - 1 = k)$
−1	.1
0	.2
1	.3
2	.2
3	.2

16.

k	$\Pr(Y - 15 = k)$
−10	.3
−5	.4
0	.1
5	.1
10	.1

17.

k	$\Pr(\frac{1}{5}Y = k)$
1	.3
2	.4
3	.1
4	.1
5	.1

18.

k	$\Pr(2X^2 = k)$
0	.1
2	.2
8	.3
18	.2
32	.2

19.

k	$\Pr((X + 1)^2 = k)$
1	.1
4	.2
9	.3
16	.2
25	.2

20.

k	$\Pr((\frac{1}{5}Y + 1)^2 = k)$
4	.3
9	.4
16	.1
25	.1
36	.1

21.

Grade	Rel Freq
0	.167
1	.250
2	.333
3	.167
4	.083

9 a.m. class

Grade	Rel Freq
0	.16
1	.23
2	.15
3	.21
4	.25

10 a.m. class

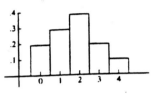

9 A.M. class

22. (a) $\dfrac{10 + 5 + 20}{10 + 15 + 20 + 10 + 5} = .75$

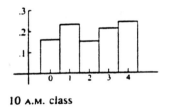

10 A.M. class

(b) $\dfrac{16 + 23 + 15}{16 + 23 + 15 + 21 + 25} = .54$

(c) $\dfrac{10 + 15}{60} = .417$

(d) $\dfrac{(20 + 10 + 5) + (15 + 21 + 25)}{160}$ .60

23. $\dfrac{6 + 4 + 10}{2 + 3 + 10 + 6 + 4} = .80$

24. $\dfrac{15}{60} = .25$

25. (a) $\dfrac{(3 + 3) + (6 + 3)}{3 + 3 + 0 + 6 + 18 + 12 + 0 + 9 + 6 + 3} = .25$

(b) $\dfrac{6 + 18 + 12}{60} = .60$

(c)

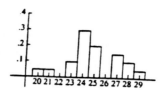

(d) About 24 or 25 calls on the average should come in within the hour. The histogram seems to be balanced at about that value.

26.

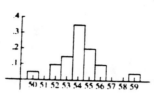

27. (a) 59   (b) $\dfrac{2}{2 + 0 + 4 + 6 + 14 + 8 + 4 + 0 + 0 + 2} = .05$

(c) 54   (d) $\dfrac{14}{40} = .35$ (e) 54 items on the average are produced each week.

28. (a)

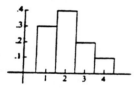

(b)

(c) P(X = 2 or 3) = .40 + .20 = .60
(d) P(Y = 2 or 3) = .20 + .20 = .40
(e) P(X ≥ 2) = .40 + .20 + .10 = .70
(f) P(X + 3 ≥ 5) = P(X ≥ 2) = .70
(g) $P(Y^2 \le 9)$ = P(Y = 1, 2, or 3) = 3(.20) = .60
(h) P(Y ≤ 10) = 1
(i)

k	Pr(2X = k)
2	.3
4	.4
6	.2
8	.1

(j)

k	$Pr((Y + 2)^2 = k)$
9	.2
16	.2
25	.2
36	.4

(k) Y appears to have the higher average value because P(Y=4) = .4.

29. (a) P(U = 4) = 1 − ($\dfrac{3}{15}$ + $\dfrac{2}{15}$ + $\dfrac{4}{15}$ + $\dfrac{5}{15}$) = $\dfrac{1}{15}$

(b) P(U ≥ 2) = $\dfrac{4}{15}$ + $\dfrac{5}{15}$ + $\dfrac{1}{15}$ = $\dfrac{2}{3}$

(c) P(U ≤ 3) = $\dfrac{3}{15}$ + $\dfrac{2}{15}$ + $\dfrac{4}{15}$ + $\dfrac{5}{15}$ = $\dfrac{14}{15}$

(d) $P(U + 2 < 4) = P(U < 2) = \frac{1}{3}$

(e)

7.2. Binomial Trials

1. $Pr(X = 2) = \binom{4}{2} \cdot (\frac{1}{6})^2 \cdot (\frac{5}{6})^2 = 6 \cdot \frac{1}{36} \cdot \frac{25}{36} = \frac{25}{216}$

    $k = 2 \qquad n = 4 \qquad p = \frac{1}{6} \qquad q = \frac{5}{6}$

2. $Pr(X = 3) = \binom{6}{3} \cdot (\frac{1}{2})^3 \cdot (\frac{1}{2})^3 = 20 \cdot \frac{1}{8} \cdot \frac{1}{8} = \frac{20}{64} = \frac{5}{16}$

    $k = 3 \qquad n = 6 \qquad p = \frac{1}{2} \qquad q = \frac{1}{2}$

3. $Pr(X = 3) = \binom{4}{3} \cdot (\frac{1}{4})^3 \cdot (\frac{3}{4})^1 = 4 \cdot (\frac{1}{64}) \cdot \frac{3}{4} = \frac{3}{64}$

    $k = 3 \qquad n = 4 \qquad p = \frac{1}{4} \qquad q = \frac{3}{4}$

4. $Pr(X = 2) = \binom{5}{2}(.7)^2(.3)^3 = (10) \cdot (.49) \cdot (.027) = .1323$

    $k = 2 \qquad n = 5 \qquad p = .7 \qquad q = .3$

5. $p = .6$ and $q = .4$

    $Pr(X \leq 2) = Pr(X = 0) + Pr(X = 1) + Pr(X = 2)$

    $= \binom{5}{2} \cdot (\frac{3}{5})^2 \cdot (\frac{2}{5})^3 + \binom{5}{1} \cdot (\frac{3}{5})^1 \cdot (\frac{2}{5})^4 + \binom{5}{0} \cdot (\frac{3}{5})^0 \cdot (\frac{2}{5})^5$

    $= 10 \cdot (\frac{9}{125}) \cdot (\frac{8}{125}) + 5 \cdot (\frac{3}{5}) \cdot \frac{16}{625} + 1 \cdot 1 \cdot (\frac{32}{3125}) = \frac{720}{3125} + \frac{240}{3125} + \frac{32}{3125} = \frac{992}{3125}$

6. $p = \dfrac{1}{2}$ and $q = \dfrac{1}{2}$ $n = 6$

$\Pr(X \ge 5) = \Pr(X = 5) + \Pr(X = 6)$

$= \binom{6}{5} \cdot (\dfrac{1}{2})^5 \cdot (\dfrac{1}{2})^1 + \binom{6}{6} \cdot (\dfrac{1}{2})^6 \cdot (\dfrac{1}{2})^0 = \dfrac{6}{64} + \dfrac{1}{64} = \dfrac{7}{64}$

7. $p = .6$ and $q = .4$ $n = 5$

$\Pr(X \le 1) = \Pr(X = 0) + \Pr(X = 1) = \binom{5}{0} \cdot (\dfrac{3}{5})^0 \cdot (\dfrac{2}{5})^5 + \binom{5}{1} \cdot (\dfrac{3}{5})^1 \cdot (\dfrac{2}{5})^4 =$

$1 \cdot 1 \cdot \dfrac{32}{3125} + 5 \cdot \dfrac{3}{5} + \dfrac{16}{625} = \dfrac{32 + 240}{3125} = .087$, selection may have been biased.

8. $p = .1$ and $q = .9$ $n = 8$

$\Pr(X = 2) = \binom{8}{2} \cdot (.1)^2 \cdot (.9)^6 = \dfrac{28 \cdot 9^6}{10^8} = .1488.$

9. $p = .3$ and $q = .7$ $n = 10.$

$\Pr(X \ge 2) = 1 - \Pr(X \le 2) = 1 - [\Pr(X = 1) + \Pr(X = 2)]$

$\Pr(X \le 2) = \binom{10}{1} \cdot (\dfrac{3}{10})^1 \cdot (\dfrac{7}{10})^9 + \binom{10}{0} \cdot (\dfrac{3}{10})^0 \cdot (\dfrac{7}{10})^{10} = (\dfrac{3 \cdot 7}{10})^9 + (\dfrac{7}{10})^{10} = .1493$

and $1 - .1493 = .8507.$

10. $\Pr(X = 5) = \begin{bmatrix} 10 \\ 5 \end{bmatrix} \cdot (.4)^5 \cdot (.6)^5 = .2007$, where $n = 10$, $p = .4$, and $q = .6$.

11. $\Pr(X \ge 2) = 1 - \Pr(X < 2).$ $\Pr(X < 2) = \begin{bmatrix} 12 \\ 0 \end{bmatrix} \cdot (1/6)^0 \cdot (5/6)^{12}$

$+ \begin{bmatrix} 12 \\ 1 \end{bmatrix} \cdot (1/6)^1 \cdot (5/6)^{11} = .1122 + .2692.$

So $\Pr(X \ge 2) = 1 - .3813 = .6187.$

12. $\Pr(X = 3) = \begin{bmatrix} 8 \\ 3 \end{bmatrix} \cdot (.15)^3 \cdot (.85)^5 = .0839$, where $n = 8$, $p = .15$, $q = .85$.

13. $\Pr(X > 2) = 1 - \Pr(X \le 2)$.

$\Pr(X \le 2) = \begin{bmatrix} 9 \\ 0 \end{bmatrix} \cdot (.2)^0 \cdot (.8)^9 + \begin{bmatrix} 9 \\ 1 \end{bmatrix} \cdot (.2)^1 \cdot (.8)^8 + \begin{bmatrix} 9 \\ 2 \end{bmatrix} \cdot (.2)^2 \cdot (.8)^7 = .7382.$

$\Pr(X > 2) = 1 - .7382 = .2618.$

k	$\Pr(X = k)$
0	.1780
1	.3560
2	.2966
3	.1318
4	.0330
5	.0044
6	.0002

14. We used n = 6 and p = 1/4.

k	$\Pr(X = k)$
0	.0168
1	.0896
2	.2090
3	.2787
4	.2322
5	.1239
6	.0413
7	.0079
8	.0007

15. We used n = 8 and p = .40.

16. (a) Use formula for $\begin{bmatrix} n \\ k \end{bmatrix}$ and $\begin{bmatrix} n \\ n - k \end{bmatrix}$.

$\begin{bmatrix} n \\ k \end{bmatrix} = \dfrac{n!}{k!(n-k)!} \cdot \begin{bmatrix} n \\ n-k \end{bmatrix} = \dfrac{n!}{(n-k)!(n-(n-k))!} = \dfrac{n!}{(n-k)!(k!)}$

(b) $n = 10 \quad p = \dfrac{1}{2} \quad$ and $\quad q = \dfrac{1}{2}$.

$\Pr(X = k) = \begin{bmatrix} n \\ k \end{bmatrix} p^k \, q^{n-k} = \begin{bmatrix} 10 \\ k \end{bmatrix} (\tfrac{1}{2})^k \, (\tfrac{1}{2})^{10-k}.$

$\Pr(X = 10 - k) = \begin{bmatrix} 10 \\ 10-k \end{bmatrix} (\tfrac{1}{2})^{10-k} \, (\tfrac{1}{2})^{10-(10-k)} = \begin{bmatrix} 10 \\ k \end{bmatrix} (\tfrac{1}{2})^{10-k} \, (\tfrac{1}{2})^k.$

17. $\Pr(X \ge 10) = \Pr(X = 10) + \Pr(X = 11) + \Pr(X = 12)$
$= \binom{12}{10} \cdot (.8)^{10} \cdot (.2)^2 + \binom{12}{11} \cdot (.8)^{11} \cdot (.2)^1 + \binom{12}{12} \cdot (.8)^{12} \cdot (.2)^0 = .5583$

18. Chance of "success" (recessive) $p = \frac{1}{4}$ $q = \frac{3}{4}$ $n = 3$

$$Pr(X \geq 1) = 1 - Pr(X = 0)$$
$$= 1 - \binom{3}{0} \cdot (\frac{1}{4})^0 \cdot (\frac{3}{4})^3$$
$$= 1 - 1 \cdot 1 \cdot \frac{27}{64} = \frac{37}{64}.$$

19. A = event 6 appears exactly 9 times, B = event 6 appears at least 9 times

$$Pr(A) = \binom{10}{9} \cdot (\frac{1}{6})^9 \cdot (\frac{5}{6})^1 = \frac{50}{6^{10}} \qquad\qquad Pr(A|B) = \frac{50}{51}$$

$$Pr(B) = \frac{50}{6^{10}} + \binom{10}{10} \cdot (\frac{1}{6})^{10} \cdot (\frac{5}{6})^0 = \frac{51}{6^{10}}.$$

20. $p = \frac{1}{2}$ and $q = \frac{1}{2}$ $n = 9$. After 9 tosses, $Pr(X = 3)$

$$= \binom{9}{3} \cdot (\frac{1}{2})^3 \cdot (\frac{1}{2})^6 = \frac{84}{512} = \frac{42}{256}.$$

$$Pr(\text{fourth head occurs on the tenth toss}) = \frac{42}{256} \cdot \frac{1}{2} = \frac{21}{256}.$$

21. Use $n = 300$, $k = 5$, $p = .01$, $q = .99$.
Then $\binom{300}{5}(0.1)^5(.99)^{295} = .1010$.

22. Use $n = 8$, $p = .005$. Then $Pr(\text{at least one error}) = 1 - Pr(\text{no errors})$
$= 1 - \binom{8}{0}(.995)^8 = 3.931\%$.

23.

0	1	2	3	4	5	6	7	8	9	10	11	12	13	14
.003	.021	.067	.134	.190	.202	.169	.112	.061	.027	.009	.003	.001	.00015	.000

24. $Pr(\text{digit 2 appears at least once}) = 1 - Pr(\text{digit 2 does not appear})$
$= 1 - \binom{4}{0}(.10)^0(.90)^4 = .3439$.

$Pr(\text{40 of 100 have at least one 2}) = \binom{100}{40}(.3439)^{40}(.6561)^{60} = .04108$.

7.3 The Mean

1. $E(x) = 0 \cdot (.15) + 1 \cdot (.2) + 2 \cdot (.1) + 3 \cdot (.25) + 4 \cdot (.3)$
   $E(x) = .2 + .2 + .75 + 1.2 = 2.35$.

2. $E(x) = -1 \cdot (.1) + \frac{-1}{2} \cdot (.4) + 0 \cdot (.25) + \frac{1}{2} \cdot (.2) + 1 \cdot (.05)$
   $E(x) = -.1 + -.2 + .1 + .05 = -.15$.

3. (a) $4 + 4 + 4 + 3 + 3 + 3 + 3 + 2 + 2 + 1 = 29$
   $\frac{29}{10} = 2.9$.

   (b)
Grade	Rel. Freq.
4	.3
3	.4
2	.2
1	.1

   (c) $4 \cdot (.3) + 3 \cdot (.4) + 2 \cdot (.2) + 1 \cdot (.1) = 2.9$.

4. (a) $9.8 + 9.8 + 9.4 + 9.2 + 9.2 + 9.0 = 56.4$
   $\frac{56.4}{6} = 9.4$.

   (b)
Scores	Rel. Freq.
9.8	1/3
9.4	1/6
9.2	1/3
9.0	1/6

   (c) $9.8 \cdot (\frac{1}{3}) + 9.4 \cdot (\frac{1}{6}) + 9.2 \cdot (\frac{1}{3}) + 9.0 \cdot (\frac{1}{6}) = 9.4$.

5. Group A
   $0 \cdot (.3) + 1 \cdot (.3) + 2 \cdot (.2) + 3 \cdot (.1) + 4 \cdot (.1) + 5 \cdot (.1) = 1.9$
   Group B
   $0 \cdot (.2) + 1 \cdot (.3) + 2 \cdot (.3) + 3 \cdot (.1) + 4 \cdot (.1) + 5 \cdot (.0) = 1.6$
   Group B had fewer cavities.

6. Investment A
   $1000 \cdot (.2) + 2000 \cdot (.5) + 3000 \cdot (.3) = 2100$
   Investment B
   $-3000 \cdot (.1) + 0 \cdot (.3) + 4000 \cdot (.6) = 2100$

   Both have mean $2100.

7.
Earnings	Rel. Freq.	$k \cdot Pr(X = k)$
$35	1/38	35/38
$-1	37/38	-37/38

   $E(x) = \frac{-37}{38} + \frac{35}{38} = \frac{-2}{38}$
   $= -\$ .0526$
   or $\mu = -5.26$ cents

8.

Earnings	Rel. Freq.
x	2/38 = 1/19
-1	36/38 = 18/19

$$E = \frac{x}{19} + \left(\frac{-18}{19}\right) = \frac{-1}{19} \quad \text{(given)}$$

Thus $x - 18 = -1$
or $x = 17$.

9.

Earnings	Probability
-50¢	$\frac{2}{6} = \frac{1}{3}$
0¢	$\left(\frac{4}{6}\right)\left(\frac{2}{5}\right) = \frac{4}{15}$
50¢	$\left(\frac{4}{6}\right)\left(\frac{3}{5}\right)\left(\frac{2}{4}\right) = \frac{1}{5}$

Earnings	Probability
$1.00	$\left(\frac{4}{6}\right)\left(\frac{3}{5}\right)\left(\frac{2}{4}\right)\left(\frac{2}{3}\right) = \frac{2}{15}$
$1.50	$\left(\frac{4}{6}\right)\left(\frac{3}{5}\right)\left(\frac{2}{4}\right)\left(\frac{1}{3}\right)\left(\frac{2}{2}\right) = \frac{1}{15}$

$$E(x) = \left(-\frac{1}{2}\right)\cdot\left(\frac{1}{3}\right) + (0)\cdot\left(\frac{4}{15}\right) + \left(\frac{1}{2}\right)\cdot\left(\frac{1}{5}\right) + (1)\cdot\left(\frac{2}{15}\right) + (1.5)\cdot\left(\frac{1}{15}\right) = .166$$
$$= 16.6\%.$$

10.

Winnings	Probability
$0	$\left(\frac{6}{8}\right)\left(\frac{5}{7}\right) = \frac{15}{28}$
$1	$\left(\frac{6}{8}\right)\left(\frac{2}{7}\right) + \left(\frac{2}{8}\right)\left(\frac{6}{7}\right) = \frac{3}{7} = \frac{12}{28}$
$2	$\left(\frac{2}{8}\right)\left(\frac{1}{7}\right) = \frac{1}{28}$

$$\mu = 0\cdot\left(\frac{15}{28}\right) + 1\cdot\left(\frac{12}{28}\right)$$
$$+ 2\cdot\left(\frac{1}{28}\right) = 50¢$$

11. The probability that he dies is $1 - .9 = .1$, he should be willing to invest $(.1\cdot\$10,000) = \$1000$.

12. The probability that the man will live 5 more years is .9 and the probability that the woman will live 5 more years is .95.

	Prob. that they will die in 5 yrs.	Earnings	$k\cdot Pr(X = k)$
man	.1	10,000	1000
woman	.05	10,000	500
both	(.1)(.05) = .005	15,000	25

They should be willing to invest $1000 + 500 - 25 = \$1475$.

13.

k	$Pr(X = k)$	$k\cdot Pr(X = k)$
1	1/36	1/36
2	3/36	6/36
3	5/36	15/36
4	7/36	28/36
5	9/36	45/36
6	11/36	66/36

$$E(x) = 161/36$$

14. Sally's average ($5168) is greater than Frank's average ($4983).

15. 2.474

16. $5(96) + 16(97) + 22(98) + 30(99) + 9(100) + 1(101) = 98.301$ degrees.

7.4. The Variance and Standard Deviation

1.

k	$Pr(X = k)$	$k \cdot Pr(X = k)$	$(k - \mu)^2$	$(k - \mu)^2 \cdot Pr(x = k)$
70	.5	35.0	1	0.5
71	.2	14.2	0	0.0
72	.1	7.2	1	0.1
73	.2	14.6	4	0.8
		$\mu = 71.0$		$\sigma^2 = 1.4$

2.

k	$Pr(X = k)$	$k \cdot Pr(X = k)$	$(k - \mu)^2$	$(k - \mu)^2 \cdot Pr(X = k)$
-1	1/8	-2/16	1	1/8
-1/2	3/8	-3/16	1/4	3/32
0	1/8	0	0	0
1/2	1/8	1/16	1/4	1/32
1	2/8	4/16	1	2/8
		$\mu = 0$		$\sigma^2 = \dfrac{16/32}{} = \dfrac{1}{2}$

3. B has the largest variance since by inspection both A and B have the same mean and the same range of values around the mean, but B's extreme values (1 and 4) have a higher probability than A's.

4. B, since the range around B's and C's mean is the same (± 2), but the probability of the extreme values is higher for B than C.

5. (a)   Investment A

k	$Pr(X = k)$	$k \cdot Pr(X = k)$	$(k - \mu)^2$	$(k - \mu)^2 \cdot Pr(X = k)$
-10	1/5	-2	625	125
20	3/5	12	25	15
25	1/5	5	100	20
		$\mu_A = 15$		$\sigma_A^2 = 160$

  Investment B

k	$Pr(X = k)$	$k \cdot Pr(X = k)$	$(k - \mu)^2$	$(k - \mu)^2 \cdot Pr(X = k)$
0	.3	0	169	50.7
10	.4	4	9	3.6
30	.3	9	289	86.7
		$\mu_B = 13$		$\sigma_B^2 = 141.0$

(b) A has the higher mean, so A also has the higher expected return
(c) B is less risky, it has the smaller variance.

6. (a)

	Golfer A				Golfer B	
k	Pr(X = k)	k · Pr(X = k)	k	Pr(X = k)	k · Pr(X = k)
39	2/20	3.90	39	0/20	0
40	6/20	12.00	40	3/20	6.00
41	7/20	14.35	41	4/20	8.20
42	1/20	2.10	42	5/20	10.50
43	3/20	6.45	43	6/20	12.90
44	1/20	2.20	44	2/20	4.40
		$\bar{x}_A = 41.00$			$\bar{x}_B = 42.00$

$$s_A^2 = \frac{1}{19} \cdot [(39-41)^2 \cdot 2 + (40-41)^2 \cdot 6 + (42-41)^2 + (43-41)^2 \cdot 3 + (44-41)^2]$$

$$= \frac{1}{19} \cdot [(-2)^2 \cdot 2 + (-1)^2 \cdot 6 + (1)^2 + (2)^2 \cdot 3 + (3)^2] = \frac{36}{19}$$

$$= 1.895$$

$$s_B^2 = \frac{1}{19} \cdot [(2)^2 \cdot 3 + (1)^2 \cdot 4 + (1)^2 \cdot 6 + (2)^2 \cdot 2] = 30/19 = 1.58.$$

(b) A is the better golfer because $\bar{x}_A < \bar{x}_B$.

(c) B is the more consistent golfer because $s_B^2 < s_A^2$.

(a) Population mean and variance
Business A

k	Pr(X = k)	k · Pr(X = k)	k^2 · Pr(X = k)
100	.1	10	1000
101	.2	20.2	2040.2
102	.3	30.6	3121.2
103	0	0	0
104	0	0	0
105	.2	21.0	2205.0
106	.2	21.2	2247.2
		$\mu_A = 103$	10613.6

$$\sigma_A^2 = 10,613.6 - (103)^2 = 4.6$$

Business B

k	Pr(X = k)	k · Pr(X = k)	k^2 · Pr(X = k)
100	0	0	0
101	.2	20.2	2040.2
102	0	0	0
103	.2	20.6	2121.8
104	.1	10.4	1081.6
105	.2	21.0	2205.0
106	.3	31.8	3370.8
		$\mu_B = \overline{104}$	$\overline{10,819.4}$

$$\sigma_B^2 = 10,819.4 - (104)^2 = 3.4$$

(b) Business B has the better sales record since $\mu_B > \mu_A$.

(c) Business B has the more consistent sales record since $\sigma_A^2 < \sigma_B^2$.

8. (a)
Student A

k	Pr(X = k)	k^2	k · Pr(X = k)	k^2 · Pr(X = k)
4	4/10 = .4	16	1.6	6.4
3	2/10 = .2	9	0.6	1.8
2	3/10 = .3	4	0.6	1.2
1	0/10 = 0	1	0.0	0.0
0	1/10 = .1	0	0.0	0.0
			$\mu_A = \overline{2.8}$	$E(X^2) = \overline{9.4}$

$$\sigma_A^2 = 9.4 - (2.8)^2 = 1.56$$

Student B

k	Pr(X = k)	k^2	k · Pr(X = k)	k^2 · Pr(X = k)
4	.6	16	2.4	9.6
3	.1	9	0.3	0.9
2	0	4	0.0	0.0
1	.3	1	0.3	0.3
0	0	0	0.0	0.0
			$\mu_B = \overline{3.0}$	$E(X^2) = \overline{10.8}$

$$\sigma_B^2 = 10.8 - (3.0)^2 = 1.8$$

(b) Student B has the better G.P.A. since $\mu_B > \mu_A$.

(c) Student A is more consistent since $\sigma_A^2 < \sigma_B^2$.

9. If $\mu = 35$ and $\sigma = 5$, the probability that an outcome falls between:

(a) 25 and 45 (c = 10) is at least $1 - (\frac{25}{100}) = \frac{3}{4} = 75\%$.

(b) 20 and 50   (c = 15)   is at least $1 - (\frac{25}{225}) = \frac{8}{9} = 88.8\%$

(c) 29 and 41   (c = 6)   is at least $1 - (\frac{25}{36}) = \frac{11}{36} = 30.5\%.$

10.   If $\mu = 8$ and $\sigma = .4$ the probability that an outcome falls between:

(a) 6 and 10   (c = 2)   is at least $1 - (\frac{.16}{4}) = .96.$

(b) 7.2 and 8.8   (c = .8)   is at least $1 - (\frac{.16}{.64}) = .75.$

(c) 7.5 and 8.5   (c = .5)   is at least $1 - (\frac{.16}{.25}) = .36.$

11. $\mu = 3000$ hrs $\sigma = 250$ hrs
The percentage that will burn out between 2000 and 4000 hours
(c=1000) is at least $1 - (\frac{250}{1000})^2 = 1 - (\frac{1}{4})^2 = \frac{15}{16}$ so at least

$5000 \cdot \frac{15}{16} = 4688$ will need replacement.

12. $\mu = 15$ and $\sigma = 10$
The chance of defects being between 0 and 30   (c = 15)
is at least $1 - (\frac{100}{225}) = \frac{5}{9}$ so out of 100 batches,

$100 \cdot \frac{5}{9} \cong 56$ will have between 0 and 30 defective transistors.

13. $\mu = 75$ and $\sigma = 6$ c = ?
The probability that an outcome will be between 75 - c and 75 + c

is $1 - (\frac{6^2}{c^2}) = \frac{7}{16}$ Solve for c: $\frac{-36}{c^2} = \frac{-9}{16}$. Hence $64 = c^2$ and c = 8.

14. $\mu = 17$ and $\sigma = .2$ ·   We want $1 - (\frac{.2^2}{c^2}) = \frac{15}{16}$, so solving for

c: $\frac{-.04}{c^2} = \frac{-1}{16}$ we see $.64 = c^2$ and c = .8

209

15. (a)

k	$\Pr(X = k)$	$k \cdot \Pr(X = k)$	$(k - \mu)^2$	$(k - \mu)^2 \cdot \Pr(X = k)$
2	1/36	2/36	25	25/36
3	2/36	6/36	16	32/36
4	3/36	12/36	9	27/36
5	4/36	20/36	4	16/36
6	5/36	30/36	1	5/36
7	6/36	42/36	0	0/36
8	5/36	40/36	1	5/36
9	4/36	36/36	4	16/36
10	3/36	30/36	9	27/36
11	2/36	22/36	16	32/36
12	1/36	12/36	25	25/36

$$\mu = 252/36 = 7 \qquad\qquad \sigma^2 = 210/36 = \frac{35}{6}$$

(b) $\Pr(4 \le x \le 10) = \Pr(x = 4) + \Pr(x = 5) + \Pr(x = 6) + \Pr(x = 7)$
$+ \Pr(x = 8) + \Pr(x = 9) + \Pr(x = 10)$

$$= \frac{3}{36} + \frac{4}{36} + \frac{5}{36} + \frac{6}{36} + \frac{5}{36} + \frac{4}{36} + \frac{3}{36} = \frac{30}{36} = \frac{5}{6}.$$

(c) $\Pr(4 \le X \le 10)$ is at least $1 - \dfrac{35/6}{9} = \dfrac{19}{54}$, with $c = 3$.

16. $\mu = 2$ and $\sigma^2 = \dfrac{5}{3}$

(a) $\Pr(0 \le x \le 4) = \Pr(x = 0) + \Pr(x = 1) + \Pr(x = 2) + \Pr(x = 3) + \Pr(x = 4) = .112 + .269 + .296 + .197 + .089 = .963.$

(b) $\Pr(0 \le x \le 4)$ $(c = 2)$ is at least $1 - \dfrac{\left(\frac{5/3}{2^2}\right)}{} = \dfrac{7}{12} = .583.$

17.

k	$\Pr(X = k)$	$k \cdot \Pr(X = k)$	$k^2 \cdot \Pr(X = k)$
0	.1	0	0
1	.3	0.3	0.3
2	.5	1.0	2.0
3	.1	0.3	0.9
		$\mu = 1.6$	$E(X)^2 = 3.2$

$$\sigma^2 = 3.2 - (1.6)^2 = .64$$

18.

k	$\Pr(X - 70 = k)$	$k \cdot \Pr(X - 70 = k)$	$(k - \mu)^2$	$(k - \mu)^2 \Pr(X = k)$
0	.5	0	1	.5
1	.2	.2	0	0
2	.1	.2	1	.1
3	.2	.6	4	.8
		$\mu = 1.0$		$\sigma^2 = 1.4$

210

19.

k	Pr(X = k)	k·Pr(2X = k)	(k − μ)²	(k − μ)²·Pr(2X = k)
−2	$\frac{1}{8}$	$-\frac{2}{8}$	4	$\frac{4}{8}$
−1	$\frac{3}{8}$	$-\frac{3}{8}$	1	$\frac{3}{8}$
0	$\frac{1}{8}$	0	0	0
1	$\frac{1}{8}$	$\frac{1}{8}$	1	$\frac{1}{8}$
2	$\frac{2}{8}$	$\frac{4}{8}$	4	$\frac{8}{8}$
		$\mu = 0$		$\sigma^2 = 2$

Variance of $2X = 2 = 4(\frac{1}{2}) = 4$(Variance of X).

20. Decreasing every value by *a* decreases the average value by *a*. Multiplying every value by *a* multiplies the average by *a*.

21. Frank's.

22. 1.893; 1.376

23. 1.262; 1.123

24. 1,985,000; 1,069,000

7.5. The Normal Distribution

1. $\Pr(z \le 1.25) = A(1.25) = .8944$

2. $\Pr(-.75 \le z \le 1) = A(1) - A(-.75) = .8413 - .2266 = .6147$

3. $\Pr(z \ge .25) = 1 - \Pr(z \le .25) = 1 - A(.25) = 1 - .5987 = .4013$

4. $\Pr(z \le -1) + \Pr(z \ge 1) = A(-1) + 1 - \Pr(z \le 1)$
$= A(-1) + 1 - A(1) = 1 - .8413 + .1587 = .3174$

5. $\Pr(.5 \le z \le 1.5) = A(1.5) - A(.5) = .9332 - .6915 = .2417$

6. $\Pr(z \le -1) = A(-1) = .1587$

7. $\Pr(z \le -.5) + \Pr(z \ge .5) = A(-.5) + 1 - \Pr(z \le .5)$
$= 1 - (A(.5) - A(-.5)) = 1 - .6915 + .3085 = .6170$

8. $\Pr(z \ge -1.25) = 1 - \Pr(z \le -1.25) = 1 - A(-1.25) = 1 - .1056 = .8944$

9. $A(-z) + (1 - A(z)) = .0228$, but $1 - A(z) = A(-z)$

$A(z) = 1 - .0401 = .9599, z = 1.75$

10. $A(-z) + (1 - A(z)) = .0456$, $A(-z) = .0456/2 = .0228, -z = -2,$ so $z = 2$

11. $A(-z) = .5 - (.5468/2) = .2266, z = .75$

12. $A(-z) = 1 - .6915 = .3085, -z = .5, z = -.5$

13. $\mu = 6, \sigma = 2$ 14. $\mu = 80, \sigma = 10$

15. $\mu = 9, \sigma = 1$ 16. $\mu = 3, \sigma = .2$

17. $\dfrac{6 - 8}{\frac{3}{4}} = \dfrac{-2}{\frac{3}{4}} = \dfrac{-8}{3}$ 18. $\dfrac{9\frac{1}{4} - 8}{\frac{3}{4}} = \dfrac{\frac{5}{4}}{\frac{3}{4}} = \dfrac{5}{3}$

19. $8 + 10 \cdot \dfrac{3}{4} = 15\frac{1}{2}$ 20. $8 - 2 \cdot \dfrac{3}{4} = 6\frac{1}{2}$

21. $\dfrac{9 - 10}{\frac{1}{2}} = \dfrac{-1}{\frac{1}{2}} = -2$ s.d.(standard deviations), $1 - A(-2) = .9772$

22. $\dfrac{32 - 30}{4} = \dfrac{2}{4} = .50$ s.d., $A(.5) = .6915$

23. $\dfrac{10 - 7}{2} = \dfrac{3}{2}$, $\dfrac{6 - 7}{2} = \dfrac{-1}{2}$ s.d. $A(1.5) - A(-.5) = .9332 - .3085$
                    $= .6247$

24. $\dfrac{4.5 - 4}{.4} = \dfrac{5}{4} = 1.25$ s.d., $\dfrac{3.5 - 4}{.4} = \dfrac{-5}{4} = -1.25$ s.d.
  $1 - (A(1.25) - A(-1.25)) = 1 - .7888 = .2112$

25. $\mu = 3.3$ meters, $\sigma = .2$ meters
  $z = \dfrac{4 - 3.3}{.2} = \dfrac{7}{2} = 3.5$ s.d. $Pr(z \geq 3.5) = 1 - Pr(z \leq 3.5)$
  $1 - A(3.5) = 1 - .9998 = .0002$

26. $z = \dfrac{16 - 16\frac{3}{4}}{1/2} = \dfrac{-3}{2} = -1.5$ s.d. $Pr(x \leq -1.5) = A(-1.5) = .0668$

27. $\mu = 6$, $\sigma = .02$

$z_1 = \dfrac{5.95 - 6}{.02} = -2.5$ s.d.

$z_2 = \dfrac{6.05 - 6}{.02} = 2.5$ s.d.

$A(2.5) - A(-2.5) = .9938 - .0062$
$= .9876$

28. $\mu = 100$, $\sigma = 10$

$z = \dfrac{125 - 100}{10} = 2.5$ s.d.

$1 - A(2.5) = 1 - .9938 = .0062$

29. $\mu = 30,000$, $\sigma = 4000$

$z = \dfrac{39,000 - 30,000}{4000} = 2.25$ s.d.

$Pr(z \geq 2.25) = 1 - Pr(z \leq 2.25)$
$= 1 - .9888 = .0122$

30. $\mu = 1200$, $\sigma = 160$

$z = \dfrac{1000 - 1200}{160} = -1.25$ s.d.

$Pr(z \leq -1.25)$
$= A(-1.25) = .1056$

31. $\mu = 520$, $\sigma = 75$

(a) From table 1:

$Pr(z \geq 1.30) = 1 - Pr(z \leq 1.30) = .0968 \cong 10\%$

So, $\dfrac{x_u - 520}{75} \cong 1.30$ s.d.   So, $x_u \cong 618$

(b) $A(1.65) = .95$, $A(-1.65) = .05$

$\dfrac{x_U - 520}{75} = 1.65$ s.d. $x_U \cong 643$

$\dfrac{x_L - 520}{75} = -1.65$ s.d. $x_L \cong 396$

The range is 396 to 643.

32. $\mu = 300$, $\sigma = 50$, we have $\dfrac{x - 300}{50} = 2.35$ s.d.,

$Pr(z \leq 2.35) = A(2.35) = .9906 \cong 99\%$. Then $x \cong 418$.

33. $\mu = 30,000$, $\sigma = 5000$

$\dfrac{x - 30,000}{5000} = 2.05$ s.d.

$1 - A(2.05) = A(-2.05) \cong .02$
$x = 40,250$ miles

34. $\mu = 4$, $\sigma = .5$ $c = 1$

(a) $1 - \left(\dfrac{(.5)^2}{1}\right) = .75$ $Pr(3 \leq x \leq 5)$ is at least 75%

213

(b) $\dfrac{5 - 4}{.5} = 2$ s.d., $\qquad$ $A(2) - A(-2) = .9772 - .0228 = .9544$

$\dfrac{3 - 4}{.5} = -2$ s.d.

(c) More exact estimate with a normal distribution.

35. $\quad 1 - A(2.6) \cong .005$
   (a) $\dfrac{6 - \mu}{.25} = 2.6$ $\qquad\qquad$ $\mu = 5.35$ ounces

   (b) $\mu = 5.35,\ \sigma = .25$
   $\dfrac{x - 5.35}{.25} = -2.35$ $\qquad\quad$ $x = 4.76$ ounces

36. 0

37. The second graph is flatter.

38. The second graph is to the right of the first.

39. 12.56, 13.56.

7.6. Normal Approximation to the Binomial

1. $n = 25$, $p = \frac{1}{5}$, $q = \frac{4}{5}$, $\quad \mu = 25 \cdot \frac{1}{5} = 5$, $\quad \sigma = \sqrt{25 \cdot \frac{1}{5} \cdot \frac{4}{5}} = 2$
   (a) $z = \dfrac{5.5 - 5}{2} = .25$ s.d.
   $\qquad A(.25) - A(-.25) = .5987 - .4013 = .1974$
   (b) $\dfrac{7.5 - 5}{2} = 1.25$ s.d. $\qquad\qquad \dfrac{2.5 - 5}{2} = -1.25$ s.d.
   $\qquad A(1.25) - A(-1.25) = .8944 - .1056 = .7888.$
   (c) $\dfrac{9.5 - 5}{2} = 2.25$ s.d. $\qquad\qquad A(2.25) = .9878.$

2. $n = 18$, $p = \frac{2}{3}$, $q = \frac{1}{3}$, $\mu = 18 \cdot \frac{2}{3} = 12$, $\quad \sigma = \sqrt{\dfrac{18 \cdot 2}{9}} = 2$

   (a) $\dfrac{10.5 - 12}{2} = -.75$ s.d. $\qquad\qquad \dfrac{9.5 - 12}{2} = -1.25$ s.d.
   $\qquad A(-.75) - A(-1.25) = .2266 - .1056 = .1210.$

   (b) $\dfrac{7.5 - 12}{2} = -2.25$ s.d. $\qquad\qquad \dfrac{16.5 - 12}{5} = 2.25$ s.d.
   $\qquad A(2.25) - A(-2.25) = .9878 - .0122 = .9756.$

214

(c) $\dfrac{12.5 - 12}{2} = .25$ s.d. $\qquad$ $1 - A(.25) = .4013.$

3. $n = 20$, $p = \dfrac{1}{6}$, $q = \dfrac{5}{6}$, $\mu = \dfrac{10}{3}$, $\sigma = \sqrt{\dfrac{100}{36}} = \dfrac{10}{6} = \dfrac{5}{3}$

$\dfrac{7.5 - 10/3}{5/3} = 2.5$ s.d. $\qquad$ $1 - A(2.5) = .0062.$

4. $n = 16$, $p = \dfrac{1}{2}$, $q = \dfrac{1}{2}$, $\mu = 8$, $\sigma = \sqrt{16 \cdot \dfrac{1}{2} \cdot \dfrac{1}{2}} = \sqrt{4} = 2$

$\dfrac{11.5 - 8}{2} = 1.75$ s.d. $\qquad$ $1 - A(1.75) = .0401.$

5. $n = 100$, $p = \dfrac{1}{2}$, $q = \dfrac{1}{2}$, $\mu = 50$, $\sigma = \sqrt{100 \cdot \dfrac{1}{2} \cdot \dfrac{1}{2}} = 5$

$\dfrac{62.5 - 50}{5} = 2.5$ s.d. $\qquad$ $1 - A(2.5) = .0062.$

6. $n = 90$, $p = \dfrac{9}{19}$, $q = \dfrac{10}{19}$, $\mu = \dfrac{810}{19}$, $\sigma = \sqrt{90 \cdot \dfrac{9}{19} \cdot \dfrac{10}{19}} = \dfrac{90}{19}$ $\qquad$ $X \geq 45$

$\dfrac{45.5 - \dfrac{810}{19}}{\dfrac{90}{19}} = \dfrac{864.5 - 810}{90} \cong .6$ s.d. $\quad$ $1 - A(.6) \cong .27.$

7. $n = 75$, $p = \dfrac{3}{4}$, $q = \dfrac{1}{4}$, $\mu = \dfrac{225}{4}$, $\sigma = \sqrt{75 \cdot \dfrac{3}{4} \cdot \dfrac{1}{4}} = \dfrac{15}{4}$

$\dfrac{67.5 - \dfrac{225}{4}}{\dfrac{15}{4}} = \dfrac{250 - 225}{15} = 3$ s.d. $\qquad$ $1 - A(3) = .0013.$

8. $n = 54$, $p = \dfrac{2}{5}$, $q = \dfrac{3}{5}$, $\mu = \dfrac{108}{5}$, $\sigma = \sqrt{54 \cdot \dfrac{2}{5} \cdot \dfrac{3}{5}} = \dfrac{18}{5}$

$\dfrac{13.5 - \dfrac{108}{5}}{\dfrac{18}{5}} = \dfrac{67.5 - 108}{18} = -2.25$ s.d. $\qquad$ $A(-2.25) = .0122.$

9. $n = 20$, $p = .310$, $q = .690$, $\mu = 6.2$, $\sigma = \sqrt{20 \cdot (.310) \cdot (.690)} \cong 2.07$

$\dfrac{5.5 - 6.2}{2.07} = -.34$ s.d. $\qquad\qquad 1 - A(-.34) = .6368$.

10. $n = 1000$, $p = \dfrac{1}{4}$, $q = \dfrac{3}{4}$, $\mu = 250$, $\sigma = \sqrt{1000 \cdot \dfrac{1}{4} \cdot \dfrac{3}{4}} \cong 13.7$

$\dfrac{289.5 - 250}{13.7} = 2.88$ s.d. $\qquad\qquad 1 - A(2.88) = .0019$ Yes.

11. $n = 1000$, $p = .02$, $q = .98$, $\mu = 20$, $\sigma = \sqrt{1000 \cdot (.02) \cdot (.98)} = 4.4$

$\dfrac{14.5 - 20}{4.4} = -1.25$ s.d. $\qquad\qquad 1 - A(-1.25) = .1056$.

12. $n = 70$, $p = .2$, $q = .8$, $\mu = 14$, $\sigma = \sqrt{70 \cdot (.2) \cdot (.8)} = 3.35$

$\dfrac{14.5 - 14}{3.35} = .15$ s.d. $\qquad \dfrac{13.5 - 14.5}{3.35} = -.15$ s.d.

$A(.15) - A(-.15) = .1192$.

13. (a) $\dfrac{50}{250} = .2$

(b) $n = 250$, $p = .25$, $\mu = 62.5$, $\sigma = 6.85$

$\dfrac{50.5 - 62.5}{6.85} = -1.75$ s.d. $\qquad A(-1.75) = .0401$

14. $p = (.01) \cdot (.02) \cdot (.01)\ 2 \cdot 10^{-6}$

$1{,}000{,}000 \cdot (2 \cdot 10^{-6}) = 2$, 2 would be expected to fail, $\mu = 2$

$\sigma = \sqrt{1{,}000{,}000 \cdot (2 \cdot 10^{-6}) \cdot (.999999)}$

$\dfrac{3.5 - 2}{1.41} = 1.06$ s.d. $\qquad\qquad 1 - A(1.06) = .1469$.

15. Exact Value

$\Pr(49 \le x \le 51) = \dbinom{100}{49}(.5)^{100} + \dbinom{100}{50}(.5)^{100} + \dbinom{100}{51}(.5)^{100}$

$\qquad\qquad = .2356$

Normal approximation: $\mu = 50$, $\sigma = \sqrt{25} = 5$

$\Phi(\dfrac{51.5 - 50}{5}) = \Phi(.3) = .6179$

$\Phi(\dfrac{48.5 - 50}{5}) = \Phi(-.3) = .3821$

$\Pr(49 \le x \le 57) \sim \Pr(-.3 \le z \le .3) = .6179 - .3821 = .2358$

16. $\Pr(17 \le x \le 21) = \binom{120}{17}(1/6)^{17}(5/6)^{103} + \binom{120}{18}(1/6)^{18}(5/6)^{102} +$

$\binom{120}{19}(1/6)^{19}(5/6)^{101} + \binom{120}{20}(1/6)^{20}(5/6)^{100} + \binom{120}{21}(1/6)^{21}(5/6)^{99}$

$= .4544.$

For normal approximations, use $\mu = 20$, $\sigma = 4.1$. $\Pr(17 \le x \le 21) = .4477$

17. $\binom{150}{30}(.20)^{30}(.80)^{120} = .08120.$

Normal approximation, use $\mu = 30$, $\sigma = \sqrt{150 \cdot (.20)(.80)} = 4.9$

$\Phi(\frac{29.5 - 30}{4.9}) - \Phi(\frac{30.5 - 30}{4.9}) = .08129.$

7. Supplementary Exercises

1.

k	Pr(x = k)	k·Pr(x = k)	$(k - \mu)^2$	$(k - \mu)^2 \cdot$ Pr(x = k)
0	$\binom{3}{0} \cdot (\frac{1}{3})^0 \cdot (\frac{2}{3})^3 = \frac{8}{7}$	0	1	$\frac{8}{27}$
1	$\binom{3}{1} \cdot (\frac{1}{3})^1 \cdot (\frac{2}{3})^2 = \frac{2}{7}$	$\frac{12}{27}$	0	0
2	$\binom{3}{2} \cdot (\frac{1}{3})^2 \cdot (\frac{2}{3})^1 = \frac{6}{7}$	$\frac{12}{27}$	1	$\frac{6}{27}$
3	$\binom{3}{3} \cdot (\frac{1}{3})^3 \cdot (\frac{2}{3})^0 = \frac{1}{7}$	$\frac{3}{27}$	4	$\frac{4}{27}$
		$\mu = 1$		$\sigma^2 = \frac{18}{27} = \frac{2}{3}$

2. $1 - A(.75) = 1 - .7734 = .2266$

3. $\frac{6.5 - 5}{3} = \frac{1.5}{3} = \frac{1}{2}$ s.d. $\qquad \frac{11 - 5}{3} = \frac{6}{3} = 2$ s.d.

$A(2) - A(.5) = .9772 - .6915 = .2857$

4. $\Pr(X = 2) = \binom{4}{2}(.3)^2(.7)^2 = 6 \cdot (.09) \cdot (.49) = .2646$

5. $\mu = 10$, $\sigma = \frac{1}{3}$, Pr(between 9 and 11), $c = 1$

$1 - (\frac{1/3}{1})^2 = 1 - \frac{1}{9} = \frac{8}{9} \ge \frac{8}{9}$

6. $\mu = 0 \cdot (.2) + 1 \cdot (.3) + 5 \cdot (.1) + 10 \cdot (.4) = 4.80$

$Ex(x^2) = 1 \cdot (.3) + 25 \cdot (.5) + 100 \cdot (.4) = 42.8$

$\sigma^2 = 42.8 - (4.80)^2 = 19.76$

7. $\mu = 5.75$, $\sigma = .2$

   $\dfrac{6 - 5.75}{.2} = 1.25$ s.d.

   $1 - A(1.25) = .1056$

   10.56%

8.

k	$Pr(X = k)$	$k \cdot Pr(X = k)$	$(k - \mu)^2$	$(k - \mu)^2 \cdot Pr(X = k)$
0	$\binom{4}{0}(\frac{1}{2})^0(\frac{1}{2})^4 = \frac{1}{16}$	0	4	$\frac{4}{16}$
1	$\binom{4}{1}(\frac{1}{2})^1(\frac{1}{2})^3 = \frac{4}{16}$	$\frac{4}{16}$	1	$\frac{4}{16}$
2	$\binom{4}{2}(\frac{1}{2})^2(\frac{1}{2})^2 = \frac{6}{16}$	$\frac{12}{16}$	0	0
3	$\binom{4}{3}(\frac{1}{2})^3(\frac{1}{2})^1 = \frac{4}{16}$	$\frac{12}{16}$	1	$\frac{12}{16}$
4	$\binom{4}{4}(\frac{1}{2})^4(\frac{1}{2})^0 = \frac{1}{16}$	$\frac{4}{16}$	4	$\frac{4}{16}$
		$\mu = 2$		$\sigma^2 = \frac{24}{16}$

9. $n = 54$, $p = \dfrac{2}{5}$, $q = \dfrac{3}{5}$, $\mu = \dfrac{108}{5}$, $\sigma = \dfrac{18}{5}$

   $\dfrac{13.5 - \frac{108}{5}}{\frac{18}{5}} = \dfrac{67.5 - 108}{18} = -2.25$ s.d. $A(-2.25) = .0122$

10. $n = 75$. $p = \dfrac{1}{4}$, $q = \dfrac{3}{4}$, $\mu = \dfrac{75}{4}$, $\sigma = \dfrac{15}{4}$

    $\dfrac{30 - 75}{15} = -3$ s.d. $\dfrac{90 - 75}{15} = 1$ s.d.

    $A(1) - A(-3) = .8413 - .0013 = .84$.

11. $\mu = 80$, $\sigma = 15$
    $A(80 + h) - .5 = .4332$ $A(80 + h) = .9332 = A(1.50)$
    $(1.50) \cdot 15 + 80 = 102.5$ $80 + h = 102.5$, $h = 22.5$

12. $1 - A(z) = .7734$ $A(z) = .2266$ $z = -.75$.

13. (a) Probability of a team winning 4 in a row is:
    $\frac{1}{2} \cdot \frac{1}{2} \cdot \frac{1}{2} \cdot \frac{1}{2} = \frac{1}{16}$, since either team can win,
    $Pr(4 \text{ games}) = \frac{1}{16} \cdot 2 = \frac{1}{8}$.

(b) For a 5 game series a team must
   lose one of the first 4 games. $\binom{4}{1} \cdot (-\frac{1}{2})^1 (\frac{1}{2})^3 (\frac{1}{2}) \cdot 2 = .25$.

(c) For a 6 game series a team must
   lose two of the first 5 games. $\binom{5}{2} \cdot (\frac{1}{2})^2 \cdot (\frac{1}{2})^2 \cdot (\frac{1}{2}) \cdot 2 = \frac{20}{64}$
   $= .3125$.

(d) For a 7 game series a team must
   lose three of the first 6 games. $\binom{6}{3} \cdot (\frac{1}{2})^3 \cdot (\frac{1}{2})^3 \cdot (\frac{1}{2}) \cdot 2 = \frac{40}{128}$
   $= .3125$.

14. Out of 10 trials
   (60%true)·(60%choose true) + (40% false)·(40% choose false)
   $= 36\% + 16\% = 52\%$.
   The probability of getting a question correct is = .52. With 10 questions the mean would be $\mu = np = 5.2$ correct. The student's expected score is 52.

MARKOV PROCESSES

8.1. The Transition Matrix

1. $\begin{bmatrix} 1 & .8 \\ 0 & .2 \end{bmatrix}$ is stochastic; it satisfies all criteria.

2. $\begin{bmatrix} \frac{1}{3} & \frac{1}{3} \\ \frac{2}{3} & \frac{2}{3} \end{bmatrix}$ is stochastic; it satisfies all criteria.

3. $\begin{bmatrix} .4 & .3 & .2 \\ .6 & .7 & .8 \end{bmatrix}$ is not stochastic; it is not a square matrix.

4. $\begin{bmatrix} .4 & .5 & .1 \\ .3 & .4 & 0 \\ .3 & .2 & .9 \end{bmatrix}$ is not stochastic; $.5 + .4 + .2 \neq 1$

5. $\begin{bmatrix} \frac{1}{6} & \frac{5}{12} & 0 \\ \frac{1}{2} & \frac{1}{4} & \frac{1}{2} \\ \frac{1}{3} & \frac{1}{3} & \frac{1}{2} \end{bmatrix}$ is stochastic.

6. $\begin{bmatrix} 1 & 0 & 0 \\ 0 & 1 & 0 \\ 0 & 0 & 1 \end{bmatrix}$ is stochastic.

7. $A \begin{bmatrix} .45 \\ .55 \end{bmatrix}_0 = \begin{bmatrix} .8 & .3 \\ .2 & .7 \end{bmatrix} \begin{bmatrix} .45 \\ .55 \end{bmatrix}_0 = \begin{bmatrix} .525 \\ .475 \end{bmatrix}_1$

The proportion of French women working in the first generation = 52.5% = 53% (round off).

$$A^2 = \begin{bmatrix} .8 & .3 \\ .2 & .7 \end{bmatrix} \begin{bmatrix} .8 & .3 \\ .2 & .7 \end{bmatrix} = \begin{bmatrix} .70 & .45 \\ .30 & .55 \end{bmatrix}$$

$$\begin{bmatrix} .70 & .45 \\ .30 & .55 \end{bmatrix} \begin{bmatrix} .45 \\ .55 \end{bmatrix}_0 = \begin{bmatrix} .5625 \\ .4375 \end{bmatrix}_2$$

so, 56.25% = 56% worked after two generations.

8. $\begin{bmatrix} .8 & .3 \\ .2 & .7 \end{bmatrix} \begin{bmatrix} .33 \\ .67 \end{bmatrix} = \begin{bmatrix} .465 \\ .535 \end{bmatrix}$

$\begin{bmatrix} .7 & .45 \\ .3 & .55 \end{bmatrix} \begin{bmatrix} .33 \\ .67 \end{bmatrix} = \begin{bmatrix} .5325 \\ .4675 \end{bmatrix}$ 47%, 53%

9. $\begin{bmatrix} .5 & .4 & .2 \\ .4 & .3 & .6 \\ .1 & .3 & .2 \end{bmatrix} \begin{bmatrix} .4 \\ .4 \\ .2 \end{bmatrix} = \begin{bmatrix} .4 \\ .4 \\ .2 \end{bmatrix}$

10. (a) $\begin{matrix} & L & R \\ L & \\ R & \end{matrix} \begin{bmatrix} .9 & .7 \\ .1 & .3 \end{bmatrix}$

(b) $\begin{bmatrix} .9 & .7 \\ .1 & .3 \end{bmatrix} \begin{bmatrix} .9 & .7 \\ .1 & .3 \end{bmatrix} = \begin{bmatrix} .88 & .84 \\ .12 & .16 \end{bmatrix}$

(c) $\begin{bmatrix} .9 & .7 \\ .1 & .3 \end{bmatrix} \begin{bmatrix} .5 \\ .5 \end{bmatrix} = \begin{bmatrix} .80 \\ .20 \end{bmatrix}_1$

(d) 0%

$\begin{bmatrix} .88 & .84 \\ .12 & .16 \end{bmatrix} \begin{bmatrix} .5 \\ .5 \end{bmatrix} = \begin{bmatrix} .86 \\ .14 \end{bmatrix}_2$

11. (a) $\begin{matrix} & S & M & L \\ S & \\ M & \\ L & \end{matrix} \begin{bmatrix} .4 & .5 & .3 \\ .6 & 0 & .2 \\ 0 & .5 & .5 \end{bmatrix}$

(b) $\begin{bmatrix} .4 & .5 & .3 \\ .6 & 0 & .2 \\ 0 & .5 & .5 \end{bmatrix} \begin{bmatrix} .4 & .5 & .3 \\ .6 & 0 & .2 \\ 0 & .5 & .5 \end{bmatrix} = \begin{bmatrix} .46 & .35 & .37 \\ .24 & .4 & .28 \\ .30 & .25 & .35 \end{bmatrix}$

$\begin{bmatrix} .46 & .35 & .37 \\ .24 & .4 & .28 \\ .30 & .25 & .35 \end{bmatrix} \begin{bmatrix} .8 \\ .1 \\ .1 \end{bmatrix} = \begin{bmatrix} .44 \\ .26 \\ .30 \end{bmatrix}$ 44% have a strenuous workout on Wednesday.

12. (a) $\begin{bmatrix} .78 & .07 & .15 \\ .12 & .85 & .05 \\ .10 & .08 & .80 \end{bmatrix} \begin{bmatrix} 1000 \\ 1000 \\ 1000 \end{bmatrix} = \begin{bmatrix} 1000 \\ 1020 \\ 980 \end{bmatrix} \begin{matrix} I \\ II \\ III \end{matrix}$ After 1 year

15% of the birds from habitat III migrate to habitat I during year.

(b) 85% of the birds from habitat II remain there.

(c). $\begin{bmatrix} .78 & .07 & .15 \\ .12 & .85 & .05 \\ .10 & .08 & .80 \end{bmatrix} \begin{bmatrix} 1000 \\ 1000 \\ 1000 \end{bmatrix} = \begin{bmatrix} 1000 \\ 1020 \\ 980 \end{bmatrix}$

$$\begin{bmatrix} .78 & .07 & .15 \\ .12 & .85 & .05 \\ .10 & .08 & .80 \end{bmatrix} \begin{bmatrix} .78 & .07 & .15 \\ .12 & .85 & .05 \\ .10 & .08 & .80 \end{bmatrix} = \begin{bmatrix} .632 & .126 & .240 \\ .200 & .735 & .101 \\ .168 & .139 & .659 \end{bmatrix}$$

$$\begin{bmatrix} .632 & .126 & .240 \\ .200 & .735 & .101 \\ .168 & .139 & .659 \end{bmatrix} \begin{bmatrix} 1000 \\ 1000 \\ 1000 \end{bmatrix} = \begin{bmatrix} 998 \\ 1036 \\ 966 \end{bmatrix} \begin{matrix} \text{I} \\ \text{II} \\ \text{III} \end{matrix} \quad \text{After 2 years.}$$

13. (a)
$$\begin{matrix} & \text{D} & \text{R} \\ \text{D} & \\ \text{R} \end{matrix} \begin{bmatrix} .70 & .40 \\ .30 & .60 \end{bmatrix}$$

(b) $A^2 = \begin{bmatrix} .70 & .40 \\ .30 & .60 \end{bmatrix} \begin{bmatrix} .70 & .40 \\ .30 & .60 \end{bmatrix} = \begin{bmatrix} .61 & .52 \\ .39 & .48 \end{bmatrix}$

$A^3 = \begin{bmatrix} .61 & .52 \\ .39 & .48 \end{bmatrix} \begin{bmatrix} .70 & .40 \\ .30 & .60 \end{bmatrix} = \begin{bmatrix} .583 & .556 \\ .417 & .444 \end{bmatrix}$

(c) $A^3 \cdot \begin{bmatrix} 1 \\ 0 \end{bmatrix} = \begin{bmatrix} .583 \\ .417 \end{bmatrix}$, 58.3% of the governors will then be Democrats

14. (a) $\begin{bmatrix} .69 & .16 & .20 \\ .12 & .74 & .14 \\ .19 & .10 & .66 \end{bmatrix}$

(b) $\begin{bmatrix} .69 & .16 & .20 \\ .12 & .74 & .14 \\ .19 & .10 & .66 \end{bmatrix} \begin{bmatrix} 1500 \\ 1500 \\ 2000 \end{bmatrix} = \begin{bmatrix} 1675 \\ 1570 \\ 1755 \end{bmatrix}$

There are 1675 people buying Crispy Flakes after one week.

$$\begin{bmatrix} .69 & .16 & .20 \\ .12 & .74 & .14 \\ .19 & .10 & .66 \end{bmatrix} \begin{bmatrix} 1675 \\ 1570 \\ 1755 \end{bmatrix} = \begin{bmatrix} 1758 \\ \\ \end{bmatrix}$$

There are 1758 people buying Crispy Flakes after two weeks.

15. (a) $\begin{bmatrix} .86 & .05 & .03 \\ .08 & .86 & .05 \\ .06 & .09 & .92 \end{bmatrix}$ (b) 11.4% will live in rural areas in 1997.

16. $\begin{bmatrix} .5 & .4 \\ .5 & .6 \end{bmatrix} \begin{bmatrix} .5 & .4 \\ .5 & .6 \end{bmatrix} = \begin{bmatrix} .45 & .44 \\ .55 & .56 \end{bmatrix}$

$$\begin{bmatrix} .45 & .44 \\ .55 & .56 \end{bmatrix} \begin{bmatrix} .5 & .4 \\ .5 & .6 \end{bmatrix} = \begin{bmatrix} .44 & .44 \\ .56 & .56 \end{bmatrix} = A^3$$

$$\begin{bmatrix} .44 & .44 \\ .56 & .56 \end{bmatrix} \begin{bmatrix} .3 \\ .7 \end{bmatrix} = \begin{bmatrix} .44 \\ .56 \end{bmatrix}_3 \qquad \begin{bmatrix} .5 & .4 \\ .5 & .6 \end{bmatrix} \begin{bmatrix} .44 \\ .56 \end{bmatrix} = \begin{bmatrix} .44 \\ .56 \end{bmatrix}_4$$

17. All are the same as the given matrix.

18. $\begin{bmatrix} 1 & .5 \\ 0 & .5 \end{bmatrix} \begin{bmatrix} 1 & .5 \\ 0 & .5 \end{bmatrix} = \begin{bmatrix} 1 & .75 \\ 0 & .25 \end{bmatrix}$

$\begin{bmatrix} 1 & .5 \\ 0 & .5 \end{bmatrix} \begin{bmatrix} 1 & .75 \\ 0 & .25 \end{bmatrix} = \begin{bmatrix} 1 & .875 \\ 0 & .125 \end{bmatrix}$

$\begin{bmatrix} 1 & .5 \\ 0 & .5 \end{bmatrix} \begin{bmatrix} 1 & .875 \\ 0 & .125 \end{bmatrix} = \begin{bmatrix} 1 & .9375 \\ 0 & .0625 \end{bmatrix}$

$\begin{bmatrix} 1 & .5 \\ 0 & .5 \end{bmatrix} \begin{bmatrix} 1 & .9375 \\ 0 & .0625 \end{bmatrix} = \begin{bmatrix} 1 & .96875 \\ 0 & .03125 \end{bmatrix}$

19. $A^2 = \begin{bmatrix} .1 & .3 \\ .9 & .7 \end{bmatrix} \begin{bmatrix} .1 & .3 \\ .9 & .7 \end{bmatrix} = \begin{bmatrix} .28 & .24 \\ .72 & .76 \end{bmatrix}$

$A^3 = \begin{bmatrix} .1 & .3 \\ .9 & .7 \end{bmatrix} \begin{bmatrix} .28 & .24 \\ .72 & .76 \end{bmatrix} = \begin{bmatrix} .24 & .25 \\ .76 & .75 \end{bmatrix}$

$A^4 = \begin{bmatrix} .1 & .3 \\ .9 & .7 \end{bmatrix} \begin{bmatrix} .24 & .25 \\ .76 & .75 \end{bmatrix} = \begin{bmatrix} .25 & .25 \\ .75 & .75 \end{bmatrix}$

$A^5 = \begin{bmatrix} .1 & .3 \\ .9 & .7 \end{bmatrix} \begin{bmatrix} .25 & .25 \\ .75 & .75 \end{bmatrix} = \begin{bmatrix} .25 & .25 \\ .75 & .75 \end{bmatrix}$

20. $A = A^3 = A^5 = \begin{bmatrix} 0 & 1 \\ 1 & 0 \end{bmatrix}, \ A^2 = A^4 = \begin{bmatrix} 1 & 0 \\ 0 & 1 \end{bmatrix}$

21. All are the same as the given matrix.

22. $\begin{bmatrix} \frac{2}{3} & 0 \\ \frac{1}{3} & 1 \end{bmatrix} \begin{bmatrix} \frac{2}{3} & 0 \\ \frac{1}{3} & 1 \end{bmatrix} = \begin{bmatrix} \frac{4}{9} & 0 \\ \frac{5}{9} & 1 \end{bmatrix} = A^2$

Not regular since not all entries of the matrix and the higher powers of the matrix are greater than zero.

23. $\begin{bmatrix} 0 & .4 \\ 1 & .6 \end{bmatrix} \begin{bmatrix} 0 & .4 \\ 1 & .6 \end{bmatrix} = \begin{bmatrix} .4 & .24 \\ .6 & .76 \end{bmatrix}$

Regular since all entries of A^2 are greater than zero.

8.2 Regular Stochastic Matrices

1. Since it is a stochastic matrix and all entries are greater than zero it is regular.

2. $\begin{bmatrix} .6 & 0 \\ .4 & 1 \end{bmatrix} \begin{bmatrix} .6 & 0 \\ .4 & 1 \end{bmatrix} = \begin{bmatrix} .36 & 0 \\ .64 & 1 \end{bmatrix}$ Not all entries are greater than zer so it is not a regular matrix.

3. $\begin{bmatrix} .3 & 1 \\ .7 & 0 \end{bmatrix} \begin{bmatrix} .3 & 1 \\ .7 & 0 \end{bmatrix} = \begin{bmatrix} .79 & .3 \\ .21 & .7 \end{bmatrix}$ It is a regular stochastic matrix.

4. $\begin{bmatrix} 1 & 0 & .7 \\ 0 & 1 & .2 \\ 0 & 0 & .1 \end{bmatrix} \begin{bmatrix} 1 & 0 & .7 \\ 0 & 1 & .2 \\ 0 & 0 & .1 \end{bmatrix} = \begin{bmatrix} 1 & 0 & .77 \\ 0 & 1 & .22 \\ 0 & 0 & .01 \end{bmatrix}$ Not all entries are great than zero, so it is not a regular matrix.

5. $\begin{bmatrix} 0 & .8 & 0 \\ 1 & .1 & .5 \\ 0 & .1 & .5 \end{bmatrix} \begin{bmatrix} 0 & .8 & 0 \\ 1 & .1 & .5 \\ 0 & .1 & .5 \end{bmatrix} = \begin{bmatrix} .8 & .08 & .4 \\ .1 & .86 & .3 \\ .1 & .06 & .3 \end{bmatrix}$ All entries are greater than zero; it is a regul matrix.

6. Since it is a stochastic matrix and all entries are greater than zero, it is regular.

7. $\begin{bmatrix} .5 & .1 \\ .5 & .9 \end{bmatrix} \begin{bmatrix} x \\ y \end{bmatrix} = \begin{bmatrix} x \\ y \end{bmatrix}$

$$-.5x + -.1y = -x$$
$$\underline{.5x + .9y = y}$$
$$.8y = y - x$$

$x + .8y = y$ so, $x = .2y$
and since $x + y = 1$, $.2y + y = 1$

$1.2y = 1$

$y = \dfrac{5}{6}$ $x = \dfrac{1}{6}$

the stable distribution is: $\begin{bmatrix} \frac{1}{6} \\ \frac{5}{6} \end{bmatrix}$

8. $\begin{bmatrix} .4 & 1 \\ .6 & 0 \end{bmatrix} \begin{bmatrix} x \\ y \end{bmatrix} = \begin{bmatrix} x \\ y \end{bmatrix}$

$$.3(.4x + y) = .3x$$
$$\underline{-.2(.6x) = -.2y}$$
$$.3y = .3x - .2y$$

$.5y = .3x$ so, $y = \frac{3}{5}x$,
and since $x + y = 1$,

$x + \frac{3}{5}x = 1$, $\frac{8}{5}x = 1$

the stable distribution is: $\begin{bmatrix} \frac{5}{8} \\ \frac{3}{8} \end{bmatrix}$

$x = \frac{5}{8}$, $y = \frac{3}{8}$

9. $\begin{bmatrix} .8 & .3 \\ .2 & .7 \end{bmatrix} \begin{bmatrix} x \\ y \end{bmatrix} = \begin{bmatrix} x \\ y \end{bmatrix}$

$\begin{array}{c} .8x + .3y = x \\ -4(.2x + .7y) = -4y \\ \hline -2.5y = x - 4y \end{array}$

$4y - 2.5x = x$ so, $1.5y = x$
and since $x + y = 1$, using substitution,
$1.5y + y = 1$
$2.5y = 1$ so $y = \frac{2}{5}$ and $x = \frac{3}{5}$

the stable distribution is : $\begin{bmatrix} \frac{3}{5} \\ \frac{2}{5} \end{bmatrix}$.

10. $\begin{bmatrix} .3 & .1 & .2 \\ .4 & .8 & .6 \\ .3 & .1 & .2 \end{bmatrix} \begin{bmatrix} x \\ y \\ z \end{bmatrix} = \begin{bmatrix} x \\ y \\ z \end{bmatrix}$

(3rd equation) $.3x + .1y + .2z = z$
so, $.3x + .1y - .8z = 0$
and $x + y + z = 1$
so, $.8x + .8y + .8z = .8$

$\begin{array}{l} .3x + .1y - .8z = 0 \\ .8x + .8y + .8z = .8 \\ \hline 1.1x + .9y = .8 \end{array}$ $*_1$

$\begin{array}{l} .4x + .8y + .6z = y \quad (2^{nd}\text{ eq.}) \\ -.9x + -.3y + -.6z = -3x \quad (1^{st}\text{ eq.})\cdot(3) \\ \hline -.5x + .5y = -3x + y \\ 2.5x - .5y = 0 \quad *_2 \end{array}$

Using $5\cdot*_1$ and $9\cdot*_2$,
$\begin{array}{l} 5(1.1x + .9y) = 5(.8) \\ 9(2.5x - .5y) = 0 \\ \hline 28x = 4 \end{array}$
so, $x = \frac{4}{28} = \frac{1}{7}$

Using $*_1$ and substitution,
$1.1\cdot(\frac{1}{7}) + .9y = .8$ $.9y = .8 - \frac{1.1}{7}$ so, $y = \frac{5}{7}$
Using $x + y + z = 1$, $\frac{1}{7} + \frac{5}{7} + z = 1$ so, $z = \frac{1}{7}$

The stable distribution is: $\begin{bmatrix} \frac{1}{7} \\ \frac{5}{7} \\ \frac{1}{7} \end{bmatrix}$.

11. $\begin{bmatrix} .1 & .4 & .7 \\ .6 & .4 & .2 \\ .3 & .2 & .1 \end{bmatrix} \begin{bmatrix} x \\ y \\ z \end{bmatrix} = \begin{bmatrix} x \\ y \\ z \end{bmatrix}$ We have three equations: $\begin{array}{l} .1x + .4y + .7z = x \\ .6x + .4y + .2z = y \\ .3x + .2y + .1z = z \end{array}$

$-.9x + .4y + .7z = 0$ Multiply the third equation
$.6x - .6y + .2z = 0$ by -2 and add to the second
$.3x + .2y - .9z = 0$ to get $2z = y$. Substitute
$x + y + z = 1$ $y = 2z$ in equations 1 and 4

to find that $2.8x = 1$ and therefore $x = 5/14$. But the 4th
equation is $x + 3z = 1$, so we can solve for $z = 3/14$ and

$y = 2z = 6/14$. The stable distribution is: $\begin{bmatrix} \dfrac{5}{14} \\[4pt] \dfrac{6}{14} \\[4pt] \dfrac{3}{14} \end{bmatrix}$.

12. $\begin{bmatrix} .9 & .7 \\ .1 & .3 \end{bmatrix} \begin{bmatrix} x \\ y \end{bmatrix} = \begin{bmatrix} x \\ y \end{bmatrix}$ $\begin{array}{l} (1^{st}\ eq.) \\ -9 \cdot (2^{nd}\ eq.) \end{array}$ $\begin{array}{l} .9x + .7y = x \\ -.9x - 2.7y = -9y \\ \hline -2.0y = x - 9y \end{array}$

We get $x = 7y$ but $x + y = 1$. So $8y = 1$ and

$\qquad\qquad\qquad\qquad\qquad\qquad\qquad y = \dfrac{1}{8}, \qquad x = \dfrac{7}{8}.$

$\dfrac{7}{8}$ or 87.5% will be going to the left.

13. $\begin{bmatrix} .4 & .5 & .3 \\ .6 & 0 & .2 \\ 0 & .5 & .5 \end{bmatrix} \begin{bmatrix} X \\ Y \\ Z \end{bmatrix} = \begin{bmatrix} X \\ Y \\ Z \end{bmatrix}$ $\begin{array}{l} 0.4x + 0.5y + 0.3z = x \\ 0.6x + 0.2z = y \\ 0.5y + 0.5z = z \end{array}$

$\left. \begin{array}{rcrcrcr} x &+& y &+& z &=& 1 \\ -.6x &+& .5y &+& .3z &=& 0 \\ .6x &-& y &+& .2z &=& 0 \\ & & .5y &-& .5z &=& 0 \\ x &+& y &+& z &=& 1 \\ & & y &-& z &=& 0 \\ & & 11y &+& 9z &=& 6 \end{array} \right\}$ $\left. \begin{array}{rcrcrcr} x &+& y &+& z &=& 1 \\ & & 11y &+& 9z &=& 6 \\ & & -16y &-& 4z &=& -6 \\ & & 5y &-& 5z &=& 0 \\ x &+& y &+& z &=& 1 \\ & & y &-& z &=& 0 \\ & & & & 20z &=& 6 \end{array} \right\}$

$\qquad\qquad\qquad\qquad$ Equivalent

$\qquad -16y - 4z = -6 \qquad\qquad\qquad -20z = -6$

$\qquad\qquad x + y + z = 1 \qquad\qquad\qquad\qquad x = \dfrac{4}{10}$

$\qquad\qquad\qquad y - z = 0 \qquad\qquad\qquad\qquad\quad y = \dfrac{3}{10}$

$\qquad\qquad\qquad\qquad z = \dfrac{3}{10} \qquad\qquad\qquad\qquad z = \dfrac{3}{10}$

14.
$\begin{bmatrix} .7 & .4 \\ .3 & .6 \end{bmatrix} \begin{bmatrix} x \\ y \end{bmatrix} = \begin{bmatrix} x \\ y \end{bmatrix}$

$3 \cdot (1^{st} eq.)$ $3(.7x + .4y) = 3x$

$-2 \cdot (2^{nd} eq.)$ $\underline{-2(.3x + .6y) = -2y}$

$1.5x = 3x - 2y$

$2y = 1.5x$ $x + y = 1$

$y = \frac{3}{4} x$ $x + \frac{3}{4} x = 1$

$x = \frac{4}{7}$ $y = \frac{3}{7}$ In the long run $\frac{4}{7}$ of the governors will be Demo.

15.
       D   H   R

$\begin{matrix} D \\ H \\ R \end{matrix} \begin{bmatrix} .5 & .25 & 0 \\ .5 & .5 & .5 \\ 0 & .25 & .5 \end{bmatrix} \begin{bmatrix} x \\ y \\ z \end{bmatrix} = \begin{bmatrix} x \\ y \\ z \end{bmatrix}$

$(x+y+z=1)$ $.5x + .5y + .5z = .5$

                $\underline{.25y - .5z = 0}$

                $.5x + .75y = .5$

$(1st\ eq.)$ $-.5x + .25y = 0$

          $\underline{.5x + .75y = .5}$

              $y = .5$

Since $-.5x + .25y = 0$, $-.5x + (.25) \cdot (.5) = 0$ or $x = .25$. So, in the long run 25% of the individuals in a generation will be dominant.

16.
     C   B

$\begin{matrix} C \\ B \end{matrix} \begin{bmatrix} .2 & .5 \\ .8 & .5 \end{bmatrix} \begin{bmatrix} x \\ y \end{bmatrix} = \begin{bmatrix} x \\ y \end{bmatrix}$

          $.2x + .5y = x$

          $\underline{-.8x - .5y = -y}$

          $-.6x = x - y$

$y = 1.6x$

$x + y = 1$, so $x + 1.6x = 1$ $2.6x = 1$, $x = \frac{10}{26} = \frac{5}{13}$

$x + y = 1$, so $\frac{5}{13} + y = 1$ $y = \frac{8}{13} = .615$

In the long run 61.5% of the people take a bus on a particular day.

17.
     R   S

$\begin{matrix} R \\ S \end{matrix} \begin{bmatrix} .1 & .6 \\ .9 & .4 \end{bmatrix} \begin{bmatrix} x \\ y \end{bmatrix} = \begin{bmatrix} x \\ y \end{bmatrix}$

          $.1x + .6y = x$

          $.9x + .4y = y$

So $-.9x + .6y = 0$
$.9x - .6y = 0$ and $x + y = 1$. So, multiply this last equation by .9 and add to the first equation to find that $1.5y = 1$. So, $y = 2/3$ and $x = 1/3$. The likelihood of rain is 2/3.

18.
     R   B

$\begin{matrix} R \\ B \end{matrix} \begin{bmatrix} .97 & .70 \\ .03 & .30 \end{bmatrix} \begin{bmatrix} x \\ y \end{bmatrix} = \begin{bmatrix} x \\ y \end{bmatrix}$

          $.97x + .70y = x$

          $.03x + .30y = y$

Let's use the second equation in the form $.03x - .70y = 0$ and $x + y = 1$ to find that $.73x = .70$, and $x = 70/73$. This means that in the long run 70/73 of the terminals are working. So 210 are working.

227

19. $\begin{bmatrix} 0 & 1 \\ 1 & 0 \end{bmatrix} \begin{bmatrix} x \\ y \end{bmatrix} = \begin{bmatrix} x \\ y \end{bmatrix}$ $\begin{array}{l} y = x \\ x = y \\ x + y = 1, \quad x = .5, \quad y = .5 \end{array}$

The stable distribution is: $\begin{bmatrix} .5 \\ .5 \end{bmatrix}$ The predicted long-term trend is independent of the initial distribution.

20. $\begin{bmatrix} .8 & .3 \\ .2 & .7 \end{bmatrix} \begin{bmatrix} x \\ y \end{bmatrix} = \begin{bmatrix} x \\ y \end{bmatrix}$ and we have equations $\begin{array}{l} .8x + .3y = x \\ \text{and} \quad .2x + .7y = y \end{array}$
and $x + y = 1$. Then $.5x = .3$ (by multiplying $x + y = 1$ by $-.3$ and adding it to the first equation). And $x = 3/5$. So $x = 60\%$.

8.3 Absorbing Stochastic Matrices

1. $\begin{bmatrix} 1 & 0 & 0 & 0 \\ 0 & 1 & 0 & 0 \\ 0 & 0 & .8 & .1 \\ 0 & 0 & .2 & .9 \end{bmatrix}$ is *not* absorbing because it is not possible to get to either absorbing state from state 3 or state 4.

2. States 1,2 and 3 are absorbing states and since column 3 can lead to states 1,2 and 3 the matrix is an absorbing stochastic matrix.

3. State 1 is absorbing, since state 3 leads to state 1 and state 2 leads to state 3 the matrix is an absorbing stochastic matrix.

4. States 1 and 2 are absorbing, but states 3 and 4 are not absorbing and do not lead to absorbing states, the matrix is not an absorbing stochastic matrix.

5. $\left[\begin{array}{cc|c} 1 & 0 & .3 \\ 0 & 1 & .2 \\ \hline 0 & 0 & .5 \end{array}\right] \begin{array}{l} \\ S \\ \\ R \end{array}$ $\begin{array}{l} [I - R]^{-1} \\ = [1 - .5]^{-1} = [2], \end{array}$ $\begin{bmatrix} 1 & 0 & .6 \\ 0 & 1 & .4 \\ 0 & 0 & 0 \end{bmatrix}$

6. $\left[\begin{array}{cc|c} 1 & 0 & \frac{1}{2} \\ 0 & 1 & \frac{1}{6} \\ \hline 0 & 0 & \frac{1}{3} \end{array}\right] \begin{array}{l} \\ S \\ \\ R \end{array}$ $\begin{array}{l} [I - R]^{-1} \\ = \left[1 - \frac{1}{3}\right]^{-1} = \left[\frac{3}{2}\right], \end{array}$ $\begin{bmatrix} 1 & 0 & \frac{3}{4} \\ 0 & 1 & \frac{1}{4} \\ 0 & 0 & 0 \end{bmatrix}$

7. $\begin{bmatrix} 1 & 0 & .1 & 0 \\ 0 & 1 & .5 & .2 \\ \hline 0 & 0 & .3 & .6 \\ 0 & 0 & .1 & .2 \end{bmatrix}$ S $[I - R] = \begin{bmatrix} .7 & -.6 \\ -.1 & .8 \end{bmatrix}$

R $\Delta = .56 - .06 = .5$

$$F = [I - R]^{-1} = \frac{1}{.5} \cdot \begin{bmatrix} .8 & .6 \\ .1 & .7 \end{bmatrix} = \begin{bmatrix} 1.6 & 1.2 \\ .2 & 1.4 \end{bmatrix}$$

$$S[I - R]^{-1} = \begin{bmatrix} .1 & 0 \\ .5 & .2 \end{bmatrix} \begin{bmatrix} 1.6 & 1.2 \\ .2 & 1.4 \end{bmatrix} = \begin{bmatrix} .16 & .12 \\ .84 & .88 \end{bmatrix}$$

The stable matrix is: $\begin{bmatrix} 1 & 0 & .16 & .12 \\ 0 & 1 & .84 & .88 \\ 0 & 0 & 0 & 0 \\ 0 & 0 & 0 & 0 \end{bmatrix}$

8. $\begin{bmatrix} 1 & 0 & \frac{1}{4} & \frac{1}{6} \\ 0 & 1 & \frac{1}{6} & 0 \\ \hline 0 & 0 & \frac{1}{4} & \frac{1}{2} \\ 0 & 0 & \frac{1}{3} & \frac{1}{3} \end{bmatrix}$ S $[I - R] = \begin{bmatrix} \frac{3}{4} & \frac{-1}{2} \\ -\frac{1}{3} & \frac{2}{3} \end{bmatrix}$

R

$\Delta = \frac{1}{2} - \frac{1}{6} = \frac{1}{3}$

$$[I - R]^{-1} = 3 \cdot \begin{bmatrix} \frac{2}{3} & \frac{1}{2} \\ \frac{1}{3} & \frac{3}{4} \end{bmatrix} = \begin{bmatrix} 2 & \frac{3}{2} \\ 1 & \frac{9}{4} \end{bmatrix}$$

$$S[I - R]^{-1} = \begin{bmatrix} \frac{1}{4} & \frac{1}{6} \\ \frac{1}{6} & 0 \end{bmatrix} \begin{bmatrix} 2 & \frac{3}{2} \\ 1 & \frac{9}{4} \end{bmatrix} = \begin{bmatrix} \frac{2}{3} & \frac{3}{4} \\ \frac{1}{3} & \frac{1}{4} \end{bmatrix}$$

The stable matrix is: $\begin{bmatrix} 1 & 0 & \frac{2}{3} & \frac{3}{4} \\ 0 & 1 & \frac{1}{3} & \frac{1}{4} \\ 0 & 0 & 0 & 0 \\ 0 & 0 & 0 & 0 \end{bmatrix}$

9.

$$\begin{bmatrix} 1 & 0 & 0 & .1 & .2 \\ 0 & 1 & 0 & .3 & 0 \\ 0 & 0 & 1 & 0 & .2 \\ \hline 0 & 0 & 0 & .5 & 0 \\ 0 & 0 & 0 & .1 & .6 \end{bmatrix} \begin{matrix} \\ \\ S \\ \\ R \end{matrix} \qquad [I - R] = \begin{bmatrix} .5 & 0 \\ -.1 & .4 \end{bmatrix} \qquad \Delta = .2$$

$$[I - R]^{-1} = 5 \cdot \begin{bmatrix} .4 & 0 \\ .1 & .5 \end{bmatrix} = \begin{bmatrix} 2 & 0 \\ .5 & 2.5 \end{bmatrix}$$

$$S[I - R]^{-1} = \begin{bmatrix} .1 & .2 \\ .3 & 0 \\ 0 & .2 \end{bmatrix} \begin{bmatrix} 2 & 0 \\ .5 & 2.5 \end{bmatrix} = \begin{bmatrix} .3 & .5 \\ .6 & 0 \\ .1 & .5 \end{bmatrix}$$

The stable matrix is:
$$\begin{bmatrix} 1 & 0 & 0 & .3 & .5 \\ 0 & 1 & 0 & .6 & 0 \\ 0 & 0 & 1 & .1 & .5 \\ \hline 0 & 0 & 0 & 0 & 0 \\ 0 & 0 & 0 & 0 & 0 \end{bmatrix}$$

10.

$$\begin{bmatrix} 1 & 0 & \frac{1}{4} & 0 & \frac{1}{3} \\ 0 & 1 & \frac{1}{4} & 0 & 0 \\ \hline 0 & 0 & 0 & \frac{1}{3} & \frac{1}{6} \\ 0 & 0 & \frac{1}{2} & \frac{1}{3} & 0 \\ 0 & 0 & 0 & \frac{1}{3} & \frac{1}{2} \end{bmatrix} \begin{matrix} \\ S \\ \\ \\ R \\ \\ \end{matrix} \qquad [I - R] = \begin{bmatrix} 1 & \frac{-1}{3} & \frac{-1}{6} \\ \frac{-1}{2} & \frac{2}{3} & 0 \\ 0 & \frac{-1}{3} & \frac{1}{2} \end{bmatrix}$$

$$[I - R]^{-1} = \begin{bmatrix} \frac{3}{2} & 1 & \frac{1}{2} \\ \frac{9}{8} & \frac{9}{4} & \frac{3}{8} \\ \frac{3}{4} & \frac{3}{2} & \frac{9}{4} \end{bmatrix}$$

$$S[I - R]^{-1} = \begin{bmatrix} \frac{1}{4} & 0 & \frac{1}{3} \\ \frac{1}{4} & 0 & 0 \end{bmatrix} \begin{bmatrix} \frac{3}{2} & 1 & \frac{1}{2} \\ \frac{9}{8} & \frac{9}{4} & \frac{3}{8} \\ \frac{3}{4} & \frac{3}{2} & \frac{9}{4} \end{bmatrix}$$

$$= \begin{bmatrix} \frac{5}{8} & \frac{3}{4} & \frac{7}{8} \\ \frac{3}{8} & \frac{1}{4} & \frac{1}{8} \end{bmatrix}$$

The stable matrix is:
$$\begin{bmatrix} 1 & 0 & \frac{5}{8} & \frac{3}{4} & \frac{7}{8} \\ 0 & 1 & \frac{3}{8} & \frac{1}{4} & \frac{1}{8} \\ 0 & 0 & 0 & 0 & 0 \\ 0 & 0 & 0 & 0 & 0 \\ 0 & 0 & 0 & 0 & 0 \end{bmatrix}$$

11. If the gambler begins with \$2, the expected number of times he will have \$1 is .79

12. 2.11

13. (a)

$$\begin{array}{c} \\ D \\ G \\ F \\ S \end{array} \begin{array}{c} D \quad G \quad F \quad S \\ \begin{bmatrix} 1 & 0 & .2 & .1 \\ 0 & 1 & 0 & .9 \\ 0 & 0 & 0 & 0 \\ 0 & 0 & .8 & 0 \end{bmatrix} \end{array} \begin{array}{c} S \\ \\ R \end{array}$$

$[I - R]^{-1} = \begin{bmatrix} 1 & 0 \\ -.8 & 1 \end{bmatrix}^{-1} = \begin{bmatrix} 1 & 0 \\ .8 & 1 \end{bmatrix}$

$$S[I - R]^{-1} = \begin{bmatrix} .2 & .1 \\ 0 & .9 \end{bmatrix} \begin{bmatrix} 1 & 0 \\ .8 & 1 \end{bmatrix} = \begin{bmatrix} .28 & .1 \\ .72 & .9 \end{bmatrix}$$

(b) The stable matrix is:
$$\begin{bmatrix} 1 & 0 & .28 & .10 \\ 0 & 1 & .72 & .90 \\ 0 & 0 & 0 & 0 \\ 0 & 0 & 0 & 0 \end{bmatrix}$$

(c) .72 probability that an entering freshman will graduate.

(d) The inverse of (I - R) is shown above to be:
$$\begin{bmatrix} 1 & 0 \\ \frac{4}{5} & 1 \end{bmatrix}.$$
The sum of the second row gives the expected number of years a student entering as a freshman attends the college before either dropping out or graduating. That is 9/5 years.

14. (a)

$$\begin{array}{c} \\ I \\ II \\ III \\ IV \end{array} \begin{array}{cccc} I & II & III & IV \\ \end{array}$$

$$\left[\begin{array}{cc|cc} 1 & 0 & 0 & .02 \\ 0 & 1 & .01994 & .03 \\ \hline 0 & 0 & .98 & 0 \\ 0 & 0 & .00006 & .95 \end{array}\right]$$

$$S \qquad [I - R]^{-1} = \begin{bmatrix} .02 & 0 \\ -.00006 & .05 \end{bmatrix}^{-1}$$

$$R \qquad = 1000 \cdot \begin{bmatrix} .05 & 0 \\ .00006 & .02 \end{bmatrix}$$

$$= \begin{bmatrix} 50 & 0 \\ .06 & 20 \end{bmatrix}$$

$$S[I - R]^{-1} = \begin{bmatrix} 0 & .02 \\ .01994 & .03 \end{bmatrix} \begin{bmatrix} 50 & 0 \\ .06 & 20 \end{bmatrix} = \begin{bmatrix} .0012 & .4 \\ .9988 & .6 \end{bmatrix}$$

(b) The stable matrix is:
$$\begin{bmatrix} 1 & 0 & .0012 & .4 \\ 0 & 1 & .9988 & .6 \\ 0 & 0 & 0 & 0 \\ 0 & 0 & 0 & 0 \end{bmatrix}$$

(c) .12% or .0012 probability that a person who is currently well will eventually become chronically insane.

(d) 50

15. (a) $\frac{13}{14}$, $\frac{11}{14}$ (b) $\frac{20}{7}$,   16. (a) $\frac{5}{13}$, $\frac{7}{26}$, $\frac{5}{26}$ (b) $\frac{60}{13}$

17. (a) $\frac{3}{4}$, $\frac{1}{2}$, $\frac{1}{4}$ (b) 4

8. Supplementary Exercises

1. It is stochastic; each column sum is one and each entry $\geq$ 0. Squarin the original, we see for any power of A the first column will always be

$$\begin{bmatrix} 1 \\ 0 \\ 0 \\ 0 \end{bmatrix}, \text{ so A is not regular.}$$

A is not absorbing since it is not possible to get from either state 3 or 4 to states 1 or 2.

2. It is stochastic; each column adds to one and each entry $\geq$ 0.

$$\begin{bmatrix} .1 & .1 & .1 & .1 \\ .2 & .2 & .2 & .2 \\ .3 & .3 & .3 & .3 \\ .4 & .4 & .4 & .4 \end{bmatrix}$$

Since all entries are greater than zero the matrix is regular.

3. It is stochastic; each column adds to one and each entry ≥ 0.

$$\begin{bmatrix} 0 & .3 \\ 1 & .7 \end{bmatrix}\begin{bmatrix} 0 & .3 \\ 1 & .7 \end{bmatrix} = \begin{bmatrix} .3 & .21 \\ .7 & .79 \end{bmatrix}$$

Since all entries in the square of the matrix are greater than zero the matrix is regular.

4. It is stochastic; each column adds to one and each entry ≥ 0.

$$\begin{bmatrix} 1 & 0 & 0 \\ 0 & 1 & \frac{1}{3} \\ 0 & 0 & \frac{2}{3} \end{bmatrix}\begin{bmatrix} 1 & 0 & 0 \\ 0 & 1 & \frac{1}{3} \\ 0 & 0 & \frac{2}{3} \end{bmatrix} = \begin{bmatrix} 1 & 0 & 0 \\ 0 & 1 & \frac{5}{9} \\ 0 & 0 & \frac{4}{9} \end{bmatrix}$$

It is not regular and it is absorbing.

5. Not stochastic, since column II adds up to $\frac{3}{2} \neq 1$, and it is not regular or absorbing, since it is not stochastic.

6. It is stochastic; each column adds to one and each entry ≥ 0.

$$\begin{bmatrix} 1 & 0 & 0 & .3 \\ 0 & 1 & 0 & .3 \\ 0 & 0 & .5 & .3 \\ 0 & 0 & .5 & .1 \end{bmatrix}\begin{bmatrix} 1 & 0 & 0 & .3 \\ 0 & 1 & 0 & .3 \\ 0 & 0 & .5 & .3 \\ 0 & 0 & .5 & .1 \end{bmatrix} = \begin{bmatrix} 1 & 0 & .15 & .33 \\ 0 & 1 & .15 & .33 \\ 0 & 0 & .40 & .18 \\ 0 & 0 & .30 & .16 \end{bmatrix}$$

Not a regular matrix and it is absorbing.

7. $$\begin{bmatrix} .6 & .5 \\ .4 & .5 \end{bmatrix}\begin{bmatrix} x \\ y \end{bmatrix} = \begin{bmatrix} x \\ y \end{bmatrix}$$

$$\begin{array}{r} .6x + .5y = x \\ -.4x - .5y = -y \\ \hline .2x = x - y \end{array}$$

$y = .8x$ $x + y = 1$

$x + .8x = 1$ $1.8x = 1$ $x = \frac{5}{9}$ $y = \frac{4}{9}$

The stable matrix is: $\begin{bmatrix} \frac{5}{9} \\ \frac{4}{9} \end{bmatrix}$.

8.

$$\left[\begin{array}{ccc|cc} 1 & 0 & 0 & \frac{1}{8} & \frac{1}{4} \\ 0 & 1 & 0 & \frac{1}{8} & 0 \\ 0 & 0 & 1 & 0 & \frac{1}{4} \\ \hline 0 & 0 & 0 & \frac{1}{4} & \frac{1}{2} \\ 0 & 0 & 0 & \frac{1}{2} & 0 \end{array}\right]$$

S

$$[I - R]^{-1} = \left[\begin{array}{cc} \frac{3}{4} & \frac{-1}{2} \\ \frac{-1}{2} & 1 \end{array}\right]^{-1}$$

R

$$= \left[\begin{array}{cc} 2 & 1 \\ 1 & \frac{3}{2} \end{array}\right]$$

$$S[I - R]^{-1} = \left[\begin{array}{cc} \frac{1}{8} & \frac{1}{4} \\ \frac{1}{8} & 0 \\ 0 & \frac{1}{4} \end{array}\right] \left[\begin{array}{cc} 2 & 1 \\ 1 & \frac{3}{2} \end{array}\right] = \left[\begin{array}{cc} \frac{1}{2} & \frac{1}{2} \\ \frac{1}{4} & \frac{1}{8} \\ \frac{1}{4} & \frac{3}{8} \end{array}\right]$$

The stable matrix is:

$$\left[\begin{array}{ccc|cc} 1 & 0 & 0 & \frac{1}{2} & \frac{1}{2} \\ 0 & 1 & 0 & \frac{1}{4} & \frac{1}{8} \\ 0 & 0 & 1 & \frac{1}{4} & \frac{3}{8} \\ \hline 0 & 0 & 0 & 0 & 0 \\ 0 & 0 & 0 & 0 & 0 \end{array}\right]$$

9. (a)

	H	M	L
H	.5	.4	.3
M	.4	.3	.5
L	.1	.3	.2

(b)

$$\left[\begin{array}{ccc} .5 & .4 & .3 \\ .4 & .3 & .5 \\ .1 & .3 & .2 \end{array}\right] \left[\begin{array}{c} .1 \\ .6 \\ .3 \end{array}\right] = \left[\begin{array}{c} .38 \\ .37 \\ .25 \end{array}\right]$$

38% of the children of this generation will have high incomes.

(c) $x + 3y - 8z = 0$ (3rd eq.) $5(-5x + 4y + 3z) = 0$ (1st eq.)
   $\underline{8x + 8y + 8z = 8}$ $\underline{-3(4x - 7y + 5z) = 0}$ (2nd eq.)
         $9x + 11y = 8$ $-37x + 41y = 0$
   $-41(9x + 11y = 8)$
   $\underline{11(-37x + 41y = 0)}$
         $776x = 328$ $x = \frac{41}{97}$, $y = \frac{37}{97}$, $z = \frac{19}{97}$

$\frac{19}{97}$ of the population will have low incomes in the long run.

10. (a)

$$\begin{array}{c} \\ P \\ N \end{array} \begin{array}{cc} P & N \end{array} \\ \begin{bmatrix} .8 & .3 \\ .2 & .7 \end{bmatrix}$$

(b) $\begin{bmatrix} .8 & .3 \\ .2 & .7 \end{bmatrix} \begin{bmatrix} .8 & .3 \\ .2 & .7 \end{bmatrix} = \begin{bmatrix} .7 & .45 \\ .3 & .55 \end{bmatrix}$

30% will need adjusting after two days

(c)
$$-.8x - .3y = -x$$
$$\underline{.8x + 2.8y = 4y}$$
$$2.5y = 4y - x$$
$$1.5y = x$$
$$1.5y + y = 1$$

$$x + y = 1$$
$$2.5y = 1 \qquad y = \frac{2}{5} \quad x = \frac{3}{5}$$

$\frac{3}{5}$ = 60% will be properly adjusted each day.

11.

$$\begin{bmatrix} 1 & 0 & \frac{1}{6} & \frac{1}{2} & \frac{2}{5} \\ 0 & 1 & 0 & 0 & \frac{2}{5} \\ 0 & 0 & 0 & 0 & 0 \\ 0 & 0 & \frac{2}{3} & \frac{1}{2} & 0 \\ 0 & 0 & \frac{1}{6} & 0 & \frac{1}{5} \end{bmatrix} \begin{array}{l} \\ \\ \\ \\ \\ \end{array} \begin{array}{l} S \\ \\ R \end{array}$$

$$[I - R]^{-1} = \begin{bmatrix} 1 & 0 & 0 \\ \frac{-2}{3} & \frac{1}{2} & 0 \\ \frac{-1}{6} & 0 & \frac{4}{5} \end{bmatrix}^{-1}$$

$$\Delta = \frac{2}{5}$$

$$[I - R]^{-1} = \begin{bmatrix} 1 & 0 & 0 & 1 & 0 & 0 \\ \frac{-2}{3} & \frac{1}{2} & 0 & 0 & 1 & 0 \\ \frac{-1}{6} & 0 & \frac{4}{5} & 0 & 0 & 1 \end{bmatrix} = \begin{bmatrix} 1 & 0 & 0 & 1 & 0 & 0 \\ 0 & \frac{1}{2} & 0 & \frac{2}{3} & 1 & 0 \\ 0 & 0 & \frac{4}{5} & \frac{1}{6} & 0 & 1 \end{bmatrix}$$

$$= \begin{bmatrix} 1 & 0 & 0 & 1 & 0 & 0 \\ 0 & 1 & 0 & \frac{4}{3} & 2 & 0 \\ 0 & 0 & 1 & \frac{5}{24} & 0 & \frac{5}{4} \end{bmatrix}$$

$$S[I - R]^{-1} = \begin{bmatrix} \frac{1}{6} & \frac{1}{2} & \frac{2}{5} \\ 0 & 0 & \frac{2}{5} \end{bmatrix} \begin{bmatrix} 1 & 0 & 0 \\ \frac{4}{3} & 2 & 0 \\ \frac{5}{24} & 0 & \frac{5}{4} \end{bmatrix}$$

$$= \begin{bmatrix} \frac{11}{12} & 1 & \frac{1}{2} \\ \frac{1}{12} & 0 & \frac{1}{2} \end{bmatrix}$$

The stable matrix is:
$$\left[\begin{array}{cc|ccc} 1 & 0 & \frac{11}{12} & 1 & \frac{1}{2} \\ 0 & 1 & \frac{1}{12} & 0 & \frac{1}{2} \\ \hline 0 & 0 & 0 & 0 & 0 \\ 0 & 0 & 0 & 0 & 0 \\ 0 & 0 & 0 & 0 & 0 \end{array}\right]$$

12. (a)
$$\begin{array}{c} \\ \text{I} \\ \text{II} \\ \text{III} \\ \text{IV} \end{array} \begin{array}{c} \begin{array}{cccc} \text{I} & \text{II} & \text{III} & \text{IV} \end{array} \\ \left[\begin{array}{cccc} 1 & 0 & 0 & \frac{1}{4} \\ 0 & 1 & \frac{1}{3} & \frac{1}{4} \\ 0 & 0 & 0 & \frac{1}{2} \\ 0 & 0 & \frac{2}{3} & 0 \end{array}\right] \end{array}$$

(b)
$$\left[\begin{array}{cccc} 1 & 0 & 0 & \frac{1}{4} \\ 0 & 1 & \frac{1}{3} & \frac{1}{4} \\ 0 & 0 & 0 & \frac{1}{2} \\ 0 & 0 & \frac{2}{3} & 0 \end{array}\right] \left[\begin{array}{cccc} 1 & 0 & 0 & \frac{1}{4} \\ 0 & 1 & \frac{1}{3} & \frac{1}{4} \\ 0 & 0 & 0 & \frac{1}{2} \\ 0 & 0 & \frac{2}{3} & 0 \end{array}\right]$$

$$= \begin{array}{c} \\ \text{I} \\ \text{II} \\ \text{III} \\ \text{IV} \end{array} \begin{array}{c} \begin{array}{cccc} \text{I} & \text{II} & \text{III} & \text{IV} \end{array} \\ \left[\begin{array}{cccc} 1 & 0 & \frac{1}{6} & \frac{1}{4} \\ 0 & 1 & \frac{1}{2} & \boxed{\frac{5}{12}} \\ 0 & 0 & \frac{1}{3} & 0 \\ 0 & 0 & 0 & \frac{1}{3} \end{array}\right] \end{array} \quad \frac{5}{12} \text{ Probability}$$

(c) $[I - R]^{-1} = \left[\begin{array}{cc} \frac{2}{3} & 0 \\ 0 & \frac{2}{3} \end{array}\right]^{-1} = \frac{9}{4} \cdot \left[\begin{array}{cc} \frac{2}{3} & 0 \\ 0 & \frac{2}{3} \end{array}\right] = \left[\begin{array}{cc} \frac{3}{2} & 0 \\ 0 & \frac{3}{2} \end{array}\right]$

$S[I - R]^{-1} = \left[\begin{array}{cc} \frac{1}{6} & \frac{1}{4} \\ \frac{1}{2} & \frac{5}{12} \end{array}\right] \left[\begin{array}{cc} \frac{3}{2} & 0 \\ 0 & \frac{3}{2} \end{array}\right] = \left[\begin{array}{cc} \frac{1}{4} & \frac{3}{8} \\ \frac{3}{4} & \boxed{\frac{5}{8}} \end{array}\right]$

The probability $= \frac{5}{8}$ that he will find the cheese in the long run.

(d) $2\frac{1}{2}$

13. (a) $\begin{bmatrix} .6 \\ .4 \\ 1 \end{bmatrix}$ $.6 + .4 + .1 \neq 1$, this cannot be the stable distribution for the regular stochastic matrix. The sum of entries should be 1 and $Ax = x$.

(b) $\begin{bmatrix} .4 & .4 & .2 \\ .1 & .1 & .3 \\ .5 & .5 & .5 \end{bmatrix} \begin{bmatrix} .2 \\ .3 \\ .5 \end{bmatrix} = \begin{bmatrix} .3 \\ .2 \\ .5 \end{bmatrix} \neq \begin{bmatrix} .2 \\ .3 \\ .5 \end{bmatrix}$; this is not the stable distribution.

(c) $\begin{bmatrix} .4 & .4 & .2 \\ .1 & .1 & .3 \\ .5 & .5 & .5 \end{bmatrix} \begin{bmatrix} .3 \\ .2 \\ .5 \end{bmatrix} = \begin{bmatrix} .3 \\ .2 \\ .5 \end{bmatrix}$; this is the stable distribution.

14. $\begin{array}{cc} & \begin{array}{cc} A & B \end{array} \\ \begin{array}{c} A \\ B \end{array} & \begin{bmatrix} .9 & .2 \\ .1 & .8 \end{bmatrix} \end{array} \begin{bmatrix} .9 & .2 \\ .1 & .8 \end{bmatrix} = \begin{bmatrix} .83 & .34 \\ .17 & .66 \end{bmatrix}$

$\begin{array}{c} A \\ B \end{array} \begin{bmatrix} .83 & .34 \\ .17 & .66 \end{bmatrix} \begin{bmatrix} .5 \\ .5 \end{bmatrix} = \begin{array}{c} A \\ B \end{array} \begin{bmatrix} .585 \\ .415 \end{bmatrix}$ 58.5% would listen to station A two days from now.

237

9

THE THEORY OF GAMES

9.1 Games and Strategies

1.
$$\begin{bmatrix} -1 & \boxed{-2} \\ \boxed{0} & \boxed{3} \end{bmatrix}$$
Row Player: smallest in each row is circled.
Row 2 is chosen (0 > -2).

Column Player: largest in each column is boxed
Column 1 is chosen (0 < 3).

Saddle point is 0 (Row 2, Column 1).

2.   R: row 2, C: column 2

3.   R: row 2, C: column 1

4.   R: row 2, C: column 3

5.   R: row 1, C: column 1

6.   R: row 2, C: column 2

7.
$$\begin{bmatrix} \boxed{1} & \boxed{0} \\ 0 & \boxed{-1} \end{bmatrix}$$
Smallest in each row is circled.
R chooses 1st row.
Largest in each column is boxed.
C chooses 2nd column.

(a)   The saddle point is row 1, column 2.
(b)   The value of the game is 0.

8.   (a)   The saddle point is row 2, column 1.
      (b)   The value of the game is 4

9.
$$\begin{array}{c} & \begin{array}{cc} H & T \end{array} \\ \begin{array}{c} H \\ T \end{array} & \begin{bmatrix} 2 & -1 \\ -1 & -4 \end{bmatrix} \end{array}$$
strictly determined; R shows heads;
C shows tails

10.
$$\begin{array}{c} & \begin{array}{ccc} S & P & St. \end{array} \\ \begin{array}{c} S \\ P \\ t. \end{array} & \begin{bmatrix} 0 & 1 & -1 \\ -1 & 0 & 1 \\ 1 & -1 & 0 \end{bmatrix} \end{array}$$
; not strictly determined

11.
$$\begin{array}{c} & \begin{array}{ccc} F & A & N \end{array} \\ \begin{array}{c} F \\ A \\ N \end{array} & \begin{bmatrix} 8000 & -1000 & 1000 \\ -7000 & 4000 & -2000 \\ 3000 & 3000 & 2000 \end{bmatrix} \end{array}$$
; strictly determined;
both should be neutral

12.
$$\begin{array}{c} & \begin{array}{cc} 1 & 2 \end{array} \\ \begin{array}{c} 1 \\ 2 \end{array} & \begin{bmatrix} 3000 & 2000 \\ 5000 & -2000 \end{bmatrix} \end{array}$$
strictly determined;
R shows quiz show at 1 o'clock, C at 2

o'clock

$$13. \quad \begin{array}{cc} & \begin{array}{ccc} R6 & B7 & B8 \end{array} \\ \begin{array}{c} R5 \\ B10 \end{array} & \begin{bmatrix} 1 & -5 & -5 \\ -6 & 3 & 2 \end{bmatrix} \end{array}$$

The largest of the least in each row is -5 in row 1. The smallest of the largest in each column is 1 in column 1. There is no saddle point, so the game is not strictly determined.

9.2 Mixed Strategies

1. (a) $[.5 \quad .5]\begin{bmatrix} 3 & -1 \\ -7 & 5 \end{bmatrix}\begin{bmatrix} .5 \\ .5 \end{bmatrix} = [-2 \quad 2]\begin{bmatrix} .5 \\ .5 \end{bmatrix} = 0$

(b) $[1 \quad 0]\begin{bmatrix} 3 & -1 \\ -7 & 5 \end{bmatrix}\begin{bmatrix} .5 \\ .5 \end{bmatrix} = [3 \quad -1]\begin{bmatrix} .5 \\ .5 \end{bmatrix} = 1$

(c) $[.3 \quad .7]\begin{bmatrix} 3 & -1 \\ -7 & 5 \end{bmatrix}\begin{bmatrix} .6 \\ .4 \end{bmatrix} = [-4 \quad 3.2]\begin{bmatrix} .6 \\ .4 \end{bmatrix} = -1.12$

(d) $[.75 \quad .25]\begin{bmatrix} 3 & -1 \\ -7 & 5 \end{bmatrix}\begin{bmatrix} .2 \\ .8 \end{bmatrix} = [.5 \quad .5]\begin{bmatrix} .2 \\ .8 \end{bmatrix} = .5$

The most advantageous to R is (b).

2. (a) .7 (b) .12 (c) -.5
(d) -.48; The most advantageous to C is (c).

3. $29,200

4. $14,700

5. 0

6. $168,000

9.3 Determining Optimal Mixed Strategies

1. Using the Simplex Method, set up the tableau for finding optimal C strategy: Maximize $z_1 + z_2$ subject to

$$2z_1 + 4z_2 \leq 1; \quad 5z_1 + 3z_2 \leq 1; \quad z_1 \geq 0; \text{ and } z_2 \geq 0$$

$$\begin{array}{c} \\ t \\ u \\ M \end{array} \begin{array}{c} \begin{array}{ccccc} z_1 & z_2 & t & u & M \end{array} \\ \left[\begin{array}{ccccc|c} 2 & 4 & 1 & 0 & 0 & 1 \\ 5 & 3 & 0 & 1 & 0 & 1 \\ \hline -1 & -1 & 0 & 0 & 1 & 0 \end{array} \right] \end{array} \sim \begin{array}{c} \begin{array}{ccccc} z_1 & z_2 & t & u & M \end{array} \\ \left[\begin{array}{ccccc|c} 2 & 4 & 1 & 0 & 0 & 1 \\ 1 & 3/5 & 0 & 1/5 & 0 & 1/5 \\ \hline -1 & -1 & 0 & 0 & 1 & 0 \end{array} \right] \end{array}$$

$$\xrightarrow[\begin{array}{c} [1] + -2 \ [2] \\ \hline [3] + [2] \end{array}]{} \begin{array}{c} \\ t \\ u \\ M \end{array} \begin{array}{c} \begin{array}{ccccc} z_1 & z_2 & t & u & M \end{array} \\ \left[\begin{array}{ccccc|c} 0 & 14/5 & 1 & -2/5 & 0 & 3/5 \\ 1 & 3/5 & 0 & 1/5 & 0 & 1/5 \\ \hline 0 & -2/5 & 0 & 1/5 & 1 & 1/5 \end{array} \right] \end{array}$$

$$\begin{array}{c}\begin{array}{cccccc} & z_1 & z_2 & t & u & M \end{array}\\ \begin{array}{c} t \\ u \\ M \end{array}\left[\begin{array}{ccccc|c} 0 & 1 & 5/14 & -1/7 & 0 & 3/14 \\ 1 & 0 & -3/14 & 2/7 & 0 & 1/14 \\ \hline 0 & 0 & 1/7 & 1/7 & 1 & 2/7 \end{array}\right]\end{array}$$

$v = 7/2$, $c_1 = vz_1 = \dfrac{7}{2} \cdot \dfrac{1}{14} = \dfrac{1}{4}$ and $c_2 = vz_2 = \dfrac{7}{2} \cdot \dfrac{3}{14} = \dfrac{3}{4}$

C's optimal strategy: $\begin{bmatrix} 1/4 \\ 3/4 \end{bmatrix}$.

$r_1 = vt = \dfrac{7}{2} \cdot \dfrac{1}{7} = \dfrac{1}{2}$ and $r_2 = vu = \dfrac{7}{2} \cdot \dfrac{1}{7} = \dfrac{1}{2}$

R's optimal strategy: $[1/2, \ 1/2]$

2. $[1/2 \quad 1/2]$; $\begin{bmatrix} 1/2 \\ 1/2 \end{bmatrix}$

3. $[1/2 \quad 1/2]$; $\begin{bmatrix} 5/9 \\ 4/9 \end{bmatrix}$

4. $[1 \quad 0]$; $\begin{bmatrix} 0 \\ 1 \end{bmatrix}$

5. $[2/5 \quad 3/5]$; $\begin{bmatrix} 3/5 \\ 2/5 \end{bmatrix}$

6. $[3/16 \quad 13/16]$; $\begin{bmatrix} 7/8 \\ 1/8 \end{bmatrix}$

7. Given: $\begin{bmatrix} 3 & 5 & -1 \\ 4 & -1 & 6 \end{bmatrix}$ Add 2 to each entry to make all entries positive.

$\begin{bmatrix} 5 & 7 & 1 \\ 6 & 1 & 8 \end{bmatrix}$ = adjusted pay-off matrix

Maximize $z_1 + z_2 + z_3$ subject to

$5z_1 + 7z_2 + z_3 \leq 1$; $6z_1 + z_2 + 8z_3 \leq 1$;

$z_1 \geq 0$; $z_2 \geq 0$; and $z_3 \geq 0$

Using the Simplex Method, set up the tableau for finding optimal C strategy; but calculate R's strategy from final tableau.

$$\begin{array}{c}\begin{array}{ccccccc} & z_1 & z_2 & z_3 & t & u & M \end{array}\\ \begin{array}{c} t \\ u \\ M \end{array}\left[\begin{array}{cccccc|c} 5 & 7 & 1 & 1 & 0 & 0 & 1 \\ 6 & 1 & 8 & 0 & 2 & 0 & 1 \\ \hline -1 & -1 & -1 & 0 & 0 & 1 & 0 \end{array}\right]\end{array} = \begin{array}{c}\begin{array}{ccccccc} z_1 & z_2 & z_3 & t & u & M \end{array}\\ \left[\begin{array}{cccccc|c} 5 & 7 & 1 & 1 & 0 & 0 & 1 \\ 3/4 & 1/8 & 1 & 0 & 1/8 & 0 & 1/8 \\ -1 & -1 & -1 & 0 & 0 & 1 & 0 \end{array}\right]\end{array}$$

$$\begin{array}{c}\begin{array}{cccccc} & z_1 & z_2 & z_3 & t & u & M \end{array}\\ \begin{array}{c} t \\ z_3 \\ M \end{array}\left[\begin{array}{cccccc|c} 17/4 & 55/8 & 0 & 1 & -1/8 & 0 & 7/8 \\ 3/4 & 1/8 & 1 & 0 & 1/8 & 0 & 1/8 \\ \hline -1/4 & -7/8 & 0 & 0 & 1/8 & 1 & 1/8 \end{array}\right]\end{array}$$

240

$$\begin{array}{c} \\ z_2 \\ z_3 \\ M \end{array} \begin{array}{ccccccc} z_1 & z_2 & z_3 & t & u & M & \\ \left[\begin{array}{cccccc|c} 34/55 & 1 & 0 & 8/55 & -1/55 & 0 & 7/55 \\ 37/55 & 0 & 1 & -1/55 & 7/55 & 0 & 6/55 \\ \hline 16/55 & 0 & 0 & 7/55 & 6/55 & 1 & 13/55 \end{array}\right] \end{array}$$

$t = 7/55;$ $u = 6/55;$ $v = 55/13$

$r_1 = vt = 7/13;$ $r_2 = vu = 6/13$

R's optimal strategy: $[7/13 \quad 6/13]$

8. $[2/5 \quad 3/5]$

9. $\begin{bmatrix} 0 \\ 1 \end{bmatrix}$

10. $\begin{bmatrix} 3/5 \\ 2/5 \end{bmatrix}$

11.   (a) $[8/17 \quad 9/17]$
      (b) $\begin{bmatrix} 8/17 \\ 9/17 \end{bmatrix}$

      (c)   \$2765

12.   (a) $[3/8 \quad 5/8]$

      (b) $\begin{bmatrix} 3/8 \\ 5/8 \end{bmatrix}$

      (c)   Ralph

13.   Given: $\begin{bmatrix} -2 & 1 \\ 2 & -3 \\ 1 & -2 \end{bmatrix}$ Add 4 to each entry to make all positive. $\begin{bmatrix} 2 & 5 \\ 6 & 1 \\ 5 & 2 \end{bmatrix}$

Maximize $z_1 + z_2$ subject to

$2z_1 + 5z_2 \le 1;$ $6z_1 + z_2 \le 1;$ $5z_1 + 2z_2 \le 1;$

$z_1 \ge 0;$ and $z_2 \ge 0$

$$\begin{array}{c} \\ t \\ u \\ v \\ M \end{array} \begin{array}{cccccc} z_1 & z_2 & t & u & w & M \\ \left[\begin{array}{cccccc|c} 2 & 5 & 1 & 0 & 0 & 0 & 1 \\ 6 & 1 & 0 & 1 & 0 & 0 & 1 \\ 5 & 2 & 0 & 0 & 1 & 0 & 1 \\ \hline -1 & -1 & 0 & 0 & 0 & 1 & 0 \end{array}\right] \end{array}$$

	z_1	z_2	t	u	w	M	
z_2	2/5	1	1/5	0	0	0	1/5
u	28/5	0	-1/5	1	0	0	4/5
w	21/5	0	-2/5	0	1	0	3/5
M	-3/5	0	1/5	0	0	1	1/5

	z_1	z_2	t	u	w	M	
z_2	2/5	1	1/5	0	0	0	1/5
u	1	0	-1/28	5/28	0	0	1/7
w	21/5	2	-2/5	0	1	0	3/5
M	-3/5	0	1/5	0	0	1	1/5

	z_1	z_2	t	u	w	M	
z_2	0	1	3/14	-1/14	0	0	1/7
z_1	1	0	-1/28	5/28	0	0	1/7
w	0	0	-1/4	-3/4	1	0	0
M	0	0	5/28	3/28	0	1	2/7

$v = 7/2;$ $z_1 = 1/7;$ $z_2 = 1/7;$ $t = 5/28;$ $u = 3/28;$

$w = 0$ $c_1 = vz_1 = 1/2;$ $c_2 = vz_2 = 1/2$

$r_1 = vt = 5/8;$ $r_2 = vu = 3/8;$ $r_3 = vw = 0$

R's strategy: $[5/8 \quad 3/8 \quad 0];$ C's strategy: $\begin{bmatrix} 1/2 \\ 1/2 \end{bmatrix}$

Payoff is $V - 4 = -1/2$

SUPPLEMENTARY EXERCISES

1. $\begin{bmatrix} 5 & -1 & 1 \\ -3 & 5 & 1 \\ 4 & 3 & 2 \end{bmatrix}$
    The 2 in R3 and C3 is both the greatest of the least
    number in the rows and the least of the greatest numbers
    in the columns. The game is strictly determined;
    R: row 3, C: column 3; the value of the game is 2.

2. Not strictly determined

3. Not strictly determined

4. Not strictly determined

5. 7

6. 4

7. $[.2 \quad .3 \quad .5] \begin{bmatrix} 1 & 0 \\ -3 & 1 \\ 0 & 5 \end{bmatrix} \begin{bmatrix} .4 \\ .6 \end{bmatrix} = [-.7 \quad 2.8] \begin{bmatrix} .4 \\ .6 \end{bmatrix} = 1.4$
    expected value = 1.4.

8. −1.3

9. $[4/11 \quad 7/11]$; $\begin{bmatrix} 6/11 \\ 5/11 \end{bmatrix}$

10. $[8/17 \quad 9/17]$, $\begin{bmatrix} 10/17 \\ 7/17 \end{bmatrix}$

11. $[0 \quad 1]$

12. $[1/4 \quad 3/4]$

13. (a) Given R $\begin{array}{c} 2 \stackrel{C}{} \\ 2 \\ 6 \end{array} \begin{bmatrix} -3 & 6 \\ 2 & -3 \end{bmatrix}$, add 4 to each element: $\begin{bmatrix} 1 & 10 \\ 6 & 1 \end{bmatrix}$

Maximize $z_1 + z_2$ subject to:

$z_1 + 10z_2 \le 1$; $6z_1 + z_2 \le 1$; $z_1 \ge 0$; and $z_2 \ge 0$

$$
\begin{array}{c}
\quad\;\; z_1 \;\; z_2 \;\; t \;\; u \;\; M \\
\begin{array}{c} t \\ u \\ M \end{array}
\left[
\begin{array}{ccccc|c}
1 & 10 & 1 & 0 & 0 & 1 \\
6 & 1 & 0 & 1 & 0 & 1 \\ \hline
-1 & -1 & 0 & 0 & 1 & 0
\end{array}
\right]
\end{array}
=
\begin{array}{c}
\quad\;\; z_1 \;\; z_2 \;\;\; t \;\;\; u \;\; M \\
\left[
\begin{array}{ccccc|c}
1 & 10 & 1 & 0 & 0 & 1 \\
1 & 1/6 & 0 & 1/6 & 0 & 1/6 \\ \hline
-1 & -1 & 0 & 0 & 1 & 0
\end{array}
\right]
\end{array}
$$

$$
\begin{array}{c}
\qquad z_1 \;\; z_2 \;\;\; t \;\;\;\; u \;\;\; M \\
\begin{array}{c} t \\ z_1 \\ M \end{array}
\left[
\begin{array}{ccccc|c}
0 & 59/6 & 1 & -1/6 & 0 & 5/6 \\
1 & 1/6 & 0 & 1/6 & 0 & 1/6 \\ \hline
0 & -5/6 & 0 & 1/6 & 1 & 1/6
\end{array}
\right]
\end{array}
$$

$$
\begin{array}{c}
\qquad z_1 \; z_2 \;\;\; t \;\;\;\;\; u \;\;\;\; M \\
\begin{array}{c} z_2 \\ z_1 \\ M \end{array}
\left[
\begin{array}{ccccc|c}
0 & 1 & 6/59 & -1/59 & 0 & 5/59 \\
1 & 0 & -1/59 & 10/59 & 0 & 9/59 \\ \hline
0 & 0 & 5/59 & 9/59 & 1 & 14/59
\end{array}
\right]
\end{array}
$$

$v = 59/14$; $z_1 = 9/59$; $z_2 = 5/59$; $t = 5/59$; $u = 9/59$

R: $[5/14 \quad 9/14]$; C: $\begin{bmatrix} 9/14 \\ 5/14 \end{bmatrix}$ Value = V − 4 = 3/14

(b) The game favors Ruth. Optimal strategy yields average pay-off for Ruth of 3/14 = \$.21 per play.

14. (a)
$$
\begin{array}{c}
\quad\;\;\; S \qquad\; Av. \qquad W \\
\begin{array}{c} A \\ B \\ C \end{array}
\begin{bmatrix}
3000 & 2000 & 1000 \\
6000 & 2000 & -3000 \\
15000 & 1000 & -10000
\end{bmatrix}
\end{array}
$$

(b) Purchase stock A (game is strictly determined).

10

THE MATHEMATICS OF FINANCE

10.1 Interest

1. (a) 12% interest compounded monthly for 2 years
      $i = .12/12 = .01$, $n = 2 \times 12 = 24$
   (b) 8% interest compounded quarterly for 5 years
      $i = .08/4 = .02$, $n = 5 \times 4 = 20$
   (c) 10% interest compounded semi-annually for 20 years
      $i = .10/2 = .05$, $n = 20 \times 2 = 40$

2. (a) $i = .06/1 = .06$, $n = 3$
   (b) $i = .06/12 = .005$, $n = 18$
   (c) $i = .09/4 = .0225$, $n = 3$

3. (a) $i = .06$, $n = 4$, $P = \$500$, $F = \$631.24$
   (b) $i = .06/12 = .005$, $n = 120$, $P = \$800$, $F = \$1455.52$
   (c) $i = .04/2$, $n = 19$, $P = \$6177.88$, $F = \$9000$

4. (a) $i = .005$, $n = 52$, $P = \$5786.63$, $F = \$7500$
   (b) $i = .06/12 = .005$, $n = 360$, $P = \$3000$, $F = \$18,067.73$
   (c) $i = .08/4 = .02$, $n = 1476$, $P = \$24$,
      $F = \$118,594,560,000,000$

5. $P = \$1000$, $i = .005$, $n = 24$, $F = \$1127.16$

6. $F = \$10,000$, $i = .04/2 = .02$, $n = 10$, $P = \$8203.48$

7. $i = .06/12 = .005$; $n = 25 \times 12 = 300$. Present value =

$$P = \left[\frac{1}{(1 + i)^n}\right] F = (.2239657)\,100,000 = \$22,396.57$$

8. $i = .073/365 = .0002$, $n = 365$. $F = \$1075.72$

9. $i = .005$, $n = 36$, $F = \$7,180.08$; $F - 6000 = \$1,180.08$.

10. $i = .02$, $n = 14$, $F = \$2,638.96$; $F - 2000 = \$638.96$.

11. (a) $i = .005$, $n = 24$, $F = 4000$, then $P = \$3548.74$.
    (b) To find interest, find $4,000 - P = \$451.26$.
    (c)

Month	Interest	Balance
0		$3548.74
1	17.74	3566.48
2	17.83	3584.31
3	17.92	3602.23

12. (a) $i = .02$, $n = 60$, $F = 10,000$. Then $P = \$3047.82$.
    (b) $10,000 - P = \$6952.18$.
    (c)

Period	Balance
1	3,108.78
2	3,170.96
3	3,234.38

13. $i = .01$, $n = 25$, $P = \$10,000$, then $F = \$12,824.32$.

14. $i = .005$, $n = 48$, $F = \$10,000$, then $P = \$7,870.98$.

15. $i = .01$, $n = 12$, $F = \$10,000$, then $P = \$8874.49$.

16. $i = .06$, $n = 20$, $P = \$100,000$. Then $F = \$320,713.55$.

17. (a) Since one month's interest is $5 on $1,000, the monthly rate of interest is $5/1000 = .005$. The annual rate is then $12 \times .005 = .06 = 6\%$
    (b) Interest is $.005(1010.03) = \$5.05$, 4/1/95 is 3 months after the initial deposit so:
    $F = (1.005) \ 1000 = (1.001508) \ 1000 = \$1015.08$
    (c) 1/1/97 is 2 full years; $i = .005$, $n = 24$
    $F = (1.05) \ 1000 = (1.12155202) \ 1000 = \$1,121.55$ Balance on 12/1/97
    .05% interest on this is $5.61, $1,127.16 due 1/1/97

18. (a) $208.08; $10.612.08
    (b) $280.05; $14,282.46

19. $i = .06$, $n = 9$, with $P = \$1,000$ yields $1,689.48. It is better to get $1,700 in 9 years.

20. $i = .01$, $n = 36$, $P = \$7,000$ yields $10, 015.38, so it is better to get $7,000 now.

21. 30% compounded annually   22. 8% compounded annually

23. 1/1/95to 4/1/95 is 3 months or 1 quarter since
    $10,100 = (1 + r) \ 10000$
    $1.01 = 1 + r$ or $r = .01$; quarterly rate is 1%

    $$P = \left[\frac{1}{(1 + i)^n} \right] F = \left[\frac{1}{(1.01)^{12}} \right] 10000 = (.88744923) \ 10000$$

    $P = \$8,874.49$

24. $2,000.00

25. (a) $r = .04$, $n = \frac{1}{2}$, $P = \$500$, $A = \$510.00$
    (b) $r = .05$, $n = 2$, $P = \$500$, $A = \$550$

26. (a) $r = .06$, $n = \frac{2}{3}$, $P = \$1000$, $A = \$1040$
    (b) $r = .04$, $n = 5$, $P = \$3000$, $A = \$3600$

27. $A = [1 + (3)(.05)] \ 1000 = \$1,150$.

28. $A = [1 + (1.5)(.06)] \ 2000 = \$2,180$.

29. Using A = (1 + nr)P, solve for P
$$3000 = [1 + 2(.10)]P$$
$$3000 = (1 + .2)P$$
$$P = 3000/1.2 = \$2500$$

30. A = \$2,000, n = 4, i = .07. Then P = \$1,562.50.

31. Solve for r: (1 +(.5)r)(980) = 1000. r = 4.0816%

32. Solve for n: (1 + n(.07)(1000) = 1210. n = 3.

33. Solve the equation for n: 2P = (1 + n (.05))P. n = 20 years.

34. $\dfrac{A-P}{nP}$

35. Using A = (1 + nr)P, solve for P. We get P = A/(1 + rn).

36. $\dfrac{A-P}{rP}$

37. i = .01, n =4, and P = 100 yields \$104.06. Solve for r:
104.06 = (1 + 1(r))(100). Then r = 4.06%

38. i = .005, n = 12, P = 100. Then F = \$106.17. Solve for r
in the equation 106.17 = (1 + (1)r)100. We get r = 6.17%

39. i = .02, n = 2, P = 1. Then F = 1.0404 so the effective
rate is 4.04%.

40. i = .005, n = 52, P = 1. Then F = 1.2961, so the effective
rate is 29.61%.

41. i = .005, n = 12, P = 1. Then F = 1.0617, so the effective
rate is 6.17%.

42. i = .02, n = 4, P = 1. Then F = 1.824, so the effective
rate is 8.24%.

43. Semi-annual compounding implies we divide a by 2
$$a = (1 + a/2)^2 P$$
Squaring the binomial, $A = (1 + a + a^2/4)P$

Thus, the effective rate is $a + (a^2/4)$ or $100\left(a+\dfrac{a^2}{4}\right)\%$

44. $P\left(1 + \dfrac{a}{n}\right)^n$ 45. $(1 + a/n)^n - 1$

46. 1065, \$1134.23, \$1207.95; 8; 12

47. \$10,252.51, \$10,511.40, \$10,776.83; 30; 53

48. 30   49. 11.75 years to double \$100

10.2 Annuities

1. (a) $1 + 2 + 4 + 8 + 16 = 2^0 + 2^1 + 2^2 + 2^3 + 2^4 = \dfrac{2^5 - 1}{2 - 1} = 31$

    (b) $1 - 2 + 4 - 8 + 16 = 1 + (-2)^1 + (-2)^2 + (-2)^3 + (-2)^4 = \dfrac{(-2)^5 - 1}{-2 - 1} = \dfrac{-33}{-3} = 11$

    (c) $1 + \dfrac{1}{2} + \dfrac{1}{4} + \dfrac{1}{8} + \dfrac{1}{16} = 1 + \dfrac{1}{2} + \left(\dfrac{1}{2}\right)^2 + \left(\dfrac{1}{2}\right)^3 + \left(\dfrac{1}{2}\right)^4 = \dfrac{(1/2)^5 - 1}{1/2} = \dfrac{1/32 - 1}{1/2} = \dfrac{-31/32}{1/2} = \dfrac{31}{16}$

    (d) $3 + \dfrac{3}{2} + \dfrac{3}{4} + \dfrac{3}{8} + \dfrac{3}{16} = 3\left(1 + \dfrac{1}{2} + \dfrac{1}{4} + \dfrac{1}{8} + \dfrac{1}{16}\right) = 3\left(\dfrac{31}{16}\right) = \dfrac{93}{16}$

2. (a) 16,105   (b) 5905
    (c) 1.9375   (d) 7.75

3. (a) $i = .005$, $n = 120$, $R = \$50$, $F = \$8193.97$
    (b) $i = .02$, $n = 20$, $R = \$2675.19$, $F = \$65,000$

4. (a) $i = .005$, $n = 240$, $R = \$520$, $P = \$72,582$
    (b) $i = .02$, $n = 20$, $R = \$700$, $P = \$11,446$

5. $i = .005$, $n = 60$, $R = 100$. Using Table 4, $F = \$6977$.

6. $F = \$10,000$, $i = .02$, $n = 14$. Using Table 5, $R = \$626.02$.

7. $i = .02$, $n = 28$, $R = \dfrac{1}{a_{\overline{n}|i}}P$

    $R = \dfrac{1}{a_{\overline{28}|.02}}(\$100,000) = (.04698967)100,000 = \$4698.97$

8. Use Table 6 with $i = .06$, $n = 10$ and $R = 1000$ to get $P = \$7,360.09$.

9. $R = 500$, $i = .005$, $n = 48$.
    (a) $F = \$27,048.92$ from Table 4.
    (b) $\$24,000$ was deposited over the 4 years. Interest is $\$3048.92$.
    (c)

Month	Interest	Balance
1	0	$500
2	2.50	1002.50
3	5.01	1507.51

10. $R = 800$, $i = .015$, $n = 20$.
    (a) $(800)(23.12366710) = \$18,498.93$ from Table 4.
    (b) The deposits were $\$16,000$. Interest = $\$2498.93$.
    (c)

Quarter	Deposit	Balance	Interest
1	800.00	800.00	8.00
2	800.00	1612.00	12.00
3	800.00	2436.18	24.18

11. R = \$305.06, Deposit = \$10,982.28, Interest = \$1,017.72.

12. i = .02, F = 5000, n = 12. Use Table 5 to get
    (.07455960)(5000), since Valerie needs \$5000. R = \$372.80.
    But (372.80)(12) = \$4473.60, so 5000 - 4473.60 = \$526.40 is
    interest.

13. \$200 per month is worth \$323.79 more. Use Table 4 with
    i = .005, n = 12, R = 200, to find F = \$2,467.11. If she
    invests \$2,000 at the some rate for the year, she has less.

14.

Month	Beg. Bal.	Withdraw	Adj. Beg. Bal.	Interest	Ending Balance
1	5000.00	0	5000.00	25.00	5025.00
2	5025.00	500	4525.00	22.63	4547.63
3	4547.63	500	4047.63	20.24	4067.87
4	4067.87	500	3567.87	17.84	3585.71

15. We are given a future value and are asked to find the rent.
    The formula is $R = \dfrac{1}{S_{\overline{n}|\,i}} F$ and i = .04/2 = .02;
    n = 2 x 15 = 30; F = 1,000,000
    $$R = \frac{1}{S_{\overline{30}|\,.02}}(1{,}000{,}000) = \frac{1}{40.56807921}(1{,}000{,}000) = \$24{,}649.92$$

16. Use Table 4 with i = .005, n = 12. He has F = \$123.36.

17. Using the software, find P, where R = \$100, i = .005, and
    n = 12 to get \$877.91. Or use Table 7.

18. 77¢

19. $F = S_{\overline{n}|\,i}; R = S_{\overline{120}|\,.01}(1000) = \$230{,}038.69$ which $\geq$ 230,000
    So \$1000 at end of each month for 10 years is better.

20. Use Table 4 to find the future value for rent of \$750 at 2%
    interest, with n = 12. We find we get \$10,059.07. So \$750
    at the end of each quarter-year for 3 years is better than
    \$10,000 lump sum at the end of 3 years.

21. We earn \$5,199.44 (use Table 4, i = .02, with n = 36 and a
    rent of \$100) plus the \$1000 plus interest compounded
    quarterly = $(1 + (.02))^{36}(1000) = \$2{,}039.89$ for a total of
    \$7239.33.

22. Use Table 4 (i = .005, n = 48, R = \$10) to find you have
    \$540.98. The \$100 has grown to $(1 + .005)^{60}(100) = \$134.89$.
    The total is \$675.87.

23. Use Table 4 with i = .005, n = 120, R = $100. That gives $16,387.93. The $1,000 at the end of the seventh year yields $1,196.68, since the number of periods is 36. The total is $17,584.61.

24. Use i = .005, n = 84, and R = $100. This is the amount in the account at the end of seven years. Subtract $1,000 and find the total future value of that based on compound interest with i = .005 and n = 36. Then find the future value of the rent of $100 for i = .005 and n = 36. Add these to get $15,191.25.

25. $P = a_{\overline{n}|i}R$ If $n = \infty$, $a_{\overline{n}|i} = \dfrac{(1 + i)^n - 1}{i(1 + i)^n} =$

$$\dfrac{1 - 1/(1 + i)^n}{i} = \dfrac{1}{i}$$

If i = 5% and P = 1/i (1200), P = 1200/.05 = $24,000

26. $P = a_{\overline{\infty}|i}R = \dfrac{1}{i}R = \dfrac{R}{i}$ dollars (see 25)

27. Deposit $10,000 at age 10. Let i = .06, compounded over n = 7 years and find the value at the end of that period to be $15,036.30. Then find

$R—= (.28859149)(15036.30) = \$ 4339.35.$

28. To get $10,000 per year for the 4 years we find (Table 6) that with i = .06, n = 4, we need P = $34,651.07 at the 18th birthday. Use Table 3 with i = .06, n = 7, to find initial deposit = (.66505711)(34651.07) = $23,044.93.

29. Use Exercise 26, with $\dfrac{R}{i} = \dfrac{6000}{.06} = \$100,000$ to see that

$100,000 is needed by Dec 1, 2000. Use the formula for compound interest to find the present value of $100,000, which is $59,189.85.

30. Principal deferred for m periods earns compound interest $F = (1 + i)^m P$, which is then paid out over n periods, given by

$$R = a_{\overline{n}|i}[(i+1)^m P] = \dfrac{i}{(1+i)^n - 1} \cdot (1+i)^{m+n} P$$

31. (a) $1 (All interest has been withdrawn.)
    (b) $A = S_{\overline{n}|i}i$ $1 is actually rent on an annuity.
    (c) $1 + S_{\overline{n}|i}$ and $F = (1 + i)^n$

$$S_{\overline{n}|i}i = (1 + i)^n - 1$$

$$S_{\overline{n}|i} = \dfrac{(1 + i)^n - 1}{i}$$

32. $$\frac{1}{a_{\overline{n}|i}} = \frac{i(1+i)^n}{(i+1)^n-1} \quad \text{and} \quad \frac{1}{s_{\overline{n}|i}} = \frac{i}{(1+i)^n-1}$$

$$\frac{1}{a_{\overline{n}|i}} - \frac{1}{s_{\overline{n}|i}} = \frac{-i + i(1+i)^n}{(i+1)^n-1} = \frac{i[(i+1)^n-1]}{(1+i)^n-1} = i$$

33. $$(i+1)\ s_{\overline{n}|i} + 1 = \frac{(1+i)[(1+i)^n-1]}{i} + 1$$

$$= \frac{(1+i)[(1+i)^n-1] + i}{i}$$

$$= \frac{(1+i)^{n+1} - 1 - i + i}{i} = \frac{(1+i)^{n+1} - 1}{i}$$

$$= s_{\overline{n+1}|i}$$

34. Annuity for the first five years has a value of $100\ s_{\overline{5}|6\%}$ at the end of five years, after which it earns compound interest at 7% (the new rate) or $(1.07)^{15} \cdot 100\ s_{\overline{5}|6\%}$. Payments for the remaining 15 years give a value of $100 \cdot s_{\overline{15}|7\%}$. Adding these two values gives a total balance.

35. Present Value of $5000 to be received in 15 years:
n=30, i=.12/2=.06, p=5000
.17411013(5000)=$870.55

Present value of 8% interest payments semianually for 15 years: n=30, i=.06, p=200; 13.76483115(200)=$2752.97

Total present value =870.55+2752.97= $3623.52

36. Use Table 6 with i = .005 and n = 60.
(51.7255608)(500) = $25,862.78

37. $50,000 = a_{\overline{n}|i} \cdot R$; n = 60; i = 1.5%

(a) $R = \dfrac{1}{a_{\overline{60}|.015}}$ (50,000) = (.02539343)(50,000) =$1269.67

(b) First, find the present value:
$P = a_{\overline{60}|.01}$(750) = (44.95503841)(750) = $33,716.28
Second, find the present value of 5 years payments, where $a_{\overline{60}|.01}$ = value of payments at beginning of 6th year and

$\dfrac{1}{1 + .01)^{60}}$ finds *that* value at beginning of 1st year.

$P = \dfrac{1}{(1 + .01)^{60}}\ a_{\overline{60}|.01}$(1269.67) =
(.550462)(44.95503841)(1269.67) = $31,418.60
Thus, $33,716.28 + $31,418.60 = $65,134.88

38. Use Table 6 with $i = .005$, $n = 60$ to get Present Value of $51,725.56

39. $1000, $2050, $3152.50; 19; 26

40. $700, $1414, $2142.28; 7, 13

41. After 33 weeks   42. After 30 months

10.3 Amortization of Loans

1. Where $i = .5\%$ and $n = 60$, $R = \dfrac{1}{a_{\overline{60}|.005}}$ $10,000 =$
    $(.019332802)(10,000) = \$193.33$ per month.

2. Use $i = .01$, $n = (25)(12)$. Then $R = \dfrac{1}{a_{\overline{n}|.01}}(100,000)$
    $= \$1053.22$.

3. $P = a_{\overline{n}|i}\, R$, where $R = \$1,000$, $i = .06$, $n = 20$.
    $P = \$11,469.22$.

4. $P = a_{\overline{n}|i}\, R = \$3144.68$, using $i = .0075$, $n = 36$. We add
    $500 to get price $= \$3644.68$.

5. (a) $(.01)(\$58,331) = \$583.31$ (b) $\$600 - 583.31 = \$16.69$
    (c) $\$58,331 - 16.69 = \$58,314.31$
    (d) $P = a_{\overline{60}|.01}(600) = (44.9550384)(600) = \$26,973.02$
    (e) $P = a_{\overline{48}|.01}(600) = (37.9739595)(600) = \$22,784.38$.
        So, we have repaid $\$26,973.02 - 22,784.38 = \$4188.65$.
    (f) At the end of 300 months the balance is $26,973.02.
        the interest is $(.01)(26973.02) = \$269.73$.

6. (a) There are 8 payments of $1,000 left at $i = .02$. So we
        have $P = a_{\overline{8}|.02}(1000) = \$7325.48$ to pay.
    (b) At the end of the 5th year the balance left unpaid is
        $7325.48. At the end of the 4th year the balance left
        unpaid is $10,575.34. The interest paid is
        $(\$1,000)(4) - (10575.34 - 7325.48) = \$750.14$.
    (c) $\$1000 - (.02)(21281.27) = \$574.37$.
    (d) $[(\$1000)(\#payments)] - [\text{amt of loan}] =$
        $\$28,000 - 21,281.27 = \$6718.73$.

7. (a) $R = \dfrac{1}{a_{\overline{36}|.01}}(800) = \$265.71$
    (b) $(36)(265.71) = \$9565.56$
    (c) $\$9565.56 - 8000 = \$1565.56$
    (d) $P = a_{\overline{24}|.01}(265.71) = \$5644.58$
    (e) $P = a_{\overline{12}|.01}(265.71) = \$2990.59$

251

(f) At the end of year #1 she owes $5,644.68. At the end of the year #2 she owes $2,990.64. So, she has paid $2,654.04 on unpaid balance. She has paid $265.71 for each of 12 months or a total of $3,188.52. The difference is the interest paid in the year = $534.53.

(g)

Payment Number	Amount	Interest	Applied to Principal	Unpaid Balance
1	$265.71	$80.00	$185.71	$7814.29
2	265.71	78.14	187.57	7626.72
3	265.71	76.27	189.44	7437.28
4	265.71	74.34	191.34	7245.94

8. (a) $R = \dfrac{1}{a_{\overline{n}|i}}(80{,}000)$ with $n = 300$, $i = .0075$.

   $R = \$671.36$

   (b) $(\$10{,}000) + (300)(671.36) = \$211{,}408.00$
   (c) $\$211{,}408 - 90{,}000 = \$121{,}408.00$
   (d) $P = a_{\overline{24}|.0075}(671.36) = \$14{,}695.50$
   (e) $P = a_{\overline{12}|.0075}(671.36) = \$7676.95$
   (f) James paid $\$14{,}695.43 - 7{,}676.91 = \$7{,}018.52$ toward the debt. But his actual payments were $(12)(671.36) = \$8{,}056.32$. The difference is the interest = $\$1037.77$.

(g)

Payment	Amount	Interest	Applied to Principal	Unpaid Balance
1	671.36	600.00	71.36	79,928.64
2	671.36	599.46	71.90	79,856.74
3	671.36	598.93	72.43	79,784.31

9. Using formula (1) with $i = 9/12 = ..75\%$

   $B_{351} = (1 + i)B_{350} - R = (1 + .75)10{,}000 - 1125 =$
   $7825 - 1125 = \$8950$

10. The interest must be $500 on $10,000 in the quarter. Thus, the interest is $500/10000 = .05$ per quarter, or 20% quarterly.

11. $P = a_{\overline{16}|.06}(1000) = \$10{,}105.90 =$ Present Value of the annuity. The Present Value of a balloon payment of $10,000 is $\dfrac{1}{(1+.06)^{16}}(10000) = \$3{,}936.46$. The difference is $14,042.36.

12. Present Value of the balloon payment is $\dfrac{1}{(1 + .01)^{60}}(10000) = \$5{,}504.50$. Annuity value = $100,000, for which the monthly payment is $\dfrac{1}{a_{\overline{60}|.01}}(100000) = \$2{,}224.44$.

13. $R = \dfrac{1}{a_{\overline{4}|\,10\%}} \cdot 1000 = 256.28109 = \$256.28$

Payment	Amount	Interest	Applied to Principal	Unpaid Balance
1	256.28	10.00	246.28	753.72
2	256.28	7.54	248.74	504.98
3	256.28	5.05	251.23	253.75
4	256.29	2.54	253.75	0.00

14.

Payment number	Amount	Interest	Applied to Principal	Unpaid Balance
1	\$5,454.37	\$600	\$4,854.37	\$5145.63
2	\$5,454.37	\$308.74	\$5,145.63	0.00

15. The amount of the loan is $120,000 - 20,000 = \$100,000$
$i = .75\%$ and $n = 360$
$$R = \dfrac{1}{a_{\overline{n}|\,i}} P = \dfrac{1}{a_{\overline{360}|\,.0075}}\ 100{,}000 = (.00804622617)\,100{,}000 =$$
$\$804.62$ per month

16. Monthly payment on the loan of \$50,000 is $\dfrac{1}{a_{\overline{300}|\,.005}} (50000) =$
$\$322.15$. Total payments to 1980 is \$38,658 of which
\$38,125.99 is interest. Unpaid balance for the remaining
180 payments is $a_{\overline{180}|\,.005}(322.15) = \$38{,}175.99$. Leaving
\$111,824.01 after the sale.

17. $a_{\overline{300}|\,.0075}(1000) = \$119{,}161.62.$

18. $B_{next} = B_{cur} + (R + [interest]_{next})$
$= B_{cur} + R + i \cdot B_{cur} = R + (1+i) \cdot B_{cur}$

19. Loan $= \$4{,}287.10$. Paying \$100 per month for 3 years ($n = 36$)
with $i = .005$ gives a Present Value of \$3,287.10 so \$1,000
remains on the loan. The balloon payment is
$(1 + .005)^{36}(1000) = \$1196.68.$

20. (a) $\dfrac{1}{a_{\overline{300}|\,.01}} (10^6) = \$10{,}532.24.$

   (b) At the end of 5 years, we have 20 years yet to pay on
   the old mortgage, with monthly payment of \$10,532.24.
   Then the balance is $a_{\overline{240}|\,.01}(10532.24) = \$956{,}531.89.$
   And the new arrangement requires
   $$\dfrac{1}{a_{\overline{120}|\,.01}} (956531.89) = \$13{,}723.45.$$

   (c) Five years are left on the loan, using $i = .01$ and $n = 60$, you would owe \$616,934.17.

21. (a) $F = S_{\overline{20}|.06}(5000) = (36.78559120)\,5000 = \$183,927.96$

(b) $R = \dfrac{1}{a_{\overline{10}|.06}}\,183,927.96 = \$24,989.92$ per year

(c) Unpaid balance after 5 years = $a_{\overline{5}|.06}(24,989.92) =$ which is the present value of an annuity of 5 payments of $24,989.92 at 6% compounded annually
Lump sum $= (4.21236379)\,24,989.92 = \$105,266.63$.

22. Use $i = .06$, $n = 20$ and find $R = \$1,359,228.00$

23. Assume $R = \$30$ million a month, with $i = .01$, $n = 180$.
The end balance is $a_{\overline{180}|.01}(30 \times 10^6) = \$2.5$ billion.

24. $R = \dfrac{1}{a_{\overline{60}|.02}}\,(5 \times 10^6) = \$143,839.85$ per quarter, if repaid in 15 years.

25. Equipment: $(1 + .06)^{10}(6 \times 10^6) = \$10,745,086$. Find $F = S_{\overline{120}|.01}(100000) = 23.038689 \times 10^6$. Yes, the sinking fund will have a surplus of $12.26 million.

26. $(1 + .10)^5(8 \times 10^6) = \$12.88408 \times 10^6 = R$ is the value of the warehouse in 5 years. $F = S_{\overline{60}|.01}R = \$157,758.47$.

27. $2105.33, $2021.12, $1936.28; 24

28. $17,204.08, $11,011.40, $3921.39; 6

29. $4258.31; after 46 months   30. 29; 54; 76

SUPPLEMENTARY EXERCISES

1. We seek the rent on an annuity with a future value of $80,000 where $n = 120$ and $i = .5\%$.
$R = \dfrac{1}{s_{\overline{n}|i}}\,F = (.00610205)\,80,000 = \$488.16$

2. $R = \dfrac{1}{a_{\overline{n}|i}}\,(150000) = \$1,206.93 \;(n = 360,\ i = .0075)$.

3. The payment should not exceed $400 per month and
$a_{\overline{360}|.0075}(400) = \$49,712.75$.

4. $(50)(1 + .0002)^{365} = \$53.79$.

5. 10% compounded annually is better. It yields $1.10 while $9\frac{1}{8}\%$ compunded daily yields $1.096.

6. $F = s_{\overline{60}|.005}(200) = \$13,954.01.$

7. (a) Given $i = 1\%$, $n = 180$

$$R = \frac{1}{a_{\overline{n}|i}} \quad P = \frac{1}{a_{\overline{180}|.01}} \, 200,000 = (.01200168) \, 200,000 =$$

$2400.34 per month for 1st 5 years.

(b) At end of 5 years, there would be 10 years left on 120 months, so we seek the present value of the annuity. Unpaid balance $= a_{\overline{120}|.01}(2400.34) =$

$$(69.70052203)(2400.34) = \$167,304.95$$

8. $(1.005)^{120}(24000) = \$43,665.52$

9. Solve for P in $50000 = (1.005)^{120}P$ to find $P = \$27,481.64.$

10. $10,000 in 2 years should cost $8,871.86 today, and $5,000 in 3 years should cost $4,178.22 today. Add to get $13,050.08.

11. $9,000 is being financed at $i = .005$, $n = 48$. Find $R = \frac{1}{a_{\overline{48}|.005}}(9000) = \$211.37.$

12. $(1.02)^4(100000) = \$108,243.22$ and $R = \frac{1}{a_{\overline{10}|.02}}(108243.22) = \$12,050.34$

13. Given $i = .5\%$ and $n = 180$, the present value of $30,000 is

$$P = \frac{1}{(1 + i)^n} \, 30,000 = (.40748243) \, 30,000 = \$12,224.47.$$

Subtract from the initial fund of $105,003.50. Find the rent on this $100,000, given $i = 1\%$, $n = 180$.

$$R = \frac{1}{a_{\overline{180}|.005}} \, 100,000 = (.00843857) \, 92,779.03 = \$782.93.$$

14. Present Value of balloon payment is $\frac{1}{(1.01)^{120}}(10000) =$

$30,299.48. $509,289.22 - 30,299.48 = \$478,989.74$. Find $R = \frac{1}{a_{\overline{120}|.01}}(478989.74) = \$6872.11$

15. $F = s_{\overline{360}|.005}(100) = \$100,451.50$

16. $a_{\overline{120}|.01}(2000) = \$139,401.04$

17. Investment A is the better investment. A generates $7,360.09 while B generates $3,736.29 for the first 5 years and $2,791.97 for 10 years giving a total of $6,528.26.

18. Yes. The present value of the bond is $879.57, which is Present Value on annuity ($240.87) plus Present Value of

$1000\ (638.70).$

19. $(1.05)^{12} = 1.1025.$ The effective rate is 10.25%.

20. $(1.015)^{12} = 1.1956.$ The effective rate is 19.56%.

21. First: $10,000 at 8% compounded quarterly for 15 years, with i = 2% and n = 60:

$A = (1 + .02)^{60}\ 10,000 = (3.28103079)\ 10,000 = \$32,810.31.$
Second: the future value of an annuity, given i = 2%, n = 6000, and R = 1000:
$F = s_{\overline{60}|.02}(1000) = (114.05153942)\ 1000 = \$114,051.54.$
Add: $32,810.31 + $114,051.54 = $146,861.85

22. Applied to Unpaid

Payment Number	Amount	Interest	Principal	Balance
1	$212.95	$35.00	$177.95	$6,822.05
2	212.95	34.11	178.84	6,643.20
3	212.95	33.22	179.74	6,463,47
4	212.95	32.32	180.64	6,282.83
5	212.95	31.41	181.54	6,101.29
6	212.95	30.51	182.45	5,918.84

23. $F = s_{\overline{120}|.01}(200) = \$46,007.74.$

At the end of 10 years this has earned interest of
$(1.01)^{120}(46007.74) = \$151,843.34.$

24. $\$300,000 = a_{\overline{60}|.005}\ R.$ So R = $5799.84.

25. $\dfrac{531,440}{3-1} = 265,720$

11

DIFFERENCE EQUATIONS AND MATHEMATICAL MODELS

11.1 Introduction to Difference Equations, I

1. $Y_{n+1} = 4Y_n - 6$ Since $a = 4$ and $b = -6$, $b/(1-a) = -6/-3 = 2$

2. -3, 16; 4

3. $-1/2$, 0; 0

4. $1/3$, 4; 6

5. $-2/3$, 15; 9

6. $.5$, -4; -8

7. Given $Y_{n+1} = (1/2)Y_n - 1$ and $Y_0 = 10$
   (a) $\quad Y_1 = 1/2(10) - 1 = 4$
   $\quad\quad Y_2 = 1/2(4) - 1 = 1$
   $\quad\quad Y_3 = 1/2(1) - 1 = -1/2$
   $\quad\quad Y_4 = 1/2(-1/2) - 1 = -5/4$
   (b)

   (c) $\quad Y_n = \dfrac{-1}{1 - 1/2} + (10 - \dfrac{1}{1 - 1/2})a^n = -2 + 12(1/2)^n$

8. (a) 2, 6, 8, 9, 9.5
   (b)

   (c) $Y_n = 10 - 8(.5)^n$

9. (a) 3.5, 4, 5, 7, 11
   (b)

   (c) $Y_n = 3 + (.5)2^n$

10. (a) 8, 8, 8, 8, 8
    (b)

    (c) $Y_n = 8$

11. (a) 17.5, 0, 7, 4.2, 5.32
    (b)

    (c) $Y_n = 5 + (12.5)(-.4)^n$

12. (a) 1/2, -1, 2, -4, 8

13. $y_{n+1} = 2y_n - 16; \quad y_0 = 15$

(a) $y_1 = 2(15) - 16 = 14$

$y_2 = 2(14) - 16 = 12$

$y_3 = 2(12) - 16 = 8$

$y_4 = 2(8) - 16 = 0$

(b)

(b)

(c) $y_n = \frac{1}{2}(-2)^n$

(c) $y_n = \frac{-16}{1-2} + (15 - \frac{-16}{1-2})2^n$

$= 16 - 2^n$

14. (a) -2, -1, 1, 5, 13

(b)

(c) $y_n = -3 + 2^n$

15. 1, 5, 5.8, 5.96, 5.992

16. 10, 1, 8.2

17. $y_{n+1} = 1.05y_n, \quad y_0 = 1000$

18. $y_{n+1} = .99y_n, \quad y_0 = 70$

19. $y_{n+1} = y_n + .05y_n + 100$

$y_{n+1} = 1.05y_n + 100$

$a = .05, \quad b = 1000, \quad y_0 = 1000$

20. $y_{n+1} = .99y_n - 1, \quad y_0 = 70$

21. (a) 1, 3, 5, 7, 9

(b)

(c) Since $a = 1$, $1 - a = 0$, then $\frac{b}{1-a} = \frac{2}{0}$, which is not

258

defined.

22. $1 - a^3$

23. $y_{n+1} = y_n + .20y_n - 36$ and $y_0 = 55$
$y_{n+1} = 1.20y_n - 36$
$y_1 = 1.2(55) - 36 = 66 - 36 = \$30$

24. $y_{n+1} = 1.20y_n - 36$, $y_0 = 55$

25. 1.4, 3.45, 4.68; $n = 57$.

26. 13, 14.32, 16.22; $n = 36$.

27. 60.22, 39.58; $n = 21$.

28. 4.88, 7.9. 9.45; if $n \geq 30$ then y is within .10 of 10.

11.2 Introduction to Difference Equations, II

1. $y_{n+1} = y_n + 5$ and $y_0 = 1$
$y_n = 1 + bn = 1 + 5n$ by formula 2

2. $y_n = 50 - 2n$

3. $80(1.0075)^{60}$

4. 96

5. $80(1 + 1/365)^{1825}$

6. $80(1.02)^{20}$

7. $y_5 = y_0 + 5(iy_0) = 80 + 5(.07)(80) = 80 + 28 = \$108$

8. $80(1.06)^{10}$

9. $A \left(1 + \dfrac{r}{k}\right)^{kt}$

10. (a) 1.40   (b) 1.44   (c) 1.46

11.

Notice that $\dfrac{b}{1-a} = \dfrac{-10}{1-2} = 10$ and that when $y_0 \neq 10$, the terms are repelled (i.e. move away) from the line $y = 10$.

259

12.

Notice that when $\frac{b}{1-a} = \frac{5}{1 - 1/2} = 10$ and that when $y \neq 10$, the terms are attracted (i.e. move toward) to the line $y=10$.

13. $y_{n+1} = .4y_n + 3$ and $y_0 = 7$

$a = .4, \quad b = 3$

$y_n = \frac{3}{1 - .4} + (7 - \frac{3}{.6})(.4)^n = \frac{3}{.6} + \left[\frac{1.2}{.6}\right](.4)^n = 5 + 2(.4)^n$

so the terms get closer to 5 as n increases..

14. $y_n = 6 + 4(3)^n$; y_n gets arbitrarily large and positive

15. $y_n = 2(-5)^n$; y_n gets arbitrarily large and alternates between being positive and negative.

16. $y_n = 2 + (-.7)^n$; y_n approaches 2.

17. $y_{n+1} = 1.0075y_n - 350$, $y_0 = 38,900$

18. $y_{240} = 0$

19. $y_{n+1} = y_n + 1/25 (50,000) = y_n - 2000$, $\quad y_0 = 50,000$;

$y_n = y_0 + bn = 50,000 - 2000n$.

20. $y_{n+1} = \frac{23}{25} y_n$, $y_n = 50,000(23/25)^n$

21. $1195; 34; 47   22. $1180; 44; 67   23. $245; 12; 23

24. $249.24; 10; 16   25. 60   26. 10

11.3 Graphing Difference Equations

1. Monotonic graphs are: A, B, D, F, H
    (A, B, D are always increasing; F,H are always decreasing)

2. A, B, D

3. B, D, E, F

4. G

5. B, D, E, F

6. F, H

7. If $|a| < 1$, the graph is asymptotic to $y = \frac{b}{1-a}$

    Graphs A, C, H, are of this type.

    If $y_0 = \frac{b}{1-a}$, then G would also qualify.

8. C, E, (possibly G)

9.

10.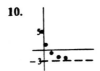

11.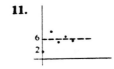

12.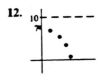

13.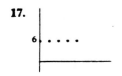

14.

15.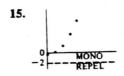

16.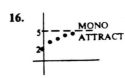

17.

18.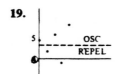

19.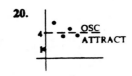

20.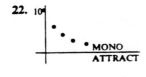

21.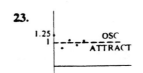

22.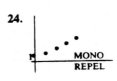

23.

24.

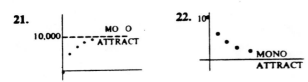

25. $Y_{n+1} = Y_n + iy_n - R = (1 + i)Y_n - R$

     $i = 9\%/12 = 3/4\%;\quad R = 450$

     $Y_{n+1} = (1.0075)y_n - 450$

     $\frac{b}{1-a} = \frac{-450}{.0075} = 60{,}000$

261

Since $a > 0$ and $|a| > 1$, this is a mono-repel graph.
If $y_0 = 60,000$, the balance will always be 60,000.
If $y_0 < 60,000$, the balance steadily decreases until paid.

26. Less than 5 million dollars

27. (a) $y_{n+1} = 1.06y_n - 120$ (b) At least $2000

28. $99.80, $20.20; $9959.80

29. - 34. have many acceptable solutions.

11.4 Mathematics of Personal Finance

1. The loan of $32,500 means $y_0 = 32,500$

   $y_{n+1} = y_n + .0075y_n - 261.50 = 1.0075y_n - 261.50$,

2. $y_{n+1} = 1.03y_n$, $y_0 = 1000$

3. $y_{n+1} = 1.015y_n + 200$, $y_0 = 4000$

4. $y_{n+1} = 1.005y_n - 100$, $y_0 = 20,000$

5. $46,000

6. $400

7. $i = 6\%$. $y_0 = 0$, $n = 20$. $1.06^{20} \approx 3.2$

   $y_{n+1} = y_n + .06y_n + 300 = 1.06y_n + 300$

   $\dfrac{b}{1-a} = \dfrac{300}{-.06} = -5000$

   $y_{20} = -5000 + [0 - (-5000)] \, 1.06^{20} = -5000 + 5000 \, (3.2)$

   $y_{20} = \$11,000$

8. $30   9. $2000   10. $25,000

11. $133.02   12. $30   13. $39.21 million; 30

14. $264.69; 7   15. $505.03, $1022.80, $1553.65; 30;37

16. $386.42; after 27 quarters; 40

11.5 Modeling with Difference Equations

1. Since we have 3% births and 1% deaths, the net increase each
   year is 2% of the population
   at the beginning of the year
   $y_{n+1} = 1.02y_n$

$a > 0$ $|a| > 1$ with $y_0 = 100$ million

monotonic increasing   repel

2.

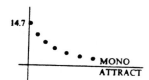

$y_{n+1} = (1.01)y_n - 600, \ y_0 = 50{,}000$

$$Y_{n+1} = (1.01)Y_n - 600$$
$$Y_0 = 50{,}000$$

3

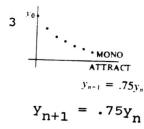

$y_{n-1} = .75y_n$

$$Y_{n+1} = .75Y_n$$

4.

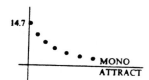

$$Y_{n+1} = .8Y_n$$
$$Y_0 = 14.7$$

5.

$$Y_{n+1} = .92Y_n + 8$$
$$Y_0 = 0$$

6.

$$Y_{n+1} = .6Y_n + 3.2$$
$$Y_0 = 3$$

7. Y_n = amount learned in 1 minute

M = maximum amount that can
       be learned

$Y_0 = 0$, $M = 12$, $k = .3$

$Y_{n+1} = Y_n + k(M - Y_n)$

$Y_{n+1} = Y_n + .3(12 - Y_n)$

$Y_{n+1} = Y_n + 3.6 - .3Y_n$

$Y_{n+1} = .7Y_n + 3.6$

$\dfrac{b}{1-a} = \dfrac{3.6}{.3} = 12$

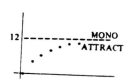

8.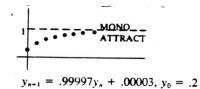

$$Y_{n+1} = .99997y_n + .00003$$
$$Y_0 = .2$$

9.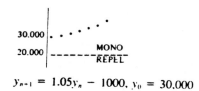

$$Y_{n+1} = 1.05y_n - 1000$$
$$Y_0 = 30,000$$

10.

11.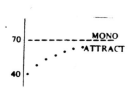

$$Y_{n+1} = 1.05y_n + 1000$$
$$Y_0 = 15,000$$

$$Y_{n+1} = .8y_n + 14$$
$$Y_0 = 40$$

12.

$$Y_{n+1} = 1.07y_n$$
$$Y_0 = 2.6$$

13. From $P_n = 20 - .1q_n$, solve for q_n

$q_n = 200 - 10P_n$

From Example 5:

$q_{n+1} = -.5q_n + 90$

$q_{n+1} = -.5(200 - 10P_n) + 90$

$q_{n+1} = -100 + 5P_n + 90$

$q_{n+1} = -10 + 5P_n$

$P_{n+1} = 20 - .1(-10 + 5P_n) = -.5P_n + 21$

$P_0 = 10 \qquad \dfrac{b}{1-a} = \dfrac{21}{3/2} = 14$

14. 332.50; 14 seconds   15. 5.37 million; 2003; 2038

16. 32.65; 15 months; 32 months

SUPPLEMENTARY EXERCISES

1. $y_{n+1} = -3y_n + 8$, $y_0 = 1$

   (a) $y_1 = -3(1) + 8 = 5$

       $y_2 = -3(5) + 8 = -7$

       $y_3 = -3(-7) + 8 = 29$

   (b) $y_n = \dfrac{b}{1-a} + (y_0 - \dfrac{b}{1-a})a^n = \dfrac{8}{1-(-3)} + (1 - \dfrac{8}{1-(-3)})(-3)^n$

       $y_n = 2 + (-1)(-3)^n = 2 - (-3)^n$

   (c) $y_4 = 2 - (-3)^4 = 2 - 81 = -79$

2. (a) $8\frac{1}{2}$, 7, $5\frac{1}{2}$ (b) $y_n = 10 - \dfrac{3}{2}n$

   (c) 1

3. $3000

4. $1110

5.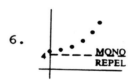

6.

7. (a) $y_{n+1} = y_n + .03y_n - 600 = 1.03y_n - 600$, $y_0 = 120{,}000$

   (b) $y_n = \dfrac{-600}{-.03} + (120{,}000 - \dfrac{-600}{-.03})\,1.03^n$

       $y_{20} = 20{,}000 + (120{,}000 - 20{,}000)\,1.03^{20}$

       $y_{20} = 20{,}000 + 100{,}000\,(1.8) = 20{,}000 + 180{,}000$

       $y_{20} = 200{,}000$

8. (a) $y_{n+1} = 1.01y_n - 360$, $y_0 = 35{,}000$

   (b) $33{,}700

9. $20

10. $215.50

11. $22,500

12. $270

13. $y_{n+1} = y_n - .1y_n + 100{,}000$,

    $y_{n+1} = y_n + k(P - y_n)$, $y_{n+1} = y_n + .1(1{,}000{,}000 - y_n)$

    $y_0 = 0$

$$y_{n+1} = .9y_n + 100,000$$

$$\frac{b}{1-a} = \frac{100,000}{.1} = 1,000,000, \; a > 0 \text{ (monotonic)}, \; |a| < 1$$

(asymptotic).

$y_{n-1} = .9y_n + 100,000, \; y_0 = 0$

14.

$y_{n+1} = .92y_n, \; y_0 = 100$

12

LOGIC

12.1 Introduction to Logic

1. Statement (it is false) 2. Statement

3. Statement 4. Statement

5. Not a statement 6. Statement

7. Not a statement 8. Statement

9. Statement 10. Statement

11. Not a statement 12. Not a statement

13. Not a statement 14. Statement

15. Statement

16. (a) Arizona does not have the largest U.S. Indian population
    (b) Arizona does not have the largest U.S. Indian population or Arizona is the site of the O.K. Corral.
    (c) Arizona is not the site of the O.K. Corral and Arizona has the largest U.S. Indian population.
    (d) Arizona has the largest U.S. Indian population or it is the site of the O.K. Corral.
    (e) Arizona does not have the largest U.S. Indian population and it is not the site of the O.K. Corral.
    (f) Arizona neither has the largest U.S. Indian population nor is it the site of the O.K. Corral.

17. (a) Ozone is opaque to ultraviolet light and life on earth requires ozone.
    (b) Ozone is not opaque to ultraviolet light or life on earth requires ozone.
    (c) Ozone is not opaque to ultraviolet light or life on earth does not require ozone.
    (d) Life on earth requires ozone.

18. (a) $\sim p$ (b) $\sim q \vee \sim p$ (c) $p \wedge \sim q$

19. (a) $p \vee q$ (b) $p \wedge \sim q$
    (c) $q \wedge \sim p$ (d) $\sim p \wedge \sim q$

12.2 Truth Tables

1.

p	q	$p \wedge \sim q$
T	T	F
T	F	T
F	T	F
F	F	F

2.

p	q	r	(p⊕q) ∧ r
T	T	T	F
T	T	F	F
T	F	T	T
T	F	F	T
F	T	T	T
F	T	F	F
F	T	F	F
F	F	F	F

3.

p	q	r	(p∧~r) ∨ q
T	T	T	T
T	T	F	T
T	F	T	F
T	F	F	T
F	T	T	T
F	T	F	T
F	F	T	F
F	F	F	F

4.

p	q	r	~(p∧r) ∨ q
T	T	T	T
T	T	F	T
T	F	T	F
T	F	F	T
F	T	T	T
F	T	F	T
F	F	T	F
F	F	F	F

5.

p	q	r	~[(p∧r) ∨ q]
T	T	T	F
T	T	F	F
T	F	T	F
T	F	F	T
F	T	T	F
F	T	F	F
F	F	T	T
F	F	F	T

6. always FALSE

7. always TRUE

p	∨	~p
T	T	F
F	T	T
(1)	(3)	(2)

8.

p	q	r	(p∨q) ∧ ~r
T	T	T	F
T	T	F	T
T	F	T	F
T	F	F	T
F	T	T	F
F	T	F	T
F	F	T	F
F	F	F	F

9.

p	q	r	p ⊕ (q∨r)
T	T	T	F
T	T	F	F
T	F	T	F
T	F	F	T
F	T	T	T
F	T	F	T
F	F	T	T
F	F	F	F

10.

p	q	r	p ∨ (q∧r)
T	T	T	T
T	T	F	T
T	F	T	T
T	F	F	T
F	T	T	T
F	T	F	F
F	F	T	F
F	F	F	F

11.

p	q	r	(p∨q) ∧ (p∨r)
T	T	T	T
T	T	F	T
T	F	T	T
T	F	F	T
F	T	T	T
F	T	F	F
F	F	T	F
F	F	F	F

12.

p	q	r	(p∧q) ∧ (p∨~r)
T	T	T	T
T	T	F	T
T	F	T	T
T	F	F	T
F	T	T	T
F	T	F	F
F	F	T	F
F	F	F	F

13.

p	q	(p∨q)	∧	~(p ∨ q)
T	T	T	F	F
T	F	T	F	F
F	T	T	F	F
F	F	F	F	T
(1)	(2)	(3)	(5)	(4)

The statement is FALSE.

14.

p	q	r	(~p∨q) ∧ r
T	T	T	T
T	T	F	F
T	F	T	F
T	F	F	F
F	T	T	T
F	T	F	F
F	F	T	T
F	F	F	F

15. TRUE in the case where p is F, q is F and r is T;
    otherwise FALSE

p	q	r	~(p∨q)		∧ r
T	T	T	F	T	F
T	T	F	F	T	F
T	F	T	F	T	F
T	F	F	F	T	F
F	T	T	F	T	F
F	T	F	F	T	F
F	F	T	T	F	T
F	F	F	T	F	F
(1)	(2)	(3)	(5)	(4)	(6)

16.

p	q	r	~[(p∨q) ∧ r]
T	T	T	F
T	T	F	T
T	F	T	F
T	F	F	T
F	T	T	F
F	T	F	T
F	F	T	T
F	F	F	T

17.

p	q	r	~p ∨ (q∧r)
T	T	T	T
T	T	F	F
T	F	T	F
T	F	F	F
F	T	T	T
F	T	F	T
F	F	T	T
F	F	F	T

18. The statement is a tautology.

19. They are identical.

p	q	~p	∨	~q	~(p	∧	q)
T	T	F	F	F	F	T	
T	F	F	T	T	T	F	
F	T	T	T	F	T	F	
F	F	T	T	T	T	F	
(1)	(2)	(3)	(5)	(4)	(7)	(6)	

20. They are identical.

21. They are identical.

22. $2^4 = 16$

23. (p∧q) ∨ r is T and p ∧ (q∨r) is F when p is F and r is T.
    Otherwise, the tables are identical.

24. (a)

p	q	p ⊖ ~q		(d) ~(p⊕q) ∧ (p⊕q)
T	T	F		F
F	T	T		T
T	F	T		T
F	F	F		F

270

(b)

p	q	r	(p⊖r) ⊖ q	(c) p ⊖ (q⊖r)
T	T	T	T	T
T	T	F	F	F
T	F	T	F	F
T	F	F	T	T
F	T	T	F	F
F	T	F	T	T
F	T	T	T	T
F	F	F	F	F

25. (a)

p	p|p
T	F
F	T

(b-d)

p	q	(p|p)|(q|q)	(p|q)|(q|q)	p|((p|q)|q)
T	T	T	T	F
T	F	T	F	F
F	T	T	F	T
F	F	F	F	T

26. ~ p has the same truth table as p|p.
     p∨q has the same truth table as (p|p)|(q|q).
     and p∧q has the same truth table as (p|q)|(p|q).

27. p has truth value T and q has truth value F
     (a) T   (b) F   (c) T   (d) F   (e) F   (f) F

28. p has truth value F and q has truth value F
     (a) F   (b) T   (c) T   (d) T

29. p has truth value F and q has truth value T
     (a) F   (b) F   (c) F   (d) F

30. p ∧ ~q   31. (p⊕q) ∧ r   32. p ⊕ (q∨r)

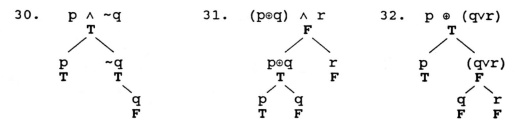

33. (p∨q) ∧ (p∨~r)

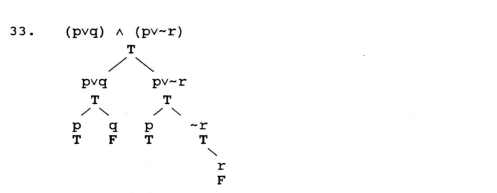

12.3 Implication

1.

p	q	p → ~q
T	T	F
T	F	T
F	T	T
F	F	T

2.

p	q	r	p ∨ (q → ~r)
T	T	T	T
T	T	F	T
T	F	T	T
T	F	F	T
F	T	T	F
F	T	F	T
F	F	T	T
F	F	F	T

3.

p	q	(p⊕q) → q
T	T	T
T	F	F
F	T	T
F	F	T

4.

p	q	r	(p⊕q) → r
T	T	T	T
T	T	F	T
T	F	T	T
T	F	F	F
F	T	T	T
F	T	F	F
F	F	T	T
F	F	F	T

5.

p	q	r	(~p∧q) → r
T	T	T	T
T	T	F	T
T	F	T	T
T	F	F	T
F	T	T	T
F	T	F	F
F	F	T	T
F	F	F	T

6.

p	q	~(p → q)
T	T	F
T	F	T
F	T	F
F	F	F

7. Tautology

p	q	(p → q)	⇔	(~p ∨ q)
T	T	T	T	F T
T	F	F	T	F F
F	T	T	T	T T
F	F	T	T	T T
(1)	(2)	(3)	(6)	(4) (5)

272

8.

p	q	r	p $\oplus$ (q $\rightarrow$ R)
T	T	T	F
T	T	F	F
T	F	T	F
T	F	F	F
F	T	T	F
F	T	F	F
F	F	T	T
F	F	F	T

9.

p	q	r	(p $\rightarrow$ q) $\rightarrow$ r
T	T	T	T
T	T	F	F
T	F	T	T
T	F	F	T
F	T	T	T
F	T	F	T
F	F	T	F
F	F	F	F

10.

p	q	r	p $\rightarrow$ (q $\rightarrow$ r)
T	T	T	T
T	T	F	F
T	F	T	T
T	F	F	T
F	T	T	T
F	T	F	T
F	F	T	T
F	F	F	T

11. ~(p∨q) $\rightarrow$ (~p∧r) is TRUE except in case p, q, and r are FALSE.

12.

p	q	p $\rightarrow$ (p⊕q)
T	T	F
T	F	T
F	T	T
F	F	T

13.

p	q	(p∨q) $\leftrightarrow$ (p∧q)
T	T	T
T	F	F
F	T	F
F	F	T

14. This is a tautology.

15. This is a tautology.

In Exercises 16-25, p is TRUE and q is FALSE.
16. F   17. T   18. T   19. T because the hypothesis is F

20. F   21. T   22. F   23. F   24. F

25.

p	q	p $\rightarrow$ [p $\wedge$ (p $\oplus$ q)]
T	F	T T T

(3)   (2)   (1)

The statement is TRUE.

26. $p \rightarrow q$ 27. $p \leftrightarrow q$ 28. $q \rightarrow p$ 29. $q \rightarrow p$

30. $p \rightarrow q$ 31. $q \rightarrow p$ 32. $q \rightarrow p$ 33. $\sim p \rightarrow \sim q$

34. $p \rightarrow q$ (T)   35. $\sim p \rightarrow \sim q$ (T)   36. $p \rightarrow p$ (T)

37. $\sim q \rightarrow \sim p$ (T)   38. $p \rightarrow q$ (T)

39. (a) hyp: A person is healthy.
         con: A person lives a long life.
     (b) hyp: The train stops at the station.
         con: A passenger requests the stop.
     (c) hyp: The plant grows.
         con: The plant is exposed to sunlight.
     (d) hyp: I will go to the store.
         con: Jane goes to the store.

40. (a) If Jane is tired, Jane runs 20 miles.
     (b) Cindy loves Fred if Fred loves Cindy.
     (c) If Jon cashes a check, the bank is open.
     (d) Errors are clear if the documentation is complete.
     (e) Sally's eating the vegetables is a sufficient
         condition for Sally's getting dessert.
     (f) Sally's eating the vegetables is a necessary condition
         for Sally's getting dessert.

41. (a) If City Sanitation collects the garbage, then the
         mayor calls.
     (b) The price of beans goes down if there is no drought.
     (c) If Lake Erie is fresh water, then goldfish swim in
         Lake Erie.
     (d) If tap water boils slowly, it is not salted.

42. (a) hyp: The weather is hot and sunny.
         con: Copa beach is crowded.
     (b) hyp: Our team wins a game.
         con: I carry a rabbit's foot.
     (c) hyp: I carry a rabbit's foot.
         con: Our team wins a game.
     (d) hyp: Ivy is green.
         con: Ivy is healthy.

43. (a) 4; the hypothesis $(z \neq 0)$ and $(x > 0)$ is FALSE.
     (b) 4; $z = 8 + (-8) = 0$, so the hypothesis is TRUE.
     (c) 4; $x = -3 \leq 0$, so the hypothesis is FALSE.
     (d) 4; same as (c).
     (e) 6; $z = 8 + (-3) = 5 \neq 0$ and $x = 8 > 0$, so the
         hypothesis is TRUE.
     (f) 6; $z = 3 + (-8) = 5 \neq 0$ and $x = 3 > 0$, so the
         hypothesis is TRUE.

44. (a) 100   (b) -100   (c) -100
     (d) -100   (e) -100   (f) 100

45. (a) 7   (b) 7   (c) 0   (d) 7   (e) 0   (f) 0

46. (a) 3   (b) 2   (c) 1/2   (d) 0
    (e) -1,000,000   (f) -1,000,000

47. (a) 6   (b) -12   (c) 0   (d) 7   (e) 0   (f) 0

48. (a) 0   (b) 4   (c) -30   (d) -3   (e) -30   (f) -30

49. (a) 3; the hypothesis (C < 0) or (B, 0) is FALSE, so D = 0
    Thus, X = 0 + 3 = 3.
    (b) 3; same as (a).
    (c) -37; C = -5 - 3 = -8 < 0, so the hypothesis is TRUE,
    and D = 5(-8) = -40. Thus X = -40 + 3 = -37.
    (d) -7; C = 3 - 5 = -2 < 0, so the hypothesis is TRUE, and
    D = 5(-2) = -10. Thus X = -10 + 3 = -7.
    (e) 43; B = -3 < 0, so the hypothesis is TRUE, and
    C = 5 - (-3) = 8, D = 5(8) = 40.
    Thus X = 40 + 3 = 43.
    (f) -7; B = -3 < 0, so the hypothesis is TRUE, and
    C = -5 - (-3) = -2, D = 5(-2) = -10.
    Thus X = -10 + 3 = -7.

50. (a) $384   (b) $768   (c) $480
    (d) $960   (e) $1160   (f) $1360

12.4 Logical Implication and Equivalence

1. When p is F and q is T, the statement is FALSE.

p	q	[(p $\longrightarrow$ q)	$\wedge$	q] $\longrightarrow$ p
T	T	T	T	T
T	F	F	F	T
F	T	T	T	F
F	F	T	F	T
(1)	(2)	(3)	(4)	(5)

2. (a)

p	q	r	p$\vee$(q$\wedge$r)		(p$\vee$q)$\wedge$(p$\vee$r)		
T	T	T	T	T	T	T	T
T	T	F	T	F	T	T	T
T	F	T	T	F	T	T	T
T	F	F	T	F	T	T	T
F	T	T	T	T	T	T	T
F	T	F	F	F	T	F	F
F	F	T	F	F	F	F	T
F	F	F	F	F	F	F	F
(1)	(2)	(3)	(7)	(4)	(5)	(8)	(6)

Since columns (7) and (8) are the same, the statements are equivalent.

(b)

p	q	r	p$\wedge$(q$\vee$r)		(p$\wedge$q)$\vee$(p$\wedge$r)		
T	T	T	T	T	T	T	T
T	T	F	T	T	T	T	F
T	F	T	T	T	F	T	T
T	F	F	F	F	F	F	F
F	T	T	F	T	F	F	F
F	T	F	F	T	F	F	F
F	F	T	F	T	F	F	F
F	F	F	F	F	F	F	F
(1)	(2)	(3)	(7)	(4)	(5)	(8)	(6)

Since columns (7) and (8) are the same, the statements are equivalent.

3.
p	q	p → q	~(p∧~q)
T	T	T	T F
T	F	F	F T
F	T	T	T F
F	F	T	T F

Since columns (3) and (5) are the same, the statements are equivalent.

4. ~[(~(p∧~q) ∧ ~(r∧p)]

5. (a)-(c) Use truth tables to show the tautologies
    (d) (p→q) ⇔ p|(q|q)
    (e) p|q ⇔ ~(p∧q)
    (f) (p⊕q) ⇔ [[(p|p)|(q|q)]|(p|q)]|[[(p|p)|(q|q)]|(p|q)]

6. [(p∨~q) ∧ r]→ p ⇔ [~(p∨~q) ∨ ~r] ∨ p ⇔ [(~p∧q) ∨ ~r] ∨ p ⇔
    [p ∨ (~p∧q)] ∨ ~r ⇔ (p∨q) ∨ ~r

7.
p	q	c	(p→q) ⇔ (p∧~q) → c]
T	T	F	T T F T
T	F	F	F T T F
F	T	F	T T F T
F	F	F	T T F T
			(1) (4) (2) (3)

8. (a) p → [(p∧q)] is a tautology.
    (b) FALSE

9. FALSE

10. TRUE

11. p ⊕ q ⇔ ~[~(p∨∘) ∨ ~(~p∨~q)]

12. (a) (~p∨q) ∨ p which is a tautology
     (b) ~(p∨~q) ∨ r
     (c) ~p ∨ r
     (d) ~q ∨ (~p∨r)

13. (a) Arizona does not border California or Arizona does not border Nevada.
     (b) There are no tickets available and the agency cannot get tickets.
     (c) The killer's hat was neither white nor gray.

14. (a) Either Montreal is not a province or Ottawa is not a province in Canada.
     (b) The sales man does not go to the customer and the customer does not call the salesman.
     (c) The hospital either admits psychiatric patients or admits orthopedic patients.

15. (a) I have a ticket to the theater and I did not spend a lot of money.
     (b) Basketball is played on an indoor court and the players do not wear sneakers.

(c)　The stock market is going up and the interest rates are not going down.

(d)　Man has enough water and man is not staying healthy.

16.　(a)　contrapositive: (T) If a rectangle is not a square, it does not have equal sides.
　　　converse: (T) If a rectangle is a square, it has equal sides.
　　　negation: (F) A rectangle has equal sides and it is not a square.

　　(b)　contrapositive: (F) If an airplane is not a Concorde, it does not fly faster than the speed of sound.
　　　converse: (T) If an airplane is a Concorde, it flies faster than the speed of sound.
　　　negation: (T) An airplane flies faster than the speed of sound, but is not a Concorde.

　　(c)　contrapositive: (T) If the union of two sets is empty, then the intersection of the two sets is empty.
　　　converse: (F) If the union of two sets is not empty, then the intersection of the two sets is not empty.
　　　negation: (F) The intersection of two sets is not empty and their union is empty.

　　(d)　contrapositive: (T) If the probability of a head is not 1/2, then the coin is not fair.
　　　converse: (T) If the probability of a head is 1/2, then the coin is fair.
　　　negation: (F) A coin is fair for which the probability of a head is not 1/2.

17.　(a)　contrapositive: (F) If a bird is not a hummingbird, then it is not small.
　　　converse: (T) If a bird is a hummingbird, then it is small.

　　(b)　contrapositive: (T) If two lines are not parallel, they do not have the same slope.
　　　converse: (T) If two lines are parallel, they have the same slope.

　　(c)　contrapositive: (T) If we are not in France, then we are not in Paris.
　　　converse:(F) If we are in France, then we are in Paris.

　　(d)　contrapositive: (T) If you can legally make a U-turn, the road is not one-way.
　　　converse: (F) If you cannot legally make a U-turn, the road is one-way.

18.　Bill is wearing a hat.

19.　Ask either guard, "Would you say your door is the door to freedom?" The honest guard would certainly answer "yes" if his door was the door to freedom and "no" if not. If the lying guard was asked "Is your door the door to freedom?" and it was, he would answer "no." So the correct answer to the full question is "no." But since he always lies, he will say "yes." In the same way, he will say "no" if the door is to death. Either way, the prisoner has gotten the correct answer.

12.5 Valid Argument

1.   s = Sue goes to the movies.   r = She reads.
        1.   s ∨ r   hyp.
        2.   ~s   hyp.
        3.   r   disj. syllogism (1,2)

2.   v = The class votes for an oral final.
      g = The teacher is glad.
      m = The exam is scheduled for Monday.
        1.   v → g   hyp.
        2.   ~m → ~g   hyp.
        3.   ~m   hyp.
        4.   ~g   mod. ponens (2,3)
        5.   ~v   mod. tollens (1,4)

3.   a = My allowance comes this week.   r = I pay rent.
      b = My bank account is in the black.   e = I am evicted.
        1.   a ∧ r → b   hyp.
        2.   ~r → e   hyp.
        3.   ~e ∧ a   hyp.
        4.   ~e   subtr. (3)
        5.   r   mod. tollens (2,4)
        6.   a   subtr. (3)
        7.   b   mod. ponens (5,6,1)

4.   s = Jane is in sixth grade.
      f = Jane understands fractions.
      r = Jane is in remedial math class.
        1.   (s → f) ∨ (s → r)   hyp.
        2.   s   hyp.
        3.   s → (f∨r)   const. dilemma
        4.   f ∨ r   mod. ponens (2,3)

5.   p = Price of oil increases.
      a = OPEC countries agree.
      u = There is a UN debate.

        1.   p → a   hyp.
        2.   ~u → p   hyp.
        3.   ~a   hyp.
        4.   ~p   mod. tollens (1,3)
        5.   u   mod. tollens (2,4)

6.   j = Jill wins.
      l = Jack loses.
      w = Peter wins.
      p = Paul loses.
        1.   j → l   hyp.
        2.   w → p   hyp.
        3.   j ∨ w   hyp.
        4.   (j∨w) → (l∨p)   constr. dilemma (1,2)
        5.   l ∨ p   mod. ponens (3,4)

7. g = The germ is present.
    f = The fever is present.
    r = The rash is present.

    1. $g \rightarrow r \wedge f$ hyp.
    2. f   hyp.
    3. ~r   hyp.
    4. ~r ∨ ~f   addition (3)
    5. ~(r∧f)   De Morgan (4)
    6. ~g   mod. tollens (1,5)

8. p = Hal is a politician.
    l = Hal is a liar.
    f = Hal is a fraud.

    1. $p \rightarrow l \vee f$ hyp.
    2. ~l   hyp.
    3. ~f   hyp.
    4. ~(l∨f)   De Morgan (2,3)
    5. ~p   mod. tollens (1,4)

9. c = The material is cotton.
    r = The material is rayon.
    d = The material can be made into a dress.

    1. $c \vee r \rightarrow d$ hyp.
    2. ~d   hyp.
    3. ~(c∨r)   mod. tollens (1.2)
    4. ~c ∧ ~r   De Morgan
    5. ~r   subtr. (4)

10. a = There is money in the account.
    c = I have a check.
    r = I pay the rent.
    e = I am evicted.

    1. $a \wedge c \rightarrow r$ hyp.
    2. $\sim c \rightarrow e$ hyp.
    3. $\sim r \rightarrow \sim(a \wedge c)$ contrapositive (1)
    4. $\sim e \rightarrow c$ contrapositive (2)
    5. $\sim r \rightarrow \sim a \vee \sim c$ De Morgan (3)
    6. (~e∧~r) $\rightarrow$ [c ∧ (~a∨~c)] contr. dilemma (4,5)
    7. c ∧ (~a∨~c) $\rightarrow$ ~a   disj. syllogism
    8. (~e∧~r) $\rightarrow$ ~a   hypoth. syllogism

11. s = The salaries go up.
    a = More people apply.
       (s $\rightarrow$ a) ∧ (s∨a) does not logically imply s.
       Invalid argument. (Suppose s is false, a is true.)

12. s = Rita studies.
    g = Rita gets good grades.

    1. $s \rightarrow g$ hyp.
    2. ~g   hyp.
    3. ~s   mod. tollens (1,2)
       The argument is valid.

13. y = The balloon is yellow
    p = The ribbon is pink.
    h = The balloon is filled with helium.

```
        1.   y ∨ p              hyp.
        2.   h ⟶ ~y             hyp.
        3.   h                  hyp.
        4.   ~y                 mod. ponens (2,3)
        5.   p                  disj. syllogism (1,4)
```
The argument is valid.

14. s = The job offer is for at least $30,000.
     f = The job offer has five weeks' vacation.
     a = I accept the job offer.
     r = I owe rent money
```
        1.   s ∨ f ⟶ a         hyp.
        2.   ~s ⟶ ~a ∧ r       hyp.
        3.   ~a                 hyp.
        4.   ~(s∨f)             mod. tollens (1,3)
        5.   ~s ∧ ~f            De Morgan (4)
        6.   ~s                 subtraction
        7.   ~a ∧ ~r            mod. ponens (2,6)
        8.   r                  subtraction
```

15. p = Papa Bear sits.
     m = Mama Bear stands.
     b = Baby Bear crawls on the floor.
```
        1.   p ⟶               hyp.
        2.   m ⟶               hyp.
        3.   ~b                 hyp.
        4.   ~m                 mod. tollens (2,3)
        5.   ~p                 mod. tollens (1,4)   The argument is valid.
```

16. s = It is snowing.
     b = I wear boots.
     The argument is invalid because (s ⟶ b) ∧ ~s does not
     logically imply ~b (let b be TRUE and s be FALSE).

17. w = Wheat prices are steady.
     e = Exports increase.
     g = GNP is steady.
     The argument is invalid because [w ⟶ (e∨g)] ∧ (w∧g)
     does not logically imply e. (Suppose w and g are TRUE,
     e is FALSE.)

18. e = We eat out.
     m = Mom treats.
     d = Dad treats.
```
        1.   e ⟶ m ∨ d         hyp.
        2.   ~(m∨d)             hyp.
        3.   ~e                 mod. tollens (1,2)
```

19. i = Tim is industrious.
     p = Tim is in line for promotion.
     q = Tim is thinking of leaving.
     The argument is invalid because (i⟶p) ∧ (p∨q) does not
     logically imply (q⟶i). (Suppose i is FALSE, q and p
     are TRUE.)

20.   h = I pass history.
        s = I go to summer school.
        f = I take French.
            1.   h → ~s   hyp.
            2.   s → f   hyp.
            3.   s → ~h   contrapositive (1)
            4.   s ∨ s → f ∨ ~h   constr. dilemma (2,3)
            5.   s → ~h ∨ f   equivalence (4)
        The argument is valid.

21.   s = Sam goes to the store.
        m = Sam needs milk.
            1.   s   by way of contradiction
            2.   s → m   hyp.
            3.   ~m   hyp.
            4.   m   mod. ponens (1,2)
            5.   Contradiction (3,4)   ∴ ~s

22.   r = It rains hard.
        p = There is a picnic.
        f = Dave brings a Frisbee.
        k = The kids are happy.
            1.   r ∨ f   by way of contradiction
            2.   r → ~p   hyp.
            3.   f → h   hyp.
            4.   ~h ∧ p   hy.
            5.   ~h   subtraction (4)
            6.   ~f   mod. tollens (3,5)
            7.   r   disj. syllogism (1,6)
            8.   p   subtraction (4)
            9.   ~r   mod. tollens (2, 8)
           10.   Contradiction (7,9)   ∴ ~r ∧ ~f

23.   n = The newspaper reports a crime.
        r = TV reports a crime.
        s = A crime is serious.
        k = A person is killed.

            1.   ~s   by way of contradiction
            2.   n ∧ t → s   hyp.
            3.   k → n   hyp.
            4.   k   hyp.
            5.   t   hyp.
            6.   ~(n∧t)   mod. tollens (1,2)
            7.   ~n ∨ ~t   De Morgan (6)
            8.   n   mod. ponens (3,4)
            9.   ~t   disj. syllogism (7,8)
           10.   Contradiction (5,9)   ∴ s.

24.   i = Linda feels ill.
        a = Linda takes aspirin.
        f = Linda runs a fever.
        b = Linda takes a bath.
            1.   ~a   by way of contradiction
            2.   i → a   hyp.
            3.   f → ~b   hyp.
            4.   ~i → b   hyp.

```
5.    f                      hyp.
6.    ~i                     mod. tollens (1,2)
7.    b                      mod. ponens (4,6)
8.    ~b                     mod. ponens (3,5)
9.    Contradiction (7,8)  ∴ a.
```

12.6 Predicate Calculus

1. (a) F   (b) T; 4 is even   (c) T; 3 is divisible by 3
    (d) T; 6 is even and divisible by 3   (e) F

2. (a) T   (b) F   (c) F   (d) F

3. (a) ∀ x p(x)   (b) ~∀ x p(x)
    (c) ∀ x [~p(x)]   (d) (c) ⟶ (b)

4. "Not all doors open" or "There are some doors that do not open."

5. ∀ x [~p(x)] ⟺ ~∃ x [p(x)]
    Abby meant to say, "Not all men cheat on their wives."

6. (a) ∀x [~p(x)]   (b) ∃x [p(x)]
    (c) ~[∀x p(x)]   (d) ∃x [~p(x)]
    (e) ∀x [~p(x)]   (f) (c) ⟺ (d) and (a) ⟺ (e)

7. (a) ∀x p(x)   (b) ∃x [~p(x)]
    (c) ∃x p(x)   (d) ~[∀x p(x)]
    (e) ∀x [~p(x)]   (f) ~[∃x p(x)] or ∀x [~p(x)]
    (g) (b) ⟺ (d) and (e) ⟺ (f) by DeMorgan's law

8. (a) T   (b) F

9. (a) T   (b) F

10. (a) T   (b) T

11. (a) T   (b) F   (c) T   (d) F
    (e) F   (f) T   (g) F   (h) T

12. (a) F   (b) F   (c) T   (d) T   (e) T
    (f) T   (g) F   (h) F   (i) T   (j) T

13. (a) Some dogs don't have their day.
    (b) All men do not fight wars, or No men fight wars.
    (c) Some mothers are unmarried.
    (d) There exists a pot without a cover.
    (e) All children have pets.
    (f) Every month has 30 days.

14. (a) There is a stitch that does not save time.
    (b) There is a book without a hard cover.
    (c) All children are unafraid of snakes.
    (d) There exists no computer without a hard disk.
    (e) All chairs have arms

15. (a) For every x and y in U, x + y is greater than 12.
       FALSE: let x = 0 and y = 3.
    (b) For all x in U, there exist a y in U such that x + y
        is greater than 12. TRUE
    (c) There exists x in U such that for all y in U, x + y is
        greater than 12. TRUE
    (d) There exist x and y in U such that x + y is greater
        than 12. TRUE

16. (a) FALSE: let x = {a, c} and let y = {a, b}.
    (b) FALSE: let x = {a, c} and let y = {a, b}.
    (c) TRUE: let x = ∅; then x ⊆ y for all y.
    (d) TRUE: let y = {a, b, c}; then x ⊆ y for every x.

17. (a) FALSE: let x = 5 and y = 6.
    (b) TRUE: given x in U, we let y = x. Then p(x, y) is
        true.
    (c) TRUE: let x = 1; then p(x, y) is true for all y in U.
    (d) FALSE: there is no such y in U such that x divides y
        regardless of the value of x in U.
    (e) TRUE: given y in U, let x = y. Then p(x, y) is true.
    (f) TRUE: x divides itself for every x in U.

18. (a) ~p ∨ q   (b) p ⊕ ~q   (c) ~p ∧ ~q   (d) ~(p ∨ q)

19. (a) x ∈ S ⟶ x ∈ T   (b) No; 13 ∈ S but 13 ∉ T

20. No; S = {1, 2, 3, 4, 6, 12} and T = {2, 4, 6, 8, 10, 12}

21. S = {2, 4, 6, 8} and T = {2, 3, 4, 6, 8}
    Therefore, x ∈ S ⟶ x ∈ T.

22. s = {a, b, d} ⊆ T

23. S = T = {3}

SUPPLEMENTARY EXERCISES

1. (a), (c), (e) are statements.

2. (a) If the lines are perpendicular, then their slopes are
       negative reciprocals of each other
   (b) If goldfish can live in a fish bowl, then the water
       is aerated.
   (c) If it rains, then Jane uses her umbrella.
   (d) If Sally gives Morris a treat, then Morris eats all
       his food.

3. (a) contrapositive: If the Yankees are not playing in
          Yankee Stadium, then they are not in New York
          City.
      converse: If the Yankees are playing in Yankee Stadium,
          then they are in New York City.
   (b) contrapositive: If the quake is not considered major,
          then the Richter scale does not indicate the
          earthquake is a 7.
      converse: If the quake is considered major, then the

Richter scale indicates the earthquake is 7.

(c) contrapositive: If the coat is not warm, it is not fur.

converse: If the coat is warm, it is made of fur.

(d) contrapositive: If Jane is not in Moscow, she is not in the USSR.

converse: If Jane is in Moscow, she is in the USSR.

4. (a) Two triangles are similar whose sides are unequal.

(b) For every real number x, $x^2 \neq 5$.

(c) There exists a positive integer n such that n is even and n^2 is not even.

(d) For every real number x, $x^2 + 4 \neq 0$.

5. (a) and (b) are tautologies.

6. (a)

p	q	r	$p \longrightarrow (\sim q \vee r)$
T	T	T	T
T	T	F	F
T	F	T	T
T	F	F	T
F	T	T	T
F	T	F	T
F	F	T	T
F	F	F	T

(b)

p	q	r	$p \wedge (q \leftrightarrow (r \wedge p))$
T	T	T	T
T	T	F	F
T	F	T	F
T	F	F	T
F	T	T	F
F	T	F	F
F	F	T	F
F	F	F	F

7. (a) is TRUE; If $p \wedge (\sim p \vee q)$ is true, then p is true and $\sim p \vee q$ is true. Since $\sim p \vee q$ is true and $\sim p$ is false, q is true. Thus $p \wedge (\sim p \vee q) \Rightarrow q$ is TRUE.

(b) is FALSE.

p	q	$[(p \longrightarrow q)$	$\wedge$	$q]$	$\longrightarrow$	p
F	T	T		T		F
(1)	(2)	(3)		(4)		(5)

8. (a) TRUE   (b) FALSE

9. (a) FALSE   (b) TRUE

10. (a) 17   (b) 100   (c) 100   (d) 100

11. (a) 50   (b) -25   (c) -15   (d) 10

12.   (a) indeterminate   (b) TRUE   (c) TRUE
      (d) indeterminate   (e) indeterminate

13.   p: The voter is over the age of 21.
      q: The voter has a driver's license.
      r: The voter is eligible for free driver education.
      Hypothesis: $(p \wedge q) \longrightarrow r$
      (a) $r \longrightarrow (p \wedge q)$ is the converse of the hypothesis, so we cannot determine the truth value of the statement.
      (b)   We cannot determine the truth value of the statement.
      (c) $\sim r \longrightarrow (\sim p \vee \sim q)$ $(p \wedge q) \longrightarrow r$ is the contrapositive. Thus, the statement is TRUE.

14.   (a) TRUE   (b) FALSE   (c) TRUE

15.   (a) indeterminate   (b) indeterminate   (c) TRUE

16.   t = Taxes go up.
      s = I sell the house.
      m = I move to India.

1.	$t \longrightarrow s \wedge m$	hyp.
2.	$\sim m$	hyp.
3.	$\sim s \vee \sim m$	addition
4.	$\sim(s \wedge m)$	De Morgan (3)
5.	$\sim t$	mod. tollens (1,4)

17.   m = I study mathematics.
      b = I study business.
      p = I can write poetry.

1.	$m \wedge b$	hyp.
2.	$b \longrightarrow \sim p \vee \sim m$	hyp.
3.	b	subtr. (1)
4.	$\sim p \vee \sim m$	mod. ponens (2,3)
5.	m	subtr. (1)
6.	$\sim p$	disj. syllogism (4,5)

18.   s = I shop for a dress.
      h = I wear high heels.
      f = I have a sore foot.

1.	$s \longrightarrow h$	hyp.
2.	$f \longrightarrow \sim h$	hyp.
3.	s	hyp.
4.	h	mod. ponens (1,3)
5.	$\sim f$	mod. tollens (2,4)

19.   a = Asters grow in the garden.
      d = Dahlias grow in the garden.
      s = It is spring.

1.	$a \vee d$	hyp.
2.	$s \longrightarrow \sim a$	hyp.
3.	s	hyp.
4.	$\sim a$	mod. ponens (2,3)
5.	d	disj. syllogism (1,4)

20.   t = The professor gives a test.
      h = Nancy studies hard.
      d = Nancy has a date.

s = Nancy takes a shower.

1.	~h	by way of contradiction
2.	t $\longrightarrow$ h	hyp.
3.	d $\longrightarrow$ s	hyp.
4.	~t $\longrightarrow$ ~s	hyp.
5.	d	hyp.
6.	s	mod. ponens (3,5)
7.	t	mod. tollens (4,6)
8.	~t	mod. tollens (1,2)
9.	Contradiction (7,8) $\therefore$ h.	

GRAPHS

13.1 Graphs as Models

1. G_1 : (a) Parallel edges cd, dc, no loops

    (b) Deg a = 1, deg b = 2, deg c = 3, deg d = 3, deg e = 1, deg f = 0, total = 10

    (c) 4

    (d) 5 = number of edges

    G_2 : (a) No parallel edges, loop at e

    (b) Deg a = deg b = deg c = deg d = 4   deg e = 6

    (c) 0

    (d) 11 = number of edges

    G_3 : (a) No parallel edges, no loops

    (b) All have deg = 2

    (c) 0

    (d) 6 = number of edges

2.

Vertex	A	B	C	Total
Degree	2	5	1	8

No. vertices of odd deg = 2

No. edges = 4

Vertex	A	B	C	D	E	F	G	Total
Degree	2	2	4	3	3	3	1	18

No. vertices of odd deg = 4

No. edges = 9

3.

4. (a) B   (b) F   (c) 9

5. The graph would have an odd number of vertices of odd degree.

6. (a) (c) No; there are an odd number of vertices of odd degree.

    (b)   Yes.

7. (a)   (b)   (c) No graph contains only one vertex of odd degree.

8. No; there are 3 vertices of odd degree.

9. 10

10. (a) 9   (b)

11.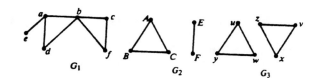

12. (a)   (b)   (c)

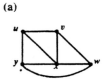 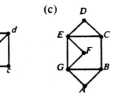

13. In G_1, deg d = 4. No vertex in G_2 has deg 4.

14. Vertices adjacent to d and v are of different degrees.

15. a ↔ z, b ↔ y, c ↔ u, d ↔ v, e ↔ x, f ↔ w

16. A ↔ V, B ↔ U, C ↔ P, D ↔ Q, E ↔ R, F ↔ S, G ↔ W, H ↔ X

17. Not equivalent, G_2 has no vertex of deg 1; G_1 does.

18. Not equivalent, G_1 has 2 vertices of degree 2, but G_2 has only 1.

19. A ↔ a, B ↔ b, C ↔ c, D ↔ d, E ↔ e, F ↔ f, G ↔ g

20. A ↔ u, B ↔ x, C ↔ z, D ↔ t, E ↔ y, F ↔ v, G ↔ w

21. A ↔ y, B ↔ v, C ↔ u, D ↔ x, E ↔ w

22. (a) Yes   (b) No, for example, one can find two different graphs with 4 vertices, two of degree 2 and two of degree 3.

23.

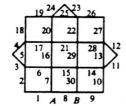

24.

25.

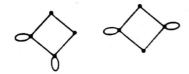

26.

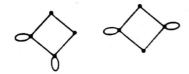

13.2 Paths and Circuits

1. In each case, the length is one less than the number of
   vertices.
   (a) 3   (b) 5   (c) 7   (d) 5   (e) 4   (f) 7

2. (a) Closed path, circuit, simple circuit
   (b) None
   (c) Simple path only
   (d) Closed path, circuit, simple circuit
   (e) Closed path, circuit, simple circuit
   (f) None

3. (a) 4, none
   (b) 3. simple path
   (c) 5, none
   (d) 5, closed path, circuit, simple circuit
   (e) 4, none
   (f) 6, closed path, circuit, simple circuit

4. (a) AE, ABC, ACDE, BDE
   (b) AEBA, ABCA, ABCDEA, EBDE, BCDB
   (c) ABCDBEA, CDBEABC

5. (a) ABCD, ACD, ACFD, ABCFED   (b) CABC, CFDC, CFEDC, yes

6.

7.   (a)   Connected
     (b)   Not connected; there is no path from x to s.
     (c)   Not connected; there is no path from A to E.

8.   No; a connected graph with 6 vertices has at least 5 edges.

9.   G cannot be disconnected; we could use at most 6 edges for 4 vertices; graph with 5 vertices and 5 edges might be disconnected.

10.   (a)   Vertex d has deg = 1.   (b)   Vertex d has deg = 3.
      (c)   The graph is disconnected.

11.   Answer is (a)

12.   None

13.   (a)   v u y x u w y v   (b)   v r s w z t u r t y x z s v

14.   No route is possible; deg b = 3 and deg c = 3

15.   a f c b e f d c a

16.   No; deg C = 3

17.   ABEDCBFGCA

18.   (a)   dbacegihafedc   (b)   fgdchaedfa

19.   D A B F E B C D E; each Euler path begins or ends at D and E; the 2 vertices are of odd degree.

20.

21.   (a)   b c d; Length = 2   (b)   d e a f g; Length = 4
     (c)   c a f g; Length = 3

13.3 Hamiltonian Circuits and Spanning Trees

1.   (a)   SRTWVUYXZS   (b)   a g i j f e d c b h a

2.   (a)   d c g h e f b a d   (b)   u v w x y z t s u
     (c)   FGAHBCDEF

3.   (a)   No Euler circuit, no Hamiltonian circuit
     (b)   Euler circuit, y r s y t u v w x s t x y;
       Hamiltonian circuit, r s t u v w x y r
     (c)   No Euler circuit;
       Hamiltonian circuit, a b c d e f g h a

4. Yes, the degree of each vertex is greater than 5/2 and
   n = 5 > 3.

5. No conclusion; G might have a Hamiltonian circuit although
   one vertex has degree less than 3.

6. G has a Hamiltonian circuit. Use Principle 2 with n = 6.

7. From Principle 2, if G has n = 8 vertices, having
   1/2(n-1)(n-2) + 2 = 1/2(7)(6) = 23 edges guarantees the
   existence of a Hamiltonian circuit.

8.

9.

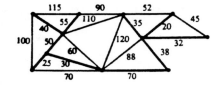

10.

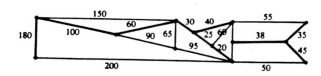

11. (a) Bipartite
    (b) 3 colors
    (c) 3 colors, 15, 4 periods

12. (a)   (b) 3

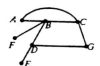

13. (a) At some point in the traversal of this graph, c and
         e are visited before reaching the end of the circuit.
         This disconnects the remaining part of the graph, making
         it impossible to complete any circuit.
    (b) As in (a), at some point before ending the traversal,
         the center point is removed, thus disconnecting the
         remaining portion of the graph.
    (c) Again there are problems with disconnection at the
         trouble spots indicated above.

14. The graphs are bipartite, but the number of vertices of one

color is not equal to the number of vertices of the other color.

15. 4 periods

13.4 Directed Graphs

1. connected: (b) (c); strongly connected: (c)

2. connected: (a) (b)

3. (a)

vertex	A	B	C	D	E	F
id	1	2	2	1	2	0
od	1	2	1	2	0	2

   (b) id of a vertex = the number of procedures called by that procedure
   od of a vertex = the number of procedures calling that procedure

4. Neither; cycles: (a) AA (b) ACDA

5. (a) cycle: ABA (b) acyclic (c) acyclic

6. (a) u v z t v w x y t w y z u
   (b) no Euler circuit and no Euler path:
   $id(e) \neq od(e)$, $id(c) \neq od(c)$, $id(b) \neq od(b)$

7. (a) u v w u p s w p r s z y x z u
   (b) By properties 2 and 3, neither a Euler circuit nor a Euler path exists:
   $id(A) = od(A) = 2$ $id(B) = od(B) = 2$
   $id(C) = 1$; $od(C) = 3$; $id(C) \neq od(C)$,
   $id(D) = od(D) = 1$ $id(E) = od(E) = 2$
   $id(F) = 3$; $od(F) = 2$; $id(F) \neq od(F)$
   $id(G) = 2$; $od(G) = 1$; $id(G) \neq od(G)$,
   $id(H) = od(H) = 1$

8. (a) connected, strongly connected, $id(D) = 2$, $od(D) = 1$, $id(A) = 2$, $od(A) = 3$, no Euler circuit, but an Euler path exists
   (b) connected, strongly connected, and all vertices have id = od, so an Euler circuit exists

9. Euler circuit: AHGAFCEDCBFGEBA

10. (a) not connected
    (b) strongly connected, no Euler paths or circuits
    (c) connected, not strongly connected
    (d) connected, not strongly connected

11. 25 days, critical path: S A_1 A_2 A_3 A_6 A_7 A_8 A_{10} A_{11} E

12. Critical path: S A_2 A_5 A_7 A_8 E takes 63 minutes.
    A_3 does not affect time; A_8 does (new time is 57 minutes).

13. 65 days critical path: ADEF

14. (a) $S A_2 A_4 A_5 E$ (b) 34 minutes   (c) yes
    (d) new critical path: $S A_2 A_6 A_8 E$; time = 28 minutes
    (e) .9960

15.
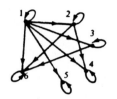

16.

17.
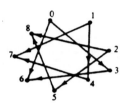

18.
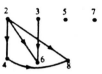

19. (a)
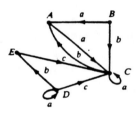

  (b) error message; A does not respond to input B.
  (c) C; it follows path B C A C.

13.5 Matrices and Graphs

1. (a) $A = \begin{bmatrix} 0 & 1 & 0 & 0 & 0 \\ 1 & 0 & 1 & 1 & 0 \\ 0 & 1 & 0 & 0 & 0 \\ 0 & 1 & 0 & 0 & 1 \\ 0 & 0 & 0 & 1 & 0 \end{bmatrix}$
  (b) $A^2 = \begin{bmatrix} 1 & 0 & 1 & 1 & 0 \\ 0 & 3 & 0 & 0 & 1 \\ 1 & 0 & 1 & 1 & 0 \\ 1 & 0 & 1 & 2 & 0 \\ 0 & 1 & 0 & 0 & 1 \end{bmatrix}$

There is one path of length 2 from v_1 to v_4.

(c) $A^3 = \begin{bmatrix} 0 & 3 & 0 & 0 & 1 \\ 3 & 0 & 3 & 4 & 0 \\ 0 & 3 & 0 & 0 & 1 \\ 0 & 4 & 0 & 0 & 2 \\ 1 & 0 & 1 & 2 & 0 \end{bmatrix}$ $A + A^2 + A^3 = \begin{bmatrix} 1 & 4 & 1 & 1 & 1 \\ 4 & 3 & 4 & 5 & 1 \\ 1 & 4 & 1 & 1 & 1 \\ 1 & 5 & 1 & 2 & 3 \\ 1 & 1 & 1 & 3 & 1 \end{bmatrix}$

R is a matrix of 1's. This is expected because the graph is connected.

2. (a) 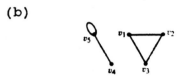 (b) 5 (c) Every entry in A^4 is nonzero; therefore, G is connected

(d) $v_1v_2v_3v_4$, $v_1v_4v_1v_4$, $v_1v_3v_1v_4$, $v_1v_2v_1v_4$, $v_1v_4v_3v_4$

3. (a) The graph is not connected. The fourth and fifth rows and columns will always have 0's.

(b)

4. (a) $A = \begin{bmatrix} 0 & 1 & 0 & 0 & 0 & 0 & 1 \\ 1 & 0 & 1 & 0 & 0 & 0 & 1 \\ 0 & 1 & 0 & 1 & 1 & 0 & 1 \\ 0 & 0 & 1 & 0 & 1 & 0 & 0 \\ 0 & 0 & 1 & 1 & 0 & 1 & 0 \\ 0 & 0 & 0 & 0 & 1 & 1 & 1 \\ 1 & 1 & 1 & 0 & 0 & 1 & 0 \end{bmatrix}$

(b) n = 3
(c) At most, three steps are needed to get from any vertex to another.

5. (a) $A = \begin{bmatrix} 0 & 1 & 1 & 0 & 0 \\ 1 & 0 & 1 & 0 & 0 \\ 1 & 1 & 0 & 1 & 0 \\ 0 & 0 & 1 & 0 & 0 \\ 0 & 0 & 0 & 0 & 1 \end{bmatrix}$

(b) The entry in the first row and fourth column of A^3 is 1.

(c) R has 1 in every position exept in the last row, where all entries but the fifth column are 0, and the last column, where all entries but the last rown are 0.

6.

7. (a) $A = \begin{bmatrix} 0 & 1 & 1 & 0 & 0 \\ 1 & 0 & 1 & 0 & 0 \\ 1 & 1 & 0 & 1 & 0 \\ 0 & 0 & 1 & 0 & 1 \\ 0 & 0 & 0 & 1 & 0 \end{bmatrix}$ (b) $A^6 = \begin{bmatrix} 31 & 30 & 32 & 23 & 7 \\ 30 & 31 & 32 & 23 & 7 \\ 32 & 32 & 52 & 16 & 16 \\ 23 & 23 & 16 & 22 & 2 \\ 7 & 7 & 16 & 2 & 6 \end{bmatrix}$

(c) We are guaranteed a path of length 6 from any vertex to any other.

8. 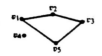   9.

10. (a) $A(D) = \begin{bmatrix} 0 & 1 & 1 & 0 & 1 \\ 0 & 0 & 1 & 0 & 0 \\ 0 & 0 & 0 & 1 & 0 \\ 0 & 0 & 0 & 0 & 0 \\ 0 & 0 & 0 & 1 & 1 \end{bmatrix}$

(b) 2_4 (c)   acd, aed
(d) A^4 is a matrix of 0's
(e)   There are no paths of length 4 in this digraph.

(f) $R(D) = \begin{bmatrix} 1 & 1 & 1 & 1 & 1 \\ 0 & 1 & 1 & 1 & 0 \\ 0 & 0 & 1 & 1 & 0 \\ 0 & 0 & 0 & 1 & 0 \\ 0 & 0 & 0 & 1 & 1 \end{bmatrix}$

(g)   D is connected, but not strongly connected. There are some 0's in R(D).

11. (a) $A = \begin{bmatrix} 0 & 1 & 1 & 0 \\ 1 & 0 & 0 & 0 \\ 0 & 1 & 0 & 0 \\ 0 & 1 & 0 & 0 \end{bmatrix}$

(b)   2

(c)   a c b a b, a b a c b

(d) $R = \begin{bmatrix} 1 & 1 & 1 & 0 \\ 1 & 1 & 1 & 0 \\ 1 & 1 & 1 & 0 \\ 1 & 1 & 1 & 1 \end{bmatrix}$

(e)   connected, not strongly connected

12. (a)

vertex	a	b	c	d
id	2	1	2	2
od	2	2	2	1

(b)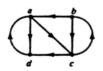

(c)   The digraph is connected and is strongly connected.
(d)   No Euler circuit.

13. (a)

vertex	v_1	v_2	v_3	v_4	v_5
id	3	2	2	3	1
od	2	2	2	3	2

(b)

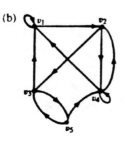

(b)

(c) 2   (d) $v_1v_2v_4v_4$, $v_1v_1v_2v_4$

13.6 Trees

1.

2.

3.

4. (a) is a tree   (b) has a cycle, is not a tree
    (c) is not connected, is not a tree

5. (a) d, e, i, j, k, h   (b) g, h, e, f, c, d
    (c) x, 6, y

6. children of x   (a) f and g   (b) g and h   (c) none
    descendants of x (a) f, g, i, j, k (b) g and h   (c) none

7. (a) a   (b) b   (c) *

8. (a) a   (b) a   (c) *

9. A tree with 7 vertices must have 6 edges. This tree cannot
    be drawn.

10. The graph cannot be drawn; it has an odd number of odd
     vertices.

11. By Property 2, if G is connected, has n vertices, and has
     n-1 edges, it is a tree.

12. An acyclic graph with 5 vertices and 4 edges is connected.

13. It cannot be drawn; a tree on 3 vertices must have 2 edges.

14.

15.

16. $[9a + y) * z] \wedge [(2 * (x/3)] = [(a + y)z]^{2(x/3)}$

17. $\dfrac{a}{b + c} - b^c$

18.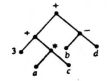

19.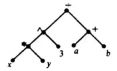

20.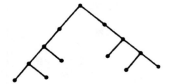

21. 7 questions, 10 questions

SUPPLEMENTARY EXERCISES

1. G_1

vertex	a	b	c	d
deg	2	3	2	5

   sum of degrees = 12
   number of edges is 6

   G_2

vertex	r	s	t	u	v	w	x
deg	3	2	3	3	4	4	3

   sum of degrees = 22
   number of edges is 11

2. G_1: (a) adc (b) adcda (c) addcba

   G_2: (a) uwv (b) uwvxwu (c) uxwrtvwu

3. G_1: weight = 9 G_2: weight = 15

  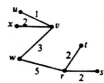

4. Euler circuits do not exist because there are vertices of odd degree in each graph.

5. G₁

vertex	a	b	c	d	e	f	g	h
degree	2	3	3	4	2	3	5	4

There are 4 vertices of odd degree.

G₂

vertex	a	b	c	d	e	f	g	h
degree	2	4	2	4	4	2	4	4

There are 0 vertices of odd degree.

6. G₁: (a) hab (b) bahcghb (c) hgcdgh (d) abhcgha

   G₂: (a) ahb (b) ghbeheg (c) ghbeheg (d) bedgehb

7. G₁: weight = 19   G₂: weight = 37

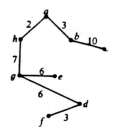

8. G₁ has no Euler circuit; some vertices have odd degree.

   G₂ has an Euler circuit: abcdfgdehgebha.

9. There are 9 paths of length 3 from v₁ to v₄ in G₁.

$$A(G_1) = \begin{bmatrix} 0 & 1 & 0 & 1 & 1 \\ 1 & 0 & 1 & 1 & 1 \\ 0 & 1 & 0 & 1 & 0 \\ 1 & 1 & 1 & 0 & 1 \\ 1 & 1 & 0 & 1 & 0 \end{bmatrix}$$

   In G₂ there are 6 paths of length 3 from v₁ to v₄.

$$A(G_2) = \begin{bmatrix} 0 & 1 & 0 & 1 & 0 \\ 1 & 0 & 1 & 1 & 0 \\ 0 & 1 & 0 & 1 & 0 \\ 1 & 1 & 1 & 0 & 1 \\ 0 & 0 & 0 & 1 & 0 \end{bmatrix}$$

10. G₂ is equivalent to G₁.

11.

G and G' are equivalent.
Associate a to w, b to u
c to x and d to v.

12. No such path exists; vertex B has degree = 1.

13. 3 colors

Color 1: F, B
Color 2: C, D, G, H
Color 3: E

14. START ABDEF END

15.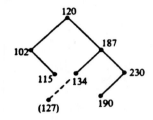

16.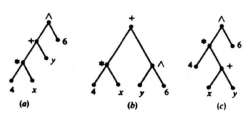

17. Start, ABDFG, End.

18. 3 cars

19. 3 colors   Color 1: B, E
                       Color 2: A, D, G
                       Color 3: C, F

20. The tournament is not transitive.
     One possible ranking is DEABC, which is not unique.